THE
HARVARD CLASSICS

Registered Edition

◆

The Five-Foot Shelf of Books

Michael Faraday

THE HARVARD CLASSICS
EDITED BY CHARLES W. ELIOT, LL.D.

Scientific Papers

Physics · Chemistry
Astronomy · Geology

With Introductions and Notes
Volume 30

P. F. Collier & Son Corporation
NEW YORK

CONTENTS

THE FORCES OF MATTER

DELIVERED BEFORE A JUVENILE AUDITORY AT THE ROYAL INSTITUTION OF GREAT BRITAIN DURING THE CHRISTMAS HOLIDAYS OF 1859–60

PAGE

LECTURE I.—THE FORCE OF GRAVITATION 7

LECTURE II.—GRAVITATION—COHESION 22

LECTURE III.—COHESION—CHEMICAL AFFINITY 37

LECTURE IV.—CHEMICAL AFFINITY—HEAT 50

LECTURE V.—MAGNETISM—ELECTRICITY 61

LECTURE VI.—THE CORRELATION OF THE PHYSICAL FORCES . . 73

THE CHEMICAL HISTORY OF A CANDLE

LECTURE I.—A CANDLE: THE FLAME—ITS SOURCES—STRUCTURE —MOBILITY—BRIGHTNESS 86

LECTURE II.—A CANDLE: BRIGHTNESS OF THE FLAME—AIR NECESSARY FOR COMBUSTION—PRODUCTION OF WATER 101

LECTURE III.—PRODUCTS: WATER FROM THE COMBUSTION—NATURE OF WATER—A COMPOUND—HYDROGEN 113

LECTURE IV.—HYDROGEN IN THE CANDLE—BURNS INTO WATER— THE OTHER PART OF WATER—OXYGEN 128

LECTURE V.—OXYGEN PRESENT IN THE AIR—NATURE OF THE ATMOSPHERE—ITS PROPERTIES—OTHER PRODUCTS FROM THE CANDLE—CARBONIC ACID—ITS PROPERTIES 141

LECTURE VI.—CARBON OR CHARCOAL—COAL-GAS—RESPIRATION AND ITS ANALOGY TO THE BURNING OF A CANDLE—CONCLUSION 156

ON THE CONSERVATION OF FORCE

INTRODUCTION TO A SERIES OF LECTURES DELIVERED AT CARLSRUHE IN THE WINTER OF 1862–1863 173

ICE AND GLACIERS

PAGE

A LECTURE DELIVERED AT FRANKFORT-ON-THE-MAIN, AND AT HEIDELBERG, IN FEBRUARY, 1865 211

THE WAVE THEORY OF LIGHT

[A LECTURE DELIVERED AT THE ACADEMY OF MUSIC, PHILADELPHIA, UNDER THE AUSPICES OF THE FRANKLIN INSTITUTE, SEPTEMBER 29TH, 1884] 251

THE TIDES

[EVENING LECTURE TO THE BRITISH ASSOCIATION AT THE SOUTHAMPTON MEETING, FRIDAY, AUGUST 25TH, 1882] 274

THE EXTENT OF THE UNIVERSE 311

GEOGRAPHICAL EVOLUTION 325

THE FORCES OF MATTER
THE CHEMICAL HISTORY OF A CANDLE

BY

MICHAEL FARADAY

INTRODUCTORY NOTE

MICHAEL FARADAY was the son of a blacksmith, and was born at Newington Butts, near London, September 22, 1791. He began life as an errand boy to a bookbinder and stationer, to whom he was later bound apprentice. After eight years in this business, he was engaged by Sir Humphry Davy as his laboratory assistant at the Royal Institution, and in 1813–15 he traveled extensively on the Continent with his master, and saw some of the most famous scientists of Europe. Shortly after his return to the Royal Institution, he began to make contributions of his own to science, his first paper appearing in 1816. He became director of the laboratory in 1825, and professor of chemistry in 1833; rising rapidly, through the number and importance of his discoveries, to a most distinguished position. But he was working at too great pressure, and in 1841 his health gave way, so that for some three years he could not work at all. He recovered, however, and made some of his most important discoveries after this interruption; and was offered, but declined, the presidency of both the Royal Society and the Royal Institution. He died August 25, 1867.

It was characteristic of Faraday's devotion to the enlargement of the bounds of human knowledge that on his discovery of magneto-electricity he abandoned the commercial work by which he had added to his small salary, in order to reserve all his energies for research. This financial loss was in part made up later by a pension of £300 a year from the British Government.

Faraday's parents were members of the obscure religious denomination of the Sandemanians, and Faraday himself, shortly after his marriage, at the age of thirty, joined the same sect, to which he adhered till his death. Religion and science he kept strictly apart, believing that the data of science were of an entirely different nature from the direct communications between God and the soul on which his religious faith was based.

The discoveries made by Faraday were so numerous, and often demand so detailed a knowledge of chemistry and physics before they can be understood, that it is impossible to attempt to describe or even enumerate them here. Among the most important are the discovery of magneto-electric induction, of the law of electro-chemical decomposition, of the magnetization of light, and of diamagnetism. Round each of these are grouped numbers of derivative but still highly important additions to scientific knowledge, and together they form so vast an achievement as

5

to lead his successor, Tyndall, to say, "Taking him for all and all, I think it will be conceded that Michael Faraday was the greatest experimental philosopher the world has ever seen; and I will add the opinion, that the progress of future research will tend, not to dim or to diminish, but to enhance and glorify the labours of this mighty investigator."

In spite of the highly technical nature of his work in research, Faraday was remarkably gifted as an expounder of science to popular audiences; and his lectures at the Royal Institution, especially those to younger audiences, were justly famous. The following examples are classics in the department of clear and fascinating scientific exposition.

THE FORCES OF MATTER

DELIVERED BEFORE A JUVENILE AUDITORY AT THE ROYAL INSTITUTION OF GREAT BRITAIN DURING THE CHRISTMAS HOLI- DAYS OF 1859–60

By Michael Faraday

LECTURE I

THE FORCE OF GRAVITATION

IT grieves me much to think that I may have been a cause of disturbance to your Christmas arrangements,* for nothing is more satisfactory to my mind than to perform what I undertake; but such things are not always left to our own power, and we must submit to circumstances as they are appointed. I will to-day do my best, and will ask you to bear with me if I am unable to give more than a few words; and, as a substitute, I will endeavor to make the *illustrations* of the sense I try to express as full as possible; and if we find by the end of this lecture that we may be justified in continuing them, thinking that next week our power shall be greater, why then, with submission to you, we will take such course as you may think fit, either to go on or discontinue them; and although I now feel much weakened by the pressure of the illness (a mere cold) upon me, both in facility of expression and clearness of thought, I shall here claim, as I always have done on these occasions, the right of addressing myself to the younger members of the audience; and for this purpose, therefore, unfitted as it may seem for an elderly, infirm man to do so, I will return to second childhood, and become, as it were, young again among the young.

Let us now consider, for a little while, how wonderfully we stand upon this world. Here it is we are born, bred, and live, and yet we

*The opening lecture was twice postponed on account of Dr. Faraday's illness.

view these things with an almost entire absence of wonder to our-
selves respecting the way in which all this happens. So small, indeed,
is our wonder, that we are never taken by surprise; and I do think
that, to a young person of ten, fifteen, or twenty years of age, per-
haps the first sight of a cataract or a mountain would occasion him
more surprise than he had ever felt concerning the means of his own
existence; how he came here; how he lives; by what means he stands
upright; and through what means he moves about from place to
place. Hence, we come into this world, we live, and depart from it,
without our thoughts being called specifically to consider how all this
takes place; and were it not for the exertions of some few inquiring
minds, who have looked *into* these things, and ascertained the very
beautiful laws and conditions by which we *do* live and stand upon
the earth, we should hardly be aware that there was any thing
wonderful in it. These inquiries, which have occupied philosophers
from the earliest days, when they first began to find out the laws by
which we grow, and exist, and enjoy ourselves, up to the present
time, have shown us that all this was effected in consequence of the
existence of certain *forces,* or *abilities* to do things, or *powers,* that
are so common that nothing can be more so; for nothing is com-
moner than the wonderful powers by which we are enabled to stand
upright: they are essential to our existence every moment.

It is my purpose to-day to make you acquainted with some of these
powers; not the vital ones, but some of the more elementary, and
what we call *physical* powers; and, in the outset, what can I do to
bring to your minds a notion of neither more nor less than that
which I mean by the word *power* or *force?* Suppose I take this
sheet of paper, and place it upright on one edge, resting against a
support before me (as the roughest possible illustration of something
to be disturbed), and suppose I then pull this piece of string which
is attached to it. I pull the paper over. I have therefore brought
into use a *power* of doing so—the *power* of my hand carried on
through this string in a way which is very remarkable when we
come to analyze it; and it is by means of these powers conjointly
(for there are several powers here employed) that I pull the paper
over. Again, if I give it a push upon the other side, I bring into
play a *power,* but a very different exertion of power from the former;

or, if I take now this bit of shell-lac [a stick of shell-lac about 12 inches long and 1 1-2 in diameter], and rub it with flannel, and hold it an inch or so in front of the upper part of this upright sheet, the paper is immediately moved towards the shell-lac, and by now drawing the latter away, the paper falls over without having been touched by any thing. You see, in the first illustration I produced an effect than which nothing could be commoner; I pull it over now, not by means of that string or the pull of my hand, but by some action in this shell-lac. The shell-lac, therefore, has a *power* wherewith it acts upon the sheet of paper; and, as an illustration of the exercise of another kind of power, I might use gunpowder with which to throw it over.

Now I want you to endeavor to comprehend that when I am speaking of a *power* or *force,* I am speaking of that which I used just now to pull over this piece of paper. I will not embarrass you at present with the *name* of that power, but it is clear there was a *something* in the shell-lac which acted by attraction, and pulled the paper over; this, then, is one of those things which we call *power,* or *force;* and you will now be able to recognize it as such in whatever form I show it to you. We are not to suppose that there are so very many different powers; on the contrary, it is wonderful to think how few are the powers by which all the phenomena of nature are governed. There is an illustration of another kind of power in that lamp; *there* is a power of heat—a power of doing something, but not the same power as that which pulled the paper over; and so, by degrees, we find that there are certain other powers (not many) in the various bodies around us; and thus, beginning with the simplest experiments of pushing and pulling, I shall gradually proceed to distinguish these powers one from the other, and compare the way in which they combine together. This world upon which we stand (and we have not much need to travel out of the world for illustrations of our subject; but the mind of man is not confined like the matter of his body, and thus he may and does travel outward, for wherever his sight can pierce, there his observations can penetrate) is pretty nearly a round globe, having its surface disposed in a manner of which this terrestrial globe by my side is a rough model; so much is land and so much is water, and by looking at it here we

see in a sort of map or picture how the world is formed upon its surface. Then, when we come to examine farther, I refer you to this sectional diagram of the geological strata of the earth, in which there is a more elaborate view of what is beneath the surface of our globe. And, when we come to dig into or examine it (as man does for his own instruction and advantage, in a variety of ways), we see that it is made up of different kinds of matter, subject to a very few powers; and all disposed in this strange and wonderful way, which gives to man a history—and such a history—as to what there is in those veins, in those rocks, the ores, the water-springs, the atmosphere around, and all varieties of material substances, held together by means of *forces* in one great mass, 8,000 miles in diameter, that the mind is overwhelmed in contemplation of the wonderful history related by these strata (some of which are fine and thin like sheets of paper), all formed in succession by the forces of which I have spoken.

I now shall try to help your attention to what I may say by directing, to-day, our thoughts to one kind of power. You see what I mean by the term *matter*—any of these things that I can lay hold of with the hand, or in a bag (for I may take hold of the air by inclosing it in a bag)—they are all portions of matter with which we have to deal at present, generally or particularly, as I may require to illustrate my subject. Here is the sort of matter which we call *water*—it is *there* ice [pointing to a block of ice upon the table], *there* water—[pointing to the water boiling in a flask]—*here* vapor— you see it issuing out from the top [of the flask]. Do not suppose that that ice and that water are two entirely different things, or that the steam rising in bubbles and ascending in vapor *there* is absolutely different from the fluid water: it may be different in some par- ticulars, having reference to the *amounts* of power which it con- tains; but it is the same, nevertheless, as the great ocean of water around our globe, and I employ it here for the sake of illustration, because if we look into it we shall find that it supplies us with examples of all the powers to which I shall have to refer. For instance, here is water—it is heavy; but let us examine it with regard to the *amount* of its heaviness or its gravity. I have before me a little glass vessel and scales [nearly equipoised scales, one of which

contained a half-pint glass vessel], and the glass vessel is at present
the lighter of the two; but if I now take some water and pour it in,
you see that that side of the scales immediately goes down; that
shows you (using common language, which I will not suppose for
the present you have hitherto applied very strictly) that it is *heavy,*
and if I put this additional weight into the opposite scale, I should
not wonder if this vessel would hold water enough to weigh *it*
down. [The lecturer poured more water into the jar, which again
went down.] Why do I hold the bottle *above* the vessel to pour the
water into it? You will say, because experience has taught me that it
is necessary. I do it for a better reason—because it is a law of nature
that the water should fall toward the earth, and therefore the very
means which I use to cause the water to enter the vessel are those
which will carry the whole body of water down. That power is
what we call *gravity,* and you see *there* [pointing to the scales] a
good deal of water gravitating toward the earth. Now *here* [ex-
hibiting a small piece of platinum([1])] is another thing which
gravitates toward the earth as much as the whole of that water. See
what a little there is of it; that little thing is heavier than so much
water [placing the metal in opposite scales to the water]. What a
wonderful thing it is to see that it requires so much water as *that*
[a half-pint vessel full] to fall toward the earth, compared with the
little mass of substance I have *here!* And again, if I take this metal
[a bar of aluminium([2]) about eight times the bulk of the platinum],
we find the water will balance that as well as it did the platinum;
so that we get, even in the very outset, an example of what we want
to understand by the words *forces* or *powers.*

I have spoken of water, and first of all of its property of falling
downward: you know very well how the oceans surround the globe
—how they fall round the surface, giving roundness to it, clothing
it like a garment; but, besides that, there are other properties of
water. *Here,* for instance, is some quicklime, and if I add some water
to it, you will find another power and property in the water.([3]) It is

[1] *Platinum,* with one exception the heaviest body known, is 21½ times heavier than
water. [2] *Aluminium* is 2½ times heavier than water.

[3] *Power or property in water.* This power—the heat by which the water is kept
in a *fluid* state—is said, under ordinary circumstances, to be *latent* or *insensible.* When,
however, the water changes its form, and, by uniting with the lime or sulphate of
copper, becomes *solid,* the heat which retained it in a liquid state is evolved.

now very hot; it is steaming up; and I could perhaps light phosphorus or a lucifer-match with it. Now that could not happen without a *force* in the water to produce the result; but that force is entirely distinct from its power of falling to the earth. Again, here is another substance [some anhydrous sulphate of copper([4])] which will illustrate another kind of power. [The lecturer here poured some water over the white sulphate of copper, which immediately became blue, evolving considerable heat at the same time.] Here is the same water with a substance which heats nearly as much as the lime does, but see how differently. So great indeed is this heat in the case of lime, that it is sufficient sometimes (as you see here) to set wood on fire; and this explains what we have sometimes heard, of barges laden with quicklime taking fire in the middle of the river, in consequence of this power of heat brought into play by a leakage of the water into the barge. You see how strangely different subjects for our consideration arise when we come to think over these various matters—the power of heat evolved by acting upon lime with water, and the power which water has of turning this salt of copper from white to blue.

I want you now to understand the nature of the most simple exertion of this power of matter called *weight* or *gravity*. Bodies are heavy; you saw that in the case of water when I placed it in the balance. Here I have what we call a *weight* [an iron half cwt.]—a thing called a weight because in it the exercise of that power of pressing downward is especially used for the purposes of weighing; and I have also one of these little inflated India-rubber bladders, which are very beautiful although very common (most beautiful things are common), and I am going to put the weight upon it, to give you a sort of illustration of the downward pressure of the iron, and of the power which the air possesses of resisting that pressure; it may burst, but we must try to avoid that. [During the last few observations the lecturer had succeeded in placing the half cwt. in a state of quiescence upon the inflated India-rubber ball, which consequently assumed a shape very much resembling a flat cheese with round edges.] There you see a bubble of air bearing half a

[4] *Anhydrous sulphate of copper:* sulphate of copper deprived of its water of crystallization. To obtain it the blue sulphate is calcined in an earthen crucible.

hundred-weight, and you must conceive for yourselves what a won-derful *power* there must be to pull this weight downward, to sink it thus in the ball of air.

Let me now give you another illustration of this power. You know what a pendulum is. I have one here (FIG. 1), and if I set it swinging, it will continue to swing to and fro. Now I wonder whether you can tell me why that body oscillates to and fro—that pendulum bob, as it is sometimes called. Observe, if I hold the straight stick horizon-tally, as high as the position of the ball at the two ends of its journey, you see that the ball is in a higher position at the two extremities than it is when in the middle. Starting from

FIG. 1

one end of the stick, the ball falls toward the centre, and then rising again to the opposite end, it constantly tries to fall to the lowest point, swinging and vibrating most beautifully, and with wonderful prop-erties in other respects—the time of its vibration, and so on—but concerning which we will not now trouble ourselves.

If a gold leaf, or piece of thread, or any other substance were hung where this ball is, it would swing to and fro in the same manner, and in the same time too. Do not be startled at this statement; I repeat, in the same manner and in the same time, and you will see by-and-by how this is. Now that power which caused the water to descend in the balance—which made the iron weight press upon and flatten the bubble of air—which caused the swinging to and fro of the pendulum, that power is entirely due to the attraction which there is between the falling body and the earth. Let us be slow and careful to comprehend this. It is not that the earth has any *particular* attraction toward bodies which fall to it, but, that *all* these bodies possess an attraction every one toward the other. It is not that the earth has any special power which these balls themselves have not; for just as much power as the earth has to attract these two balls [dropping two ivory balls], just so much power have they in pro-portion to their bulks to draw themselves one to the other; and the only reason why they fall so quickly to the earth is owing to its greater size. Now if I were to place these two balls near together,

I should not be able, by the most delicate arrangement of apparatus, to make you, or myself, sensible that these balls did attract one another; and yet we know that such is the case, because if, instead of taking a small ivory ball, we take a mountain, and put a ball like this near it, we find that, owing to the vast size of the mountain as compared with the billiard ball, the latter is drawn slightly toward it, showing clearly that an attraction *does* exist, just as it did between the shell-lac which I rubbed and the piece of paper which was over-turned by it.

Now it is not very easy to make these things quite clear at the outset and I must take care not to leave anything unexplained as I proceed, and, therefore, I must make you clearly understand that all bodies are attracted to the earth, or, to use a more learned term, *gravitate*. You will not mind my using this word, for when I say that this penny-piece *gravitates,* I mean nothing more nor less than that it falls toward the earth, and, if not intercepted, it would go on falling, falling, until it arrived at what we call the *centre of gravity* of the earth, which I will explain to you by-and-by.

I want you to understand that this property of gravitation is never lost; that every substance possesses it; that there is never any change in the quantity of it; and, first of all, I will take as illustration a piece of marble. Now this marble has weight, as you will see if I put it in these scales; it weighs the balance down, and if I take it off, the balance goes back again and resumes its equilibrium. I can decompose this marble and change it in the same manner as I can change ice into water and water into steam. I can convert a part of it into *its own* steam easily, and show you that this steam from the marble has the property of remaining in the same place at common temperatures, which *water* steam has not. If I add a little liquid to the marble and decompose it (5), I get that which you see—[the lecturer here put several lumps of marble into a glass jar, and poured

5 *Add a little liquid to the marble and decompose it.* Marble is composed of *carbonic acid* and *lime,* and, in chemical language, is called *carbonate of lime.* When sulphuric acid is added to it, the carbonic acid is set free, and the sulphuric acid unites with the lime to form sulphate of lime.

Carbonic acid, under ordinary circumstances, is a colorless invisible gas, about half as heavy again as air. Dr. Faraday first showed that under great pressure it could be obtained in a liquid state. Thilorier, a French chemist, afterward found that it could be solidified.

water and then acid over them; the carbonic acid immediately com-
menced to escape with considerable effervescence]—the appearance
of boiling, which is only the separation of one part of the marble
from another. Now this [marble] steam, and that [water] steam,
and all other steams, *gravitate* just like any other substance does;
they all are attracted the one toward the other, and all fall toward the
earth, and what I want you to see is that *this* steam gravitates. I
have here (FIG. 2) a large vessel placed upon a balance, and the

FIG. 2

moment I pour this steam into it you see that the steam gravitates.
Just watch the index, and see whether it tilts over or not. [The
lecturer here poured the carbonic acid out of the glass in which it
was being generated into the vessel suspended on the balance, when
the gravitation of the carbonic acid was at once apparent.] Look
how it is going down. How pretty that is! I poured nothing in but
the invisible steam, or vapor, or gas which came from the marble,
but you see that part of the marble, although it has taken the shape
of air, still gravitates as it did before. Now will it weigh down that
bit of paper? [placing a piece of paper in the opposite scale.] Yes,
more than that; it nearly weighs down this bit of paper [placing
another piece of paper in]. And thus you see that *other* forms of
matter besides solids and liquids tend to fall to the earth; and,
therefore, you will accept from me the fact that *all* things gravitate,
whatever may be their form or condition. Now *here* is another
chemical test which is very readily applied. [Some of the carbonic
acid was poured from one vessel into another, and its presence in
the latter shown by introducing into it a lighted taper, which was
immediately extinguished.] You see from this result also that it

gravitates. All these experiments show you that, tried by the balance, tried by pouring like water from one vessel to another, this steam, or vapor, or gas is, like all other things, attracted to the earth.

There is another point I want in the next place to draw your attention to. I have here a quantity of shot; each of these falls separately, and each has its own gravitating power, as you perceive when I let them fall loosely on a sheet of paper. If I put them into a bottle, I collect them together as one mass, and philosophers have discovered that there is a certain point in the middle of the whole collection of shots that may be considered as the *one point* in which all their *gravitating power* is centred, and that point they call the *centre of gravity;* it is not at all a bad name, and rather a short one—the centre of gravity. Now suppose I take a sheet of pasteboard, or any other thing easily dealt with, and run a bradawl through it at

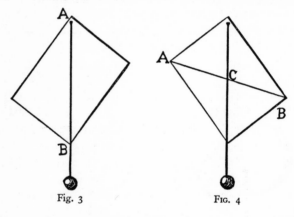

Fig. 3 FIG. 4

one corner, A (FIG. 3), and Mr. Anderson holds that up in his hand before us, and I then take a piece of thread and an ivory ball, and hang that upon the awl, then the centre of gravity of both the pasteboard and the ball and string are as near as they can get to the centre of the earth; that is to say, the whole of the attracting power of the earth is, as it were, centred in a single point of the cardboard, and this point is exactly below the point of suspension. All I have to do, therefore, is to draw a line, A B, corresponding with the string, and we shall find that the centre of gravity is somewhere in

that line. But where? To find that out, all we have to do is to take
another place for the awl (FIG. 4), hang the plumb-line, and make
the same experiment, and there [at the point C] is the centre of
gravity,—there where the two lines which I have traced cross each
other; and if I take that pasteboard and make a hole with the brad-
awl through it at that point, you will see that it will be supported
in any position in which it may be placed. Now, knowing that,
what do I do when I try to stand upon one leg? Do you not see
that I push myself over to the left side, and quietly take up the
right leg, and thus bring some central point in my body over this
left leg? What is that point which I throw over? You will know
at once that it is the *centre of gravity*—that point in me where the
whole gravitating force of my body is centred, and which I thus
bring in a line over my foot.

Here is a toy I happened to see the other day, which will, I think,
serve to illustrate our subject very well. That toy *ought* to lie some-
thing in this manner (FIG. 5), and would do so if it were uniform
in substance; but you see it does not; it will get up again. And now

FIG. 5 FIG. 6

philosophy comes to our aid, and I am perfectly sure, without look-
ing inside the figure, that there is some arrangement by which the
centre of gravity is at the lowest point when the image is standing
upright; and we may be certain, when I am tilting it over (see
FIG. 6), that I am lifting up the centre of gravity (*a*), and raising
it from the earth. All this is effected by putting a piece of lead
inside the lower part of the image, and making the base of large
curvature, and there you have the whole secret. But what will

happen if I try to make the figure stand upon a sharp point? You observe I must get that point exactly under the centre of gravity, or it will fall over thus [endeavoring unsuccessfully to balance it]; and

this, you see, is a difficult matter; I can not make it stand steadily; but if I embarrass this poor old lady with a world of trouble, and hang this wire with bullets at each end about her neck, it is very evident that, owing to there being those balls of lead hanging down on either side, in addition to the lead inside, I have lowered the centre of gravity, and now she will stand upon this point (FIG. 7), and, what is more, she proves the truth of our philosophy by standing sideways.

I remember an experiment which puzzled me very much when a boy. I read it in a conjuring book, and this

FIG. 7

was how the problem was put to us: "How," as the book said, "how to hang a pail of water, by means of a stick, upon the side of a table" (FIG. 8). Now I have here a table, a piece of stick, and a pail, and the

FIG. 8 FIG. 9

proposition is, how can that pail be hung to the edge of this table? It is to be done, and can you at all anticipate what arrangement I shall make to enable me to succeed? Why this. I take a stick, and put it in

the pail between the bottom and the horizontal piece of wood, and thus give it a stiff handle, and there it is; and, what is more, the more water I put into the pail, the better it will hang. It is very true that before I quite succeeded I had the misfortune to push the bottoms of several pails out; but here it is hanging firmly (Fig. 9), and you now see how you can hang up the pail in the way which the conjuring books require.

Again, if you are really so inclined (and I do hope all of you are), you will find a great deal of philosophy in this [holding up a cork and a pointed thin stick about a foot long]. Do not refer to your toy-books, and say you have seen that before. Answer me rather, if I ask you, have you *understood* it before? It is an experiment which appeared very wonderful to me when I was a boy. I used to take a piece of cork (and I remember I thought at first that it was very important that it should be cut out in the shape of a man, but by degrees I got rid of that idea), and the problem was to balance it on the

Fig. 10

point of a stick. Now you will see I have only to place two sharp-pointed sticks one on each side, and give it wings, thus, and you will find this beautiful condition fulfilled.

We come now to another point. All bodies, whether heavy or light, fall to the earth by this force which we call gravity. By observation, moreover, we see that bodies do not occupy the same time in falling; I think you will be able to see that this piece of paper and that ivory ball fall with different velocities to the table [dropping them]; and if, again, I take a feather and an ivory ball, and let them fall, you see they reach the table or earth at different times; that is to say, the ball falls faster than the feather. Now that should not be so, for all bodies do fall equally fast to the earth. There are one or two beautiful points included in that statement. First of all, it is manifest that an ounce, or a pound, or a ton, or a thousand tons, all fall equally fast, no one faster than another: here are two balls of lead, a very light one and a very heavy one, and you perceive they

both fall to the earth in the same time. Now if I were to put into a little bag a number of these balls sufficient to make up a bulk equal to the large one, they would also fall in the same time; for if an avalanche fall from the mountains, the rocks, snow, and ice, together falling toward the earth, fall with the same velocity, whatever be their size.

I can not take a better illustration of this than that of gold leaf, because it brings before us the reason of this apparent difference in the time of the fall. Here is a piece of gold leaf. Now if I take a lump of gold and this gold leaf, and let them fall through the air together, you see that the lump of gold—the sovereign or coin—will fall much faster than the gold leaf. But why? They are both gold, whether sovereign or gold leaf. Why should they not fall to the earth with the same quickness? *They would do so,* but that the air around our globe interferes very much where we have the piece of gold so extended and enlarged as to offer much obstruction on falling through it. I will, however, show you that gold leaf *does* fall as fast when the resistance of the air is excluded; for if I take a piece of gold leaf and hang it in the centre of a bottle so that the gold, and the bottle, and the air within shall all have an equal chance of falling, then the gold leaf will fall as fast as anything else. And if I suspend the bottle containing the gold leaf to a string, and set it oscillating like a pendulum, I may make it vibrate as hard as I please and the gold leaf will not be disturbed, but will swing as steadily as a piece of iron would do; and I might even swing it round my head with any degree of force, and it would remain undisturbed. Or I can try another kind of experiment: if I raise the gold leaf in this way [pulling the bottle up to the ceiling of the theatre by means of a cord and pulley, and then suddenly letting it fall within a few inches of the lecture table], and allow it then to fall from the ceiling downward (I will put something beneath to catch it, supposing I should be *maladroit*), you will perceive that the gold leaf is not in the least disturbed. The resistance of the air having been avoided, the glass bottle and gold leaf all fall exactly in the same time.

Here is another illustration: I have hung a piece of gold leaf in the upper part of this long glass vessel, and I have the means by a little arrangement at the top, of letting the gold leaf loose. Before

we let it loose we will remove the air by means of an air-pump, and, while that is being done, let me show you another experiment of the same kind. Take a penny-piece, or a half crown, and a round piece of paper a trifle smaller in diameter than the coin, and try them side by side to see whether they fall at the same time [dropping them]. You see they do not—the penny-piece goes down first. But, now place this paper flat on the top of the coin, so that it shall not meet with any resistance from the air, and upon *then* dropping them you see they *do* both fall in the same time [exhibiting the effect]. I dare say, if I were to put this piece of gold leaf, instead of the paper, on the coin, it would do as well. It is very difficult to lay the gold leaf so flat that the air shall not get under it and lift it up in falling, and I am rather doubtful as to the success of this, because the gold leaf is puckery, but will risk the experiment. There they go together! [letting them fall] and you see at once that they both reach the table at the same moment.

We have now pumped the air out of the vessel, and you will perceive that the gold leaf will fall as quickly in this vacuum as the coin does in the air. I am now going to let it loose, and you must watch to see how rapidly it falls. There! [letting the gold loose] there it is, falling as gold should fall.

I am sorry to see our time for parting is drawing so near. As we proceed, I intend to write upon the board behind me certain words, so as to recall to your minds what we have already examined; and I put the word FORCES as a heading, and I will then add beneath the names of the special forces according to the order in which we consider them; and although I fear that I have not sufficiently pointed out to you the more important circumstances connected with the force of GRAVITATION, especially the law which governs its attraction (for which, I think, I must take up a little time at our next meeting), still I will put that word on the board, and hope you will now remember that we have in some degree considered the *force of gravitation*—that force which causes all bodies to attract each other when they are at sensible distances apart, and tends to draw them together.

LECTURE II

GRAVITATION—COHESION

D O me the favor to pay me as much attention as you did at our last meeting, and I shall not repent of that which I have proposed to undertake. It will be impossible for us to consider the Laws of Nature, and what they effect, unless we now and then give our sole attention, so as to obtain a clear idea upon the subject. Give me now that attention, and then I trust we shall not part without our knowing something about those laws, and the manner in which they act. You recollect, upon the last occasion, I explained that all bodies attracted each other, and that this power we called *gravitation*. I told you that when we brought these two bodies [two equal-sized ivory balls suspended by threads] near together, they attracted each other, and that we might suppose that the whole power of this attraction was exerted between their respective centres of gravity; and, furthermore, you learned from me that if, instead of a small ball I took a larger one, like *that* [changing one of the balls for a much larger one], there was much more of this attraction exerted; or, if I made this ball larger and larger, until, if it were possible, it became as large as the Earth itself—or I might take the Earth itself as the large ball—that *then* the attraction would become so powerful as to cause them to rush together in this manner [dropping the ivory ball]. You sit *there* upright, and I stand upright *here,* because we keep our centres of gravity properly balanced with respect to the earth; and I need not tell you that on the other side of this world the people are standing and moving about with their feet toward our feet, in a reversed position as compared with us, and all by means of this power of gravitation to the centre of the earth.

I must not, however, leave the subject of gravitation without telling you something about its laws and regularity; and, first, as regards its power with respect to the distance that bodies are apart. If I take one of these balls and place it within an inch of the other,

they attract each other with a certain power. If I hold it at a greater distance off, they attract with less power; and if I hold it at a greater distance still, their attraction is still less. Now this fact is of the greatest consequence; for, knowing this law, philosophers have discovered most wonderful things. You know that there is a planet, Uranus, revolving round the sun with us, but eighteen hundred millions of miles off, and because there is another planet as far off as three thousand millions of miles, this law of attraction, or gravitation, still holds good, and philosophers actually discovered this latter planet, Neptune, by reason of the effects of its attraction at this overwhelming distance. Now I want you clearly to understand what this law is. They say (and they are right) that two bodies attract each other *inversely as the square of the distance*—a sad jumble of words until you understand them; but I think we shall soon comprehend what this law is, and what is the meaning of the "inverse square of the distance."

I have here (Fig. 11) a lamp, A, shining most intensely upon this disc, B, C, D, and this light acts as a sun by which I can get a

shadow from this little screen B F (merely a square piece of card), which, as you know, when I place it close to the large screen, just shadows as much of it as is exactly equal to its own size; but now let me take this card, E, which is equal to the other one in size, and place it midway between the lamp and the screen; now look at the

size of the shadow B D—it is four times the original size. Here, then, comes the "inverse square of the distance." This distance, A E, is *one,* and that distance, A B, is *two,* but that size E being *one,* this size B D of shadow is *four* instead of *two,* which is the *square* of the distance, and, if I put the screen at one-third of the distance from the lamp, the shadow on the large screen would be *nine* times the size. Again, if I hold this screen *here,* at B F, a certain amount of light falls on it; and if I hold it nearer the lamp at E, *more* light shines upon it. And you see at once how much—exactly the quantity which I have shut off from the part of this screen, B D, now in shadow; moreover, you see that if I put a single screen here, at G, by the side of the shadow, it can only receive *one-fourth* of the proportion of light which is obstructed. That, then, is what is meant by the *inverse* of the square of the distance. This screen E is the brightest because it is the nearest, and there is the whole secret of this curious expression, *inversely as the square of the distance.* Now if you can not perfectly recollect this when you go home, get a candle and throw a shadow of something—your profile, if you like—on the wall and then recede or advance, and you will find that your shadow is exactly in proportion to the *square* of the distance you are off the wall; and then, if you consider how much light shines on you at one distance, and how much at another, you get the inverse accordingly. So it is as regards the attraction of these two balls; they attract according to the square of the distance, inversely. I want you to try and remember these words, and then you will be able to go into all the calculations of astronomers as to the planets and other bodies, and tell why they move so fast, and why they go *round* the sun without falling into it and be prepared to enter upon many other interesting inquiries of the like nature.

Let us now leave this subject which I have written upon the board under the word FORCE—GRAVITATION—and go a step farther. All bodies attract each other at sensible distances. I showed you the electric attraction on the last occasion (though I did not call it so); that attracts at a distance; and in order to make our progress a little more gradual, suppose I take a few iron particles [dropping some small fragments of iron on the table]. There! I have already told you that in all cases where bodies fall it is the *particles* that are

attracted. You may consider these, then, as separate particles magni-
fied, so as to be evident to your sight; they are loose from each other
—they all gravitate—they all fall to the earth—for the force of gravi-
tation *never* fails. Now I have here a centre of power which I will
not name at present, and when these particles are placed upon it,
see what an attraction they have for each other.

Here I have an arch of iron filings (FIG. 12) regularly built up like
an iron bridge, because I have put them within a sphere of action
which will cause them to attract each other. See! I could let a mouse
run through it; and yet, if I try to do the same thing with them
here [on the table], they do not attract each other at all. It is *that*

[the magnet] which makes them hold
together. Now just as these iron particles
hold together in the form of an elliptical
bridge, so do the different particles of
iron which constitute this nail hold to-
gether and make it one. And here is a
bar of iron; why, it is only because the
different parts of *this* iron are so wrought
as to keep close together by the attraction
between the particles that it is held to-
gether in one mass. It is kept together, in
fact, merely by the attraction of one

FIG. 12

particle to another, and that is the point I want now to illustrate.
If I take a piece of flint, and strike it with a hammer, and break it
thus [breaking off a piece of the flint], I have done nothing more
than separate the particles which compose these two pieces so far
apart that their attraction is too weak to cause them to hold together,
and it is only for that reason that there are now two pieces in the
place of one. I will show you an experiment to prove that this
attraction does still exist in those particles; for here is a piece of glass
(for what was true of the flint and the bar of iron is true of the
piece of glass, and is true of every other solid—they are all held
together in the lump by the attraction between their parts), and I
can show you the attraction between its separate particles; for if I
take these portions of glass which I have reduced to very fine powder,
you see that I can actually build them up into a solid wall by pressure

between two flat surfaces. The power which I thus have of building up this wall is due to the attraction of the particles, forming, as it were, the cement which holds them together; and so in this case, where I have taken no very great pains to bring the particles together, you see perhaps a couple of ounces of finely pounded glass standing as an upright wall: is not this attraction most wonderful? *That* bar of iron one inch square has such power of attraction in its particles— giving to it such strength—that it will hold up twenty tons' weight before the little set of particles in the small space equal to one division across which it can be pulled apart will separate. In this manner suspension bridges and chains are held together by the attraction of their particles, and I am going to make an experiment which will show how strong is this attraction of the particles. [The lecturer here placed his foot on a loop of wire fastened to a support above, and swung with his whole weight resting upon it for some moments.] You see, while hanging here, all my weight is supported by these little particles of the wire, just as in pantomimes they sometimes suspend gentlemen and damsels.

How can we make this attraction of the particles a little more simple? There are many things which, if brought together properly, will show this attraction. Here is a boy's experiment (and I like a boy's experiment). Get a tobacco-pipe, fill it with lead, melt it, and then pour it out upon a stone, and thus get a clean piece of lead (this is a better plan than scraping it; scraping alters the condition of the surface of the lead). I have here some pieces of lead which I melted this morning for the sake of making them clean. Now these pieces of lead hang together by the attraction of their particles, and if I press these two separate pieces close together, so as to bring their particles within the sphere of attraction, you will see how soon they become one. I have merely to give them a good squeeze, and draw the upper piece slightly round at the same time, and here they are as one, and all the bending and twisting I can give them will not separate them again; I have joined the lead together, not with solder, but simply by means of the attraction of the particles.

This, however, is not the best way of bringing those particles together; we have many better plans than that; and I will show you one that will do very well for juvenile experiments. There is some

alum crystallized very beautifully by nature (for all things are far more beautiful in their natural than their artificial form), and here I have some of the same alum broken into fine powder. In it I have destroyed that force of which I have placed the name on this board —COHESION, or the attraction exerted between the particles of bodies to hold them together. Now I am going to show you that if we take this powdered alum and some hot water, and mix them together, I shall dissolve the alum; all the particles will be separated by the water far more completely than they are here in the powder; but then, being in the water, they will have the opportunity as it cools (for that is the condition which favors their coalescence) of uniting together again and forming one mass ([6]).

Now, having brought the alum into solution, I will pour it into this glass basin, and you will, to-morrow, find that these particles of alum which I have put into the water, and so separated that they are no longer solid, will, as the water cools, come together and cohere, and by to-morrow morning we shall have a great deal of the alum crystallized out—that is to say, come back to the solid form. [The lecturer here poured a little of the hot solution of alum into the glass dish, and when the latter had thus been made warm, the remainder of the solution was added.] I am now doing that which I advise you to do if you use a glass vessel, namely, warming it slowly and gradually; and in repeating this experiment, do as I do—pour the liquid out gently, leaving all the dirt behind in the basin; and remember that the more carefully and quietly you make this experiment at home, the better the crystals. To-morrow you will see the particles of alum drawn together; and if I put two pieces of coke in some part of the solution (the coke ought first to be washed very clean, and dried), you will find to-morrow that we shall have a beautiful crystallization over the coke, making it exactly resemble a natural mineral.

Now how curiously our ideas expand by watching these conditions of the attraction of cohesion! how many new phenomena it gives

[6] *Crystallization of alum.* The solution must be saturated—that is, it must contain as much alum as can possibly be dissolved. In making the solution, it is best to add powdered alum to hot water as long as it dissolves; and when no more is taken up, allow the solution to stand a few minutes, and then pour it off from the dirt and undissolved alum.

us beyond those of the attraction of gravitation! See how it gives us great strength. The things we deal with in building up the structures on the earth are of strength—we use iron, stone, and other things of great strength; and only think that all those structures you have about you—think of the *Great Eastern,* if you please, which is of such size and power as to be almost more than man can manage— are the result of this power of cohesion and attraction.

I have here a body in which I believe you will see a change taking place in its condition of cohesion at the moment it is made. It is at first yellow; it then becomes a fine crimson red. Just watch when I pour these two liquids together—both colorless as water. [The lecturer here mixed together solutions of perchloride of mercury and iodide of potassium, when a yellow precipitate of biniodide of mercury fell down, which almost immediately became crimson red.] Now there is a substance which is very beautiful, but see how it is changing color. It was reddish-yellow at first, but it has now become red ([7]). I have previously prepared a little of this red substance, which you see formed in the liquid, and have put some of it upon paper [exhibiting several sheets of paper coated with scarlet biniodide of mercury ([8])]. There it is—the same substance spread upon paper; and there, too, is the same substance; and here is some more of it [exhibiting a piece of paper as large as the other sheets, but having only very little red color on it, the greater part being yellow]—a *little* more of it, you will say. Do not be mistaken; there is as much upon the surface of one of these pieces of paper as upon the other. What you see yellow is the same thing as the red body, only the attraction of cohesion is in a certain degree changed, for I will take this red body, and apply heat to it (you may perhaps see a little

[7] *Red precipitate of biniodide of mercury.* A little care is necessary to obtain this precipitate. The solution of iodide of potassium should be added to the solution of perchloride of mercury (corrosive sublimate) very gradually. The red precipitate which first falls is redissolved when the liquid is stirred: when a little more of the iodide of potassium is added a pale red precipitate is formed, which, on the farther addition of the iodide, changes into the brilliant scarlet biniodide of mercury. If too much iodide of potassium is added, the scarlet precipitate disappears, and a colorless solution is left.

[8] *Paper coated with scarlet biniodide of mercury.* In order to fix the biniodide on paper, it must be mixed with a little weak gum water, and then spread over the paper, which must be dried without heat.

Biniodide of mercury is said to be *dimorphous;* that is, is able to assume two different forms.

smoke arise, but that is of no consequence), and if you look at it it
will first of all darken—but see how it is becoming yellow. I have
now made it all yellow, and, what is more, it will remain so; but if I
take any hard substance, and rub the yellow part with it, it will
immediately go back again to the red condition [exhibiting the ex-
periment]. There it is. You see the red is not *put back,* but *brought
back* by the change in the substance. Now [warming it over the
spirit lamp] here it is becoming yellow again, and that is all because
its attraction of cohesion is changed. And what will you say to me
when I tell you that this piece of common charcoal is just the same
thing, only differently coalesced, as the diamonds which you wear?
(I have put a specimen outside of a piece of straw which was
charred in a particular way—it is just like black lead.) Now this
charred straw, this charcoal, and these diamonds, are all of them the
same substance, changed but in their properties as respects the force
of cohesion.

Here is a piece of glass [producing a piece of plate-glass about two
inches square]. (I shall want this afterward to look to and examine

FIG. 13 FIG. 14

its internal condition), and here is some of the same sort of glass
differing only in its power of cohesion, because while yet melted it
had been dropped into cold water [exhibiting a "Prince Rupert's
drop,"([9]) (FIG. 13)], and if I take one of these little tear-like pieces
and break off ever so little from the point, the whole will at once
burst and fall to pieces. I will now break off a piece of this. [The

[9] *"Prince Rupert's Drops."* These are made by pouring drops of melted green
glass into cold water. They were not, as is commonly supposed, invented by Prince
Rupert, but were first brought to England by him in 1660. They excited a great
deal of curiosity, and were considered "a kind of miracle in nature."

lecturer nipped off a small piece from the end of one of Rupert's drops, whereupon the whole immediately fell to pieces.] There! you see the solid glass has suddenly become powder, and more than that, it has knocked a hole in the glass vessel in which it was held. I can show the effect better in this bottle of water, and it is very likely the whole bottle will go. [A 6-oz. vial was filled with water, and a Rupert's drop placed in it with the point of the tail just projecting out; upon breaking the tip off, the drop burst, and the shock, being transmitted through the water to the sides of the bottle, shattered the latter to pieces.]

Here is another form of the same kind of experiment. I have here some more glass which has not been annealed [showing some thick glass vessels([10]) (FIG. 14)], and if I take one of these glass vessels and drop a piece of pounded glass into it (or I will take some of these small pieces of rock crystal; they have the advantage of being harder than glass), and so make the least scratch upon the inside, the whole bottle will break to pieces—it can not hold together. [The lecturer here dropped a small fragment of rock crystal into one of these glass vessels, when the bottom immediately came out and fell upon the plate.] There! it goes through, just as it would through a sieve.

Now I have shown you these things for the purpose of bringing your minds to see that bodies are not merely held together by this power of cohesion, but that they are held together in very curious ways. And suppose I take some things that are held together by this force, and examine them more minutely. I will first take a bit of glass, and if I give it a blow with a hammer I shall just break it to pieces. You saw how it was in the case of the flint when I broke the piece off; a piece of a similar kind would come off, just as you would expect; and if I were to break it up still more, it would be, as you have seen, simply a collection of small particles of no definite shape or form. But supposing I take some other thing—this stone, for instance (FIG. 15) [taking a piece of mica([11])], and if I hammer this stone I may batter it a great deal before I can break it up. I may even bend it without breaking it—that is to say, I may bend it in

[10] *Thick glass vessels.* They are called *Proofs* or *Bologna phials.*

[11] *Mica.* A silicate of alumina and magnesia. It has a bright metallic lustre; hence its name, from *mico,* to shine.

one particular direction without breaking it much, although I feel in my hands that I am doing it some injury. But now, if I take it by the edges, I find that it breaks up into leaf after leaf in a most extraordinary manner. Why should it break up like that? Not because all stones do, or all crystals; for there is some salt (FIG. 16)— you know what common salt is ([12]); here is a piece of this salt, which by natural circumstances has had its particles so brought together

FIG. 15 FIG. 16 FIG. 17

that they have been allowed free opportunity of combining or coalescing, and you shall see what happens if I take this piece of salt and break it. It does not break as flint did, or as the mica did, but with a clean sharp angle and exact surfaces, beautiful and glittering as diamonds [breaking it by gentle blows with a hammer]; there is a square prism which I may break up into a square cube. You see these fragments are all square; one side may be longer than the other, but they will only split up so as to form square or oblong pieces with cubical sides. Now I go a little farther, and I find another stone (FIG. 17) [Iceland or calc-spar] ([13]) which I may break in a similar way, but *not* with the same result. Here is a piece which I have broken off, and you see there are plain surfaces perfectly regular with respect to each other, but it is not cubical—it is what we call a rhomboid. It still breaks in three directions most beautifully and regularly with polished surfaces, but with *sloping* sides, not like the salt. Why not? It is very manifest that this is owing to the attraction of the particles one for the other being less in the direction in which they give way than in other directions. I have on the table before me a number of little bits of calcareous spar, and

[12] *Common salt* or chloride of sodium crystallizes in the form of solid cubes, which, aggregated together, form a mass, which may be broken up into the separate cubes.
[13] *Iceland* or *calc-spar*. Native carbonate of lime in its primitive crystalline form.

I recommend each of you to take a piece home, and then you can take a knife and try to divide it in the direction of any of the surfaces already existing. You will be able to do it at once; but if you try to cut it *across* the crystals, you can not; by hammering you may bruise and break it up, but you can only divide it into these beautiful little rhomboids.

Now I want you to understand a little more how this is, and for this purpose I am going to use the electric light again. You see we can not look into the *middle* of a body like this piece of glass. We perceive the outside form and the inside form, and we look *through* it, but we can not well find out how these forms become so, and I

FIG. 18

want you, therefore, to take a lesson in the way in which we use a ray of light for the purpose of seeing what is in the interior of bodies. Light is a thing which is, so to say, attracted by every substance that gravitates (and we do not know any thing that does not). All matter affects light more or less by what we may consider as a kind of attraction, and I have arranged (FIG. 18) a very simple experiment upon the floor of the room for the purpose of illustrating this. I have put into that basin a few things which those who are in the body of the theatre will not be able to see, and I am going to make use of this power which matter possesses of attracting a ray of light. If Mr. Anderson pours some water, gently and steadily, into the basin, the water will attract the rays of light downward, and the piece of silver and the sealing-wax will appear to rise up into the sight of those who were before not high enough to see over the side of the basin to its bottom. [Mr. Anderson here poured water into the basin, and upon the lecturer asking whether any body could

see the silver and sealing-wax, he was answered by a general affirm-
ative.] Now I suppose that every body can see that they are not at all
disturbed, while from the way they appear to have risen up you
would imagine the bottom of the basin and the articles in it were
two inches thick, although they are only one of our small silver
dishes and a piece of sealing-wax which I have put there. The light
which now goes to you from that piece of silver was obstructed by
the edge of the basin when there was no water there, and you were
unable to see anything of it; but when we poured in water the rays
were attracted down by it over the edge of the basin, and you were
thus enabled to see the articles at the bottom.

I have shown you this experiment first, so that you might under-
stand how glass attracts light, and might then see how other sub-
stances like rock-salt and calcareous spar, mica, and other stones,
would affect the light; and, if Dr. Tyndall will be good enough to
let us use his light again, we will first of all show you how it may
be bent by a piece of glass (FIG. 19). [The electric lamp was again

FIG. 19

lit, and the beam of parallel rays of light which it emitted was bent
about and decomposed by means of the prism.] Now, here you see,
if I send the light through this piece of plain glass, A, it goes straight
through without being bent (unless the glass be held obliquely, and
then the phenomenon becomes more complicated); but if I take this
piece of glass, B [a prism], you see it will show a very different
effect. It no longer goes to that wall, but it is bent to this screen, C,
and how much more beautiful it is now [throwing the prismatic
spectrum on the screen]. This ray of light is bent out of its course
by the attraction of the glass upon it; and you see I can turn and
twist the rays to and fro in different parts of the room, just as I
please. Now it goes there, now here. [The lecturer projected the

prismatic spectrum about the theatre.] Here I have the rays once more bent on to the screen, and you see how wonderfully and beautifully that piece of glass not only bends the light by virtue of its attraction, but actually splits it up into different colors. Now I want you to understand that this piece of glass [the prism], being perfectly uniform in its internal structure, tells us about the action of these other bodies which are not uniform—which do not merely *cohere,* but also have within them, in different parts, different *degrees of cohesion,* and thus attract and bend the light with varying powers. We will now let the light pass through one or two of these things which I just now showed you broke so curiously; and, first of all, I will take a piece of mica. Here, you see, is our ray of light: we have first to make it what we call *polarized;* but about that you need not trouble yourselves; it is only to make our illustration more clear. Here, then, we have our polarized ray of light, and I can so adjust it as to make the screen upon which it is shining either light or dark, although I have nothing in the course of this ray of light but what is perfectly transparent [turning the *analyzer* round]. I will now make it so that it is quite dark, and we will, in the first instance, put a piece of common glass into the polarized ray so as to show you that it does not enable the light to get through. You see the screen remains dark. The glass, then, internally, has no effect upon light. [The glass was removed and a piece of mica introduced.] Now there is the mica which we split up so curiously into leaf after leaf, and see how that enables the light to pass through to the screen, and how, as Dr. Tyndall turns it round in his hand, you have those different colors, pink, and purple, and green, coming and going most beautifully; not that the mica is more transparent than the glass, but because of the different manner in which its particles are arranged by the force of cohesion.

Now we will see how calcareous spar acts upon this light—that stone which split up into rhombs, and of which you are each of you going to take a little piece home. [The mica was removed, and a piece of calc-spar introduced at A.] See how that turns the light round and round, and produces these rings and that black cross (FIG. 20). Look at those colors: are they not most beautiful for you and for me? (for I enjoy these things as much as you do). In what

a wonderful manner they open out to us the internal arrangement of the particles of this calcareous spar by the force of cohesion.

And now I will show you another experiment. Here is that piece of glass which before had no action upon the light. You shall see what it will do when we apply pressure to it. Here, then, we have our ray of polarized light, and I will first of all show you that the

Fig. 20

glass has no effect upon it in its ordinary state; when I place it in the course of the light, the screen still remains dark. Now Dr. Tyndall will press that bit of glass between three little points, one point against two, so as to bring a strain upon the parts, and you will see what a curious effect that has. [Upon the screen two white dots gradually appeared.] Ah! these points show the position of the strain; in these parts the force of cohesion is being exerted in a different degree to what it is in the other parts, and hence it allows the light to pass through. How beautiful that is! how it makes the light come through some parts and leaves it dark in others, and all because we weaken the force of cohesion between particle and particle. Whether you have this mechanical power of straining, or whether we take other means, we get the same result; and, indeed, I will show you by another experiment that if we heat the glass in one part, it will alter its internal structure and produce a similar effect. Here is a piece of common glass, and if I insert this in the path of the polarized ray, I believe it will do nothing. There is the common glass [introducing it]. No light passes through; the screen remains quite dark; but I am going to warm this glass in the lamp, and you know yourselves that when you pour warm water upon

glass you put a strain upon it sufficient to break it sometimes—something like there was in the case of the Prince Rupert's drops. [The glass was warmed in the spirit lamp, and again placed across the ray of light.] Now you see how beautifully the light goes through those parts which are hot, making dark and light lines just as the crystal did, and all because of the alteration I have effected in its internal condition; for these dark and light parts are a proof of the presence of forces acting and dragging in different directions within the solid mass.

LECTURE III

COHESION—CHEMICAL AFFINITY

WE will first return for a few minutes to one of the experiments made yesterday. You remember what we put together on that occasion—powdered alum and warm water. Here is one of the basins then used. Nothing has been done to it since; but you will find, on examining it, that it no longer contains any powder, but a number of beautiful crystals. Here also are the pieces of coke which I put into the other basin; they have a fine mass of crystals about them. That other basin I will leave as it is. I will not pour the water from it, because it will show you that the particles of alum have done something more than merely crystallize together. They have pushed the dirty matter from them, laying it around the outside or outer edge of the lower crystals—squeezed out, as it were, by the strong attraction which the particles of alum have for each other.

And now for another experiment. We have already gained a knowledge of the manner in which the particles of bodies—of solid bodies—attract each other, and we have learned that it makes calcareous spar, and so forth, crystallize in these regular forms. Now let me gradually lead your minds to a knowledge of the means we possess of making this attraction alter a little in its force; either of increasing, or diminishing, or, apparently, of destroying it altogether. I will take this piece of iron [a rod of iron about two feet long and a quarter of an inch in diameter]. It has at present a great deal of strength, due to its attraction of cohesion; but if Mr. Anderson will make part of this red-hot in the fire, we shall then find that it will become soft, just as sealing-wax will when heated, and we shall also find that the more it is heated the softer it becomes. Ah! but what does *soft* mean? Why, that the attraction between the particles is so weakened that it is no longer sufficient to resist the power we bring to bear upon it. [Mr. Anderson handed to the

37

lecturer the iron rod, with one end red-hot, which he showed could be easily twisted about with a pair of pliers.] You see I now find no difficulty in bending this end about as I like, whereas I can not bend the cold part at all. And you know how the smith takes a piece of iron and heats it in order to render it soft for his purpose: he acts upon our principle of lessening the adhesion of the particles, although he is not exactly acquainted with the terms by which we express it.

And now we have another point to examine, and this water is again a very good substance to take as an illustration (as philosophers we call it all water, even though it be in the form of ice or steam). Why is this water hard? [pointing to a block of ice]; because the attraction of the particles to each other is sufficient to make them retain their places in opposition to force applied to it. But what happens when we make the ice warm? Why, in that case we diminish to such a large extent the power of attraction that the solid substance is destroyed altogether. Let me illustrate this: I will take a red-hot ball of iron [Mr. Anderson, by means of a pair of tongs, handed to the lecturer a red-hot ball of iron, about two inches in diameter], because it will serve as a convenient source of heat [placing the red-hot iron in the centre of the block of ice]. You see I am now melting the ice where the iron touches it. You see the iron sinking into it; and while part of the solid water is becoming liquid, the heat of the ball is rapidly going off. A certain part of the water is actually rising in steam, the attraction of some of the particles is so much diminished that they can not even hold together in the liquid form, but escape as vapor. At the same time, you see I can not melt all this ice by the heat contained in this ball. In the course of a very short time I shall find it will have become quite cold.

Here is the water which we have produced by destroying some of the attraction which existed between the particles of the ice, for below a certain temperature the particles of water increase in their mutual attraction and become ice; and above a certain temperature the attraction decreases and the water becomes steam. And exactly the same thing happens with platinum, and nearly every substance in nature; if the temperature is increased to a certain point it becomes

liquid and a farther increase converts it into a gas. Is it not a glorious thing for us to look at the sea, the rivers, and so forth, and to know that this same body in the northern regions is all solid ice and ice-bergs, while here, in a warmer climate, it has its attraction of cohesion so much diminished as to be liquid water? Well, in dimin-ishing this force of attraction between the particles of ice, we made use of another force, namely, that of *heat;* and I want you now to understand that this force of heat is always concerned when water passes from the solid to the liquid state. If I melt ice in *other* ways I can not do without heat (for we have the means of making ice liquid without heat—that is to say, without using heat as a *direct* cause). Suppose, for illustration, I make a vessel out of this piece of tinfoil [bending the foil up into the shape of a dish]. I am making it metallic, because I want the heat which I am about to deal with to pass readily through it; and I am going to pour a little water on this board, and then place the tin vessel on it. Now if I put some of this ice into the metal dish, and then proceed to make it liquid by any of the various means we have at our command, it still must take the necessary quantity of heat from something, and in this case it will take the heat from the tray, and from the water underneath, and from the other things round about. Well, a little salt added to the ice has the power of causing it to melt, and we shall very shortly see the mixture become quite fluid, and you will then find that the water beneath will be frozen—frozen because it has been forced to give up that heat which is necessary to keep it in the liquid state to the ice on becoming liquid. I remember once, when I was a boy, hearing of a trick in a country ale-house: the point was how to melt ice in a quart pot by the fire and freeze it to the stool. Well, the way they did it was this: they put some pounded ice in a pewter pot, and added some salt to it, and the consequence was that when the salt was mixed with it, the ice in the pot melted (they did not tell me any thing about the salt and they set the pot by the fire, just to make the result more mysterious), and in a short time the pot and the stool were frozen together, as we shall very shortly find it to be the case here, and all because salt has the power of lessening the attraction between the particles of ice. Here you see the tin dish is frozen to the board; I can even lift the little stool up by it.

This experiment can not, I think, fail to impress upon your minds the fact that whenever a solid body loses some of that force of attraction by means of which it remains solid, heat is absorbed; and if, on the other hand, we convert a liquid into a solid, *e. g.,* water into ice, a corresponding amount of heat is given out. I have an experiment showing this to be the case. Here (FIG. 21) is a bulb, A, filled

FIG. 21

with air, the tube from which dips into some colored liquid in the vessel B. And I dare say you know that if I put my hand on the bulb A, and warm it, the colored liquid which is now standing in the tube at C will travel forward. Now we have discovered a means, by great care and research into the properties of various bodies, of preparing a solution of a salt ([14]) which, if shaken or disturbed, will at once become a solid; and as I explained to you just now (for what is true of water is true of every other liquid), by reason of its becoming solid heat is evolved, and I can make this evident to you by pouring it over this bulb; there! it is becoming solid; and look at the colored liquid, how it is being driven down the tube, and how it is bubbling out through the water at the end; and so we learn this beautiful law of our philosophy, that whenever we diminish the attraction of cohesion we absorb heat, and whenever we increase that attraction heat is evolved. This, then, is a great step in advance, for you have learned a great deal in addition to the mere circumstance that particles attract each other. But you must not now suppose that because they are liquid they have lost their attraction

[14] *Solution of a salt.* Acetate of soda. A solution saturated, or nearly so, at the boiling point, is necessary, and it must be allowed to cool, and remain at rest until the experiment is made.

of cohesion; for here is the fluid mercury, and if I pour it from one vessel into another, I find that it will form a stream from the bottle down to the glass—a continuous rod of fluid mercury, the particles of which have attraction sufficient to make them hold together all the way through the air down to the glass itself; and if I pour water quietly from a jug, I can cause it to run in a continuous stream in the same manner. Again: let me put a little water on this piece of plate glass, and then take another plate of glass and put it on the water; there! the upper plate is quite free to move, gliding about on the lower one from side to side; and yet, if I take hold of the upper plate and lift it up straight, the cohesion is so great that the lower one is held up by it. See how it runs about as I move the upper one, and this is all owing to the strong attraction of the particles of the water. Let me show you another experiment. If I take a little soap and water—not that the soap makes the particles of the water more adhesive one for the other, but it certainly has the power of continuing in a better manner the attraction of the particles (and let me advise you, when about to experiment with soap-bubbles, to take care to have every thing clean and soapy). I will now blow a bubble, and that I may be able to talk and blow a bubble too, I will take a plate with a little of the soapsuds in it, and will just soap the edges of the pipe and blow a bubble on to the plate. Now there is our bubble. Why does it hold together in this manner? Why, because the water of which it is composed has an attraction of particle for particle—so great, indeed, that it gives to this bubble the very power of an India-rubber ball; for you see, if I introduce one end of this glass tube into the bubble, that it has the power of contracting so powerfully as to force enough air through the tube to blow out a light (FIG. 22); the light is blown out. And look! see how the bubble is disappearing—see how it is getting smaller and smaller.

There are twenty other experiments I might show you to illustrate this power of cohesion of the particles of liquids. For instance, what would you propose to me if, having lost the stopper out of this alcohol bottle, I should want to close it speedily with something near at hand. Well, a bit of paper would not do, but a piece of linen cloth would, or some of this cotton wool which I have here. I will put a

tuft of it into the neck of the alcohol bottle, and you see, when I turn it upside down, that it is perfectly well stoppered so far as the alcohol is concerned; the air can pass through, but the alcohol can not. And if I were to take an oil vessel this plan would do equally well, for in former times they used to send us oil from Italy in flasks stoppered only with cotton wool (at the present time the cotton is put in after the oil has arrived here, but formerly it used to be sent so stoppered). Now if it were not for the particles of liquid cohering together, this alcohol would run out; and if I had time I

FIG. 22 FIG. 23

could have shown you a vessel with the top, bottom, and sides altogether formed like a sieve, and yet it would hold water, owing to the cohesion.

You have now seen that the solid water can become fluid by the addition of heat, owing to this lessening the attractive force between its particles, and yet you see that there is a good deal of attractive force remaining behind. I want now to take you another step beyond. We saw that if we continued applying heat to the water (as indeed happened with our piece of ice here), that we did at last break up that attraction which holds the liquid together, and I am about to take some other (any other liquid would do, but ether makes a better experiment for my purpose) in order to illustrate what will happen when this cohesion is broken up. Now this liquid ether, if exposed to a very low temperature, will become a solid; but if we apply heat to it, it becomes vapor; and I want to show you the enormous bulk of the substance in this new form: when we make ice into water, we lessen its bulk; but when we convert water into steam, we increase it to an enormous extent. You see it is very clear that as I apply heat to the liquid I diminish its attraction of co-

hesion; it is now boiling, and I will set fire to the vapor, so that you may be enabled to judge of the space occupied by the ether in this form by the size of its flame; and you now see what an enormously bulky flame I get from that small volume of ether below. The heat from the spirit lamp is now being consumed, not in making the ether any warmer, but in converting it into vapor; and if I desired to catch this vapor and condense it (as I could without much difficulty), I should have to do the same as if I wished to convert steam into water and water into ice: in either case it would be necessary to increase the attraction of the particles by cold or otherwise. So largely is the bulk occupied by the particles increased by giving them this diminished attraction, that if I were to take a portion of water a cubic inch in bulk (A, FIG. 23), I should produce a volume of steam of that size, B [1,700 cubic inches; nearly a cubic foot], so greatly is the attraction of cohesion diminished by heat; and yet it still remains water. You can easily imagine the consequences which are due to this change in volume by heat—the mighty powers of steam and the tremendous explosions which are sometimes produced by this force of water. I want you now to see another experiment, which will perhaps give you a better illustration of the bulk occupied by a body when in the state of vapor. Here is a substance which we call iodine, and I am about to submit this solid body to the same kind of condition as regards heat that I did the water and the ether [putting a few grains of iodine into a hot glass globe, which immediately became filled with the violet vapor], and you see the same kind of change produced. Moreover, it gives us the opportunity of observing how beautiful is the violet-colored vapor from this black substance, or rather the mixture of the vapor with air (for I would not wish you to understand that this globe is entirely filled with the vapor of iodine).

If I had taken mercury and converted it into vapor (as I could easily do), I should have a perfectly colorless vapor; for you must understand this about vapors, that bodies in what we call the vaporous or the gaseous state are always perfectly transparent, never cloudy or smoky; they are, however, often colored, and we can frequently have colored vapors or gases produced by colorless particles themselves mixing together, as in this case [the lecturer here

inverted a glass cylinder full of binoxide of nitrogen ([15]) over a cylinder of oxygen, when the dark red vapor of hyponitrous acid was produced]. Here also you see a very excellent illustration of the effect of a power of nature which we have not as yet come to, but which stands next on our list—CHEMICAL AFFINITY. And thus you see we can have a violet vapor or an orange vapor, and different other kinds of vapor, but they are always perfectly transparent, or else they would cease to be vapors.

I am now going to lead you a step beyond this consideration of the attraction of the particles for each other. You see we have come to understand that, if we take water as an illustration, whether it be ice, or water, or steam, it is always to be considered by us as water. Well, now prepare your minds to go a little deeper into the subject. We have means of searching into the constitution of water beyond any that are afforded us by the action of heat, and among these one of the most important is that force which we call voltaic electricity, which we used at our last meeting for the purpose of obtaining light, and which we carried about the room by means of these wires. This force is produced by the battery behind me, to which, however, I will not now refer more particularly; before we have done we shall know more about this battery, but it must grow up in our knowledge as we proceed. Now here (FIG. 24) is a portion of water in this little vessel, C, and besides the water there are two plates of the metal platinum, which are connected with the wires (A and B) coming outside, and I want to examine that water, and the state and the condition in which its particles are arranged. If I were to apply heat to it you know what we should get; it would assume the state of vapor, but it would nevertheless remain water, and would return to the liquid state as soon as the heat was removed. Now by means of these wires (which are connected with the battery behind me, and come under the floor and up through the table) we shall have a certain amount of this new power at our disposal. Here

[15] *Binoxide of nitrogen* and *hyponitrous acid*. Binoxide of nitrogen is formed when nitric acid and a little water are added to some copper turnings. It produces deep red fumes as soon as it comes in contact with the air, by combining with the oxygen of the latter to form hyponitrous acid. *Binoxide of nitrogen* is composed of two parts of oxygen and one part of nitrogen; *hyponitrous acid* is composed of one part of nitrogen and three parts of oxygen.

you see it is [causing the ends of the wires to touch]—that is the electric light we used yesterday, and by means of these wires we can cause water to submit itself to this power; for the moment I put them into metallic connection (at A and B), you see the water boiling in that little vessel (C), and you hear the bubbling of the gas that is going through the tube (D). See how I am converting the water into vapor; and if I take a little vessel (E), and fill it with water, and put it into the trough over the end of the tube (D),

Fig. 24

there goes the vapor ascending into the vessel. And yet that is not steam, for you know that if steam is brought near cold water, it would at once condense, and return back again to water; this, then, can not be steam, for it is bubbling through the cold water in this trough; but it is a vaporous substance, and we must therefore examine it carefully, to see in what way the water has been changed. And now, in order to give you a proof that it is not steam, I am going to show you that it is combustible; for if I take this small vessel to a light, the vapor inside explodes in a manner that steam could never do.

I will now fill this large bell-jar (F) with water; and I propose letting the gas ascend into it, and I will then show you that we can reproduce the water back again from the vapor or air that is there. Here is a strong glass vessel (G), and into it we will let the gas (from F) pass. We will there fire it by the electric spark, and then,

after the explosion, you will find that we have got the water back again; it will not be much, however, for you will recollect that I showed you how small a portion of water produced a very large volume of vapor. Mr. Anderson will now pump all the air out of this vessel (G), and when I have screwed it on to the top of our jar of gas (F), you will see, upon opening the stop-cocks (H H H), the water will jump up, showing that some of the gas has passed into the glass vessel. I will now shut these stop-cocks, and we shall be able to send the electric spark through the gas by means of the wires (I, K) in the upper part of the vessel, and you will see it burn with a most intense flash. [Mr. Anderson here brought a Leyden jar, which he discharged through the confined gas by means of the wires I, K.] You saw the flash, and now that you may see that there is no longer any gas remaining, if I place it over the jar and open the stop-cocks again, up will go the gas, and we can have a second combustion; and so I might go on again and again, and I should continue to accumulate more and more of the water to which the gas has returned. Now is not this curious? In this vessel (C) we can go on making from water a large bulk of *permanent gas,* as we call it, and then we can reconvert it into water in this way. [Mr. Anderson brought in another Leyden jar, which, however, from some cause, would not ignite the gas. It was therefore recharged, when the explosion took place in the desired manner.] How beautifully we get our results when we are right in our proceedings! It is not that Nature is wrong when we make a mistake. Now I will lay this vessel (G) down by my right hand, and you can examine it by-and-by; there is not very much water flowing down, but there is quite sufficient for you to see.

Another wonderful thing about this mode of changing the condition of the water is this: that we are able to get the separate parts of which it is composed at a distance the one from the other, and to examine them, and see what they are like, and how many of them there are; and for this purpose I have here some more water in a slightly different apparatus to the former one (FIG. 25), and if I place this in connection with the wires of the battery (at A, B), I shall get a similar decomposition of the water at the two platinum plates.

Now I will put this little tube (O) over there, and that will collect
the gas together that comes from this side (A), and this tube (H)
will collect the gas that comes from the other side (B), and I think
we shall soon be able to see a difference. In this apparatus the wires
are a good way apart from each other,
and it now seems that *each* of them is
capable of drawing off particles from the
water and sending them off, and you see
that one set of particles (H) is coming off
twice as fast as those collected in the other
tube (O). Something is coming out of
the water *there* (at H) which burns [set-
ting fire to the gas]; but what comes out
of the water *here* (at O), although it will
not burn, will support combustion very
vigorously. [The lecturer here placed a match with a glowing tip in
the gas, when it immediately rekindled.]

Fig. 25

Here, then, we have two things, neither of them being water
alone, but which we get out of the water. Water is therefore com-
posed of two substances different to itself, which appear at separate
places when it is made to submit to the force which I have in these
wires; and if I take an inverted tube of water and collect this gas
(H), you will see that it is by no means the same as the one we
collected in the former apparatus (Fig. 24). That exploded with a
loud noise when it was lighted, but this will burn quite noiselessly: it
is called *hydrogen;* and the other we call *oxygen*—that gas which so
beautifully brightens up all combustion, but does not burn of itself.
So now we see that water consists of two kinds of particles attracting
each other in a very different manner to the attraction of gravitation
or cohesion, and this new attraction we call *chemical affinity,* or the
force of chemical action between different bodies; we are now no
longer concerned with the attraction of iron for iron, water for water,
wood for wood, or like bodies for each other, as we were when deal-
ing with the force of cohesion; we are dealing with another kind
of attraction—the attraction between particles of a *different* nature
one to the other. Chemical affinity depends entirely upon the energy

with which particles of *different* kinds attract each other. Oxygen and hydrogen are particles of different kinds, and it is their attraction to each other which makes them chemically combine and produce water.

I must now show you a little more at large what chemical affinity is. I can prepare these gases from other substances as well as from water; and we will now prepare some oxygen: here is another substance which contains oxygen—chlorate of potash; I will put some of it into this glass retort, and Mr. Anderson will apply heat to it: we have here different jars filled with water, and when, by the application of heat, the chlorate of potash is decomposed, we will displace the water, and fill the jars with gas.

Now, when water is opened out in this way by means of the battery, which adds nothing to it materially, which takes nothing from it materially (I mean no *matter;* I am not speaking of *force*), which adds no *matter* to the water, it is changed in this way—the gas which you saw burning a little while ago, called *hydrogen*, is evolved in large quantity, and the other gas, *oxygen,* is evolved in only half the quantity; so that these two areas represent water, and these are always the proportions between the two gases.

Oxygen	88.9
Hydrogen		11.1
Water	100.0

But oxygen is sixteen times the weight of the other—eight times as heavy as the particles of hydrogen in the water; and you therefore know that water is composed of nine parts by weight—one of hydrogen and eight of oxygen; thus:

Hydrogen46.2 cubic inches= 1 grain
Oxygen23.1 " " = 8 grains

Water *(steam)*........69.3 " " = 9 grains

Now Mr. Anderson has prepared some oxygen, and we will pro-

ceed to examine what is the character of this gas. First of all, you remember I told you that it does not burn, but that it affects the burning of other bodies. I will just set fire to the point of this little bit of wood, and then plunge it into the jar of oxygen, and you will see what this gas does in increasing the brilliancy of the combustion. It does not burn, it does not take fire as the hydrogen would; but how vividly the combustion of the match goes on! Again, if I were to take this wax taper and light it, and turn it upside down in the air, it would, in all probability, put itself out, owing to the wax run-

ning down into the wick. [The lecturer here turned the lighted taper upside down, when in a few seconds it went out.] Now that will not happen in oxygen gas; you will see how differently it acts (Fig. 26). [The taper was again lighted, turned upside down, and then introduced into a jar of oxygen.] Look at that! See how the very wax itself burns, and falls down in a dazzling stream of fire, so powerfully does the oxygen sup-

Fig. 26

port combustion. Again, here is another experiment which will serve to illustrate the force, if I may so call it, of oxygen. I have here a circular flame of spirit of wine, and with it I am about to show you the way in which iron burns, because it will serve very well as a comparison between the effect produced by air and oxygen. If I take this ring flame, I can shake, by means of a sieve, the fine particles of iron filings through it, and you will see the way in which they burn. [The lecturer here shook through the flame some iron filings, which took fire and fell through with beautiful scintillations.] But if I now hold the flame over a jar of oxygen [the experiment was repeated over a jar of oxygen, when the combustion of the filings as they fell into the oxygen became almost insupportably brilliant], you see how wonderfully different the effect is in the jar, because there we have oxygen instead of common air.

LECTURE IV

CHEMICAL AFFINITY—HEAT

WE shall have to pay a little more attention to the forces existing in water before we can have a clear idea on the subject. Besides the attraction which there is between its particles to make it hold together as a liquid or a solid, there is also another force, different from the former—one which, yesterday, by means of the voltaic battery, we overcame, drawing from the water two different substances, which, when heated by means of the electric spark, attracted each other, and rushed into combination to reproduce water. Now I propose to-day to continue this subject, and trace the various phenomena of chemical affinity; and for this purpose, as we yesterday considered the character of oxygen, of which I have here two jars (oxygen being those particles derived from the water which enable other bodies to burn), we will now consider the other constituent of water, and, without embarrassing you too much with the way in which these things are made, I will proceed now to show you our common way of making *hydrogen*. (I called it hydrogen yesterday: it is so called because it helps to generate water.)* I put into this retort some zinc, water, and oil of vitriol, and immediately an action takes place, which produces an abundant evolution of gas, now coming over into this jar, and bubbling up in appearance exactly like the oxygen we obtained yesterday (Fig. 27).

The processes, you see, are very different, though the result is the same, in so far as it gives us certain gaseous particles. Here, then, is the hydrogen. I showed you yesterday certain qualities of this gas; now let me exhibit you some other properties. Unlike oxygen, which is a supporter of combustion and will not burn, hydrogen itself is combustible. There is a jar full of it; and if I carry it along in this manner and put a light to it, I think you will see it take fire (Fig. 27) —not with a bright light; you will, at all events, hear it if you do not

* Ὕδωρ, "water," and γεννάω, "I generate."

see it. Now that is a body entirely different from oxygen; it is extremely light; for, although yesterday you saw twice as much of this hydrogen produced on the one side as on the other by the voltaic

Fig. 27

battery, it was only one-eighth the weight of the oxygen. I carry this jar upside down. Why? Because I know that it is a very light body, and that it will continue in this jar upside down quite as effectually as the water will in that jar which is not upside down; and just as I can pour water from one vessel into another in the right position to receive it, so can I pour this gas from one jar into another when they are upside down. See what I am about to do. There is no hydrogen in this jar at present, but I will gently turn this jar of hydrogen up under this other jar (Fig. 28), and then we will examine the two. We shall see, on applying a light, that the hydrogen has left the jar in which it was at first, and has poured upward into the other, and there we shall find it.

Fig. 28

You now understand that we can have particles of very different kinds, and that they can have different bulks and weights; and there are two or three very interesting experiments which serve to illustrate this. For instance, if I blow soap bubbles with the breath from my mouth, you will see them fall, because I fill them with common air, and the water which forms the bubble carries it down. But now, if I inhale hydrogen gas into my lungs (it does no harm to the lungs, although it does no good to them), see what happens. [The lecturer inhaled some hydrogen, and, after one or two ineffectual attempts,

succeeded in blowing a splendid bubble, which rose majestically and slowly to the ceiling of the theatre, where it burst.] That shows you very well how light a substance this is; for, notwithstanding all the heavy bad air from my lungs, and the weight of the bubble, you saw how it was carried up. I want you now to consider this phenomenon of weight as indicating how exceedingly different particles are one

FIG. 29

from the other; and I will take as illustrations these very common things, air, water, the heaviest body, platinum, and this gas, and observe how they differ in this respect; for if I take a piece of platinum of that size (Fig. 29), it is equal to the weight of portions of water, air, and hydrogen of the bulks I have represented in these spheres; and this illustration gives you a very good idea of the extraordinary difference with regard to the gravity of the articles having this enormous difference in bulk. [The following tabular statement having reference to this illustration appeared on the diagram board.]

Hydrogen...........................1			
Air....................................14.4	1		
Water.............................11943	829	1	
Platinum.........................256774	17831	21.5	

Whenever oxygen and hydrogen unite together they produce water, and you have seen the extraordinary difference between the

bulk and appearance of the water so produced and the particles of which it consists chemically. Now we have never yet been able to reduce either oxygen or hydrogen to the liquid state; and yet their first impulse, when chemically combined, is to take up first this liquid condition and then the solid condition. We never combine these different particles together without producing water; and it is curious to think how often you must have made the experiment of combining oxygen and hydrogen to form water without knowing it. Take a candle, for instance, and a clean silver spoon (or a piece of clean tin will do), and, if you hold it over the flame, you immediately cover it with dew—not a smoke—which presently evaporates. This, perhaps, will serve to show it better. Mr. Anderson will put a candle under that jar,

FIG. 30

and you will see how soon the water is produced (FIG. 30). Look at that dimness on the sides of the glass, which will soon produce drops, and trickle down into the plate. Well, that dimness and these drops are *water,* formed by the union of the oxygen of the air with the hydrogen existing in the wax of which that candle is formed.

And now, having brought you, in the first place, to the consideration of chemical attraction, I must enlarge your ideas so as to include all substances which have this attraction for each other; for it changes the character of bodies, and alters them in this way and that way in the most extraordinary manner, and produces other phenomena wonderful to think about. Here is some chlorate of potash, and there some sulphuret of antimony([16]). We will mix these two different sets of particles together and I want to show you, in a general sort of way, some of the phenomena which take place when we make different particles act together. Now I can make these bodies act upon each other in several ways. In this case I am going to apply heat to the mixture; but if I were to give a blow with a hammer, the same result would follow. [A lighted match

[16] *Chlorate of potash and sulphuret of antimony.* Great care must be taken in mixing these substances, as the mixture is dangerously explosive. They must be powdered separately and mixed together with a feather on a sheet of paper, or by passing them several times through a small sieve.

was brought to the mixture, which immediately exploded with a sudden flash, evolving a dense white smoke.] There you see the result of the action of chemical affinity overcoming the attraction of cohesion of the particles. Again, here is a little sugar([17]), quite a different substance from the black sulphuret of antimony, and you shall see what takes place when we put the two together. [The mixture was touched with sulphuric acid, when it took fire, and burnt gradually and with a brighter flame than in the former instance.] Observe this chemical affinity traveling about the mass, and setting it on fire, and throwing it into such wonderful agitation!

I must now come to a few circumstances which require careful consideration. We have already examined one of the effects of this chemical affinity, but, to make the matter more clear, we must point out some others. And here are two salts dissolved in water([18]). They are both colorless solutions, and in these glasses you can not see any difference between them. But if I mix them, I shall have chemical attraction take place. I will pour the two together into this glass, and you will at once see, I have no doubt, a certain amount of change. Look, they are already becoming milky, but they are sluggish in their action—not quick as the others were—for we have endless varieties of rapidity in chemical action. Now, if I mix them together, and stir them so as to bring them properly together, you will soon see what a different result is produced. As I mix them they get thicker and thicker, and you see the liquid is hardening and stiffening, and before long I shall have it quite hard; and before the end of the lecture it will be a solid stone—a wet stone, no doubt, but more or less solid—in consequence of the chemical affinity. Is not this changing two liquids into a solid body a wonderful manifestation of chemical affinity?

There is another remarkable circumstance in chemical affinity, which is, that it is capable of either waiting or acting at once. And this is very singular, because we know of nothing of the kind in the forces either of gravitation or cohesion. For instance: here are

[17] The mixture of chlorate of potash and sugar does not require the same precautions. They may be rubbed together in a pestle and mortar without fear. One part of chlorate of potash and three parts of sugar will answer. The mixture need only be touched with a glass rod dipped in oil of vitriol.

[18] *Two salts dissolved in water.* Sulphate of soda and chloride of calcium. The solutions must be saturated for the experiment to succeed well.

some oxygen particles, and here is a lump of carbon particles. I am going to put the carbon particles into the oxygen; they *can* act, but they *do* not—they are just like this unlighted candle. It stands here quietly on the table, waiting until we want to light it. But it is not so in this other case: here is a substance, gaseous like the oxygen, and if I put these particles of metal into it the two combine at once. The copper and the chlorine unite by their power of chemical affinity, and produce a body entirely unlike either of the substances used. And in this other case, it is not that there is any deficiency of affinity between the carbon and oxygen, for the moment I choose to put them in a condition to exert their affinity, you will see the difference. [The piece of charcoal was ignited, and introduced into the jar of oxygen, when the combustion proceeded with vivid scintillations.]

Now this chemical action is set going exactly as it would be if I had lighted the candle, or as it is when the servant puts coals on and lights the fire: the substances wait until we do something which is able to start the action. Can any thing be more beautiful than this combustion of charcoal in oxygen? You must understand that each of these little sparks is a portion of the charcoal, or the bark of the charcoal thrown off white hot into the oxygen, and burning in it most brilliantly, as you see. And now let me tell you another thing, or you will go away with a very imperfect notion of the powers and effects of this affinity. There you see some charcoal burning in oxygen. Well, a piece of lead will burn in oxygen just as well as the charcoal does, or indeed better, for absolutely that piece of lead will act at once upon the oxygen as the copper did in the other vessel with regard to the chlorine. And here, also, a piece of iron—if I light it and put it into the oxygen, it will burn away just as the carbon did. And I will take some lead, and show you that it will burn in the common atmospheric oxygen at the ordinary temperature. These are the lumps of lead which you remember we had the other day—the two pieces which clung together. Now these pieces, if I take them to-day and press them together, will not stick, and the reason is that they have attracted from the atmosphere a part of the oxygen there present, and have become coated as with a varnish by the oxide of lead, which is formed on the surface by a real process of combustion or combination. There you see the iron

burning very well in oxygen, and I will tell you the reason why those
scissors and that lead do not take fire while they are lying on the
table. Here the lead is in a lump, and the coating of oxide remains
on its surface, while there you see the melted oxide is clearing itself
off from the iron, and allowing more and more to go on burning.
In this case, however, [holding up a small glass tube containing
lead pyrophorus([19])], the lead has been very carefully produced in
fine powder, and put into a glass tube, and hermetically sealed so as
to preserve it, and I expect you will see it take fire at once. This has
been made about a month ago, and has thus had time to sink down
to its normal temperature; what you see, therefore, is the result
of chemical affinity alone. [The tube was broken at the end, and
the lead poured out on to a piece of paper, whereupon it immediately
took fire.] Look! look at the lead burning! Why, it has set fire to
the paper! Now that is nothing more than the common affinity
always existing between very clean lead and the atmospheric oxygen;
and the reason why this iron does not burn until it is made red hot
is because it has got a coating of oxide about it, which stops the action
of the oxygen—putting a varnish, as it were, upon its surface, as we
varnish a picture—absolutely forming a substance which prevents
the natural chemical affinity between the bodies from acting.

I must now take you a little farther in this kind of illustration, or
consideration I would rather call it, of chemical affinity. This attrac-
tion between different particles exists also most curiously in cases
where they are previously combined with other substances. Here
is a little chlorate of potash containing the oxygen which we found
yesterday could be procured from it; it contains the oxygen there
combined and held down by its chemical affinity with other things,
but still it can combine with sugar, as you saw. This affinity can thus
act *across* substances, and I want you to see how curiously what we
call combustion acts with respect to this force of chemical affinity.
If I take a piece of phosphorus and set fire to it, and then place a
jar of air over the phosphorus, you see the combustion which we
are having there on account of chemical affinity (combustion being
in all cases the result of chemical affinity). The phosphorus is

[19] *Lead pyrophorus.* This is tartrate of lead which has been heated in a glass tube
to dull redness as long as vapors are emitted. As soon as they cease to be evolved
the end of the tube is sealed, and it is allowed to cool.

escaping in that vapor, which will condense into a snowlike mass at the close of the lecture. But suppose I limit the atmosphere, what then? why, even the phosphorus will go out. Here is a piece of camphor, which will burn very well in the atmosphere, and even on water it will float about and burn, by reason of some of its particles gaining access to the air. But if I limit the quantity of air by placing a jar over it, as I am now doing, you will soon find the camphor will go out. Well, why does it go out? not for want of air, for there is plenty of air remaining in the jar. Perhaps you will be shrewd enough to say for want of oxygen.

This, therefore, leads us to the inquiry as to whether oxygen can do more than a certain amount of work. The oxygen there (Fig. 30) can not go on burning an unlimited quantity of candle, for that has gone out, as you see; and its amount of chemical attraction or affinity is just as strikingly limited: it can no more be fallen short of or exceeded than can the attraction of gravitation. You might as soon attempt to destroy gravitation, or weight, or all things that exist, as to destroy the exact amount of force exerted by this oxygen. And when I pointed out to you that eight by weight of oxygen to one by weight of hydrogen went to form water, I meant this, that neither of them would combine in different proportions with the other, for you can not get ten of hydrogen to combine with six of oxygen, or ten of oxygen to combine with six of hydrogen; it must be eight of oxygen and one of hydrogen. Now suppose I limit the action in this way: this piece of cotton wool burns, as you see, very well in the atmosphere; and I have known of cases of cotton-mills being fired as if with gunpowder through the very finely divided particles of cotton being diffused through the atmosphere in the mill, when it has sometimes happened that a flame has caught these raised particles, and it has run from one end of the mill to the other and blown it up. That, then, is on account of the affinity which the cotton has for the oxygen; but suppose I set fire to this piece of cotton which is rolled up tightly; it does not go on burning, because I have limited the supply of oxygen, and the inside is prevented from having access to the oxygen, just as it was in the case of the lead by the oxide. But here is some cotton which has been imbued with oxygen in a certain manner. I need not trouble you

now with the way it is prepared; it is called guncotton([20]). See how
that burns [setting fire to a piece]; it is very different from the
other, because the oxygen which must be present in its proper
amount is put there beforehand. And I have here some pieces of
paper which are prepared like the guncotton([21]), and imbued with
bodies containing oxygen. Here is some which has been soaked in
nitrate of strontia: you will see the beautiful red color of its flame;
and here is another which I think contains baryta, which gives that
fine green light; and I have here some more which has been soaked
in nitrate of copper: it does not burn quite so brightly, but still very
beautifully. In all these cases the combustion goes on independent
of the oxygen of the atmosphere. And here we have some gun-
powder put into a case, in order to show that it is capable of burning
under water. You know that we put it into a gun, shutting off the
atmosphere with shot, and yet the oxygen which it contains supplies
the particles with that without which chemical action could not
proceed. Now I have a vessel of water here, and am going to make
the experiment of putting this fuse under the water, and you will
see whether that water can extinguish it; here it is burning out of
the water, and there it is burning under the water; and so it will
continue until exhausted, and all by reason of the requisite amount
of oxygen being contained within the substance. It is by this kind
of attraction of the different particles one to the other that we are
enabled to trace the laws of chemical affinity, and the wonderful
variety of the exertions of these laws.

Now I want you to observe that one great exertion of this power
which is known as *chemical affinity* is to produce HEAT and light;
you know, as a matter of fact, no doubt, that when bodies burn they
give out heat, but it is a curious thing that this heat does not con-
tinue; the heat goes away as soon as the action stops, and you see,
thereby, that it depends upon the action *during the time* it is going

[20] *Guncotton* is made by immersing cotton wool in a mixture of sulphuric acid and
the strongest nitric acid or of sulphuric acid and nitrate of potash.

[21] *Paper prepared like guncotton.* It should be bibulous paper, and must be soaked
for ten minutes in a mixture of ten parts, by measure, of oil of vitriol with five parts
of strong fuming nitric acid. The paper must afterward be thoroughly washed with
warm distilled water, and then carefully dried at a gentle heat. The paper is then
saturated with chlorate of strontia, or chlorate of baryta, or nitrate of copper, by im-
mersion in a warm solution of these salts. (See Chemical News, vol. i., p. 36.)

on. It is not so with gravitation; this force is continuous, and is just as effective in making that lead press on the table as it was when it first fell there. Nothing occurs there which disappears when the action of falling is over; the pressure is upon the table, and will remain there until the lead is removed; whereas, in the action of chemical affinity to give light and heat, they go away immediately the action is over. This lamp *seems* to evolve heat and light continuously, but it is owing to a constant stream of air coming into it on all sides, and this work of producing light and heat by chemical affinity will subside as soon as the stream of air is interrupted. What, then, is this curious condition of heat? Why, it is the evolution of another power of matter—of a power new to us, and which we must consider as if it were now for the very first time brought under our notice. What is heat? We recognize heat by its power of liquefying solid bodies and vaporizing liquid bodies; by its power of setting in action, and very often overcoming, chemical affinity. Then how do we obtain heat? We obtain it in various ways; most abundantly by means of the chemical affinity we have just before been speaking about, but we can also obtain it in many other ways. Friction will produce heat. The Indians rub pieces of wood together until they make them hot enough to take fire; and such things have been known as two branches of a tree rubbing together so hard as to set the tree on fire. I do not suppose I shall set these two pieces of wood on fire by friction, but I can readily produce heat enough to ignite some phosphorus. [The lecturer here rubbed two pieces of cedar wood strongly against each other for a minute, and then placed on them a piece of phosphorus, which immediately took fire.] And if you take a smooth metal button stuck on a cork, and rub it on a piece of soft deal wood, you will make it so hot as to scorch wood and paper, and burn a match.

I am now going to show you that we can obtain heat, not by chemical affinity alone, but by the pressure of air. Suppose I take a pellet of cotton and moisten it with a little ether, and put it into a glass tube (Fig. 31), and then take a piston and press it down suddenly, I expect I shall be able to burn a little of that ether in the vessel. It wants a suddenness of pressure, or we shall not do what we require. [The piston was forcibly pressed down, when a flame,

due to the combustion of the ether, was visible in the lower part of the syringe.] All we want is to get a little ether in vapor, and give fresh air each time, and so we may go on again and again, getting heat enough by the compression of air to fire the ether-vapor.

This, then, I think, will be sufficient, accompanied with all you have previously seen, to show you how we procure heat. And now for the effects of this power. We need not consider many of them on the present occasion, because, when you have seen its power of changing ice into water and water into steam, you have seen the two principal results of the application of heat. I want you now to see how it expands all bodies—all bodies but one, and that under limited circumstances. Mr. Anderson will hold a lamp under that retort, and you will see, the moment he does so, that the air will issue abundantly from the neck which is under water, because the heat which he

Fig. 31 applies to the air causes it to expand. And here is a brass rod (Fig. 32) which goes through that hole, and fits also accurately into this gauge; but if I make it warm with this spirit lamp, it will only go in the gauge or through the hole with difficulty; and if I were to put it into boiling water it would not go through at all. Again, as soon as the heat escapes from bodies, they collapse: see how the air

Fig. 32

is contracting in the vessel now that Mr. Anderson has taken away his lamp; the stem of it is filling with water. Notice too, now, that although I cannot get the tube through this hole or into the gauge, the moment I cool it, by dipping it into water, it goes through with perfect facility, so that we have a perfect proof of this power of heat to contract and expand bodies.

LECTURE V

MAGNETISM—ELECTRICITY

I WONDER whether we shall be too deep to-day or not. Remember that we spoke of the attraction by gravitation of *all* bodies to all bodies by their simple approach. Remember that we spoke of the attraction of particles of the *same* kind to each other— that power which keeps them together in masses—iron attracted to iron, brass to brass, or water to water. Remember that we found, on looking into water, that there were particles of two different kinds attracted to each other; and this was a great step beyond the first simple attraction of gravitation, because here we deal with attraction between *different* kinds of matter. The hydrogen could attract the oxygen and reduce it to water, but it could not attract any of its own particles, so that there we obtained a first indication of the existence of *two* attractions.

To-day we come to a kind of attraction even more curious than the last, namely, the attraction which we find to be of a double nature—of a curious and dual nature. And I want, first of all, to make the nature of this doubleness clear to you. Bodies are some- times endowed with a wonderful attraction, which is not found in them in their ordinary state. For instance, here is a piece of shellac, having the attraction of gravitation, having the attraction of cohesion, and if I set fire to it, it would have the attraction of chemical affinity to the oxygen in the atmosphere. Now all these powers we find *in* it as if they were parts of its substance; but there is another property which I will try and make evident by means of this ball, this bubble of air [a light India-rubber ball, inflated and suspended by a thread]. There is no attraction between this ball and this shellac at present; there may be a little wind in the rooms slightly moving the ball about, but there is no attraction. But if I rub the shellac with a piece of flannel [rubbing the shellac, and then holding it near the ball], look at the attraction which has arisen out of the shellac simply

by this friction, and which I may take away as easily by drawing it gently through my hand. [The lecturer repeated the experiment of exciting the shellac, and then removing the attractive power by drawing it through his hand.] Again, you will see I can repeat this experiment with another substance; for if I take a glass rod, and rub it with a piece of silk covered with what we call amalgam, look at the attraction which it has; how it draws the ball toward it; and then, as before, by quietly rubbing it through the hand, the attraction will be all removed again, to come back by friction with this silk.

But now we come to another fact. I will take this piece of shellac, and make it attractive by friction; and remember that, whenever we get an attraction of gravity, chemical affinity, adhesion, or electricity (as in this case), the body which attracts is attracted also, and just as much as that ball was attracted by the shellac, the shellac was attracted by the ball. Now I will suspend this piece of excited shellac in a little paper stirrup, in this way (Fig. 33), in order to make it move easily, and I will take another piece of shellac, and, after

Fig. 33

rubbing it with flannel, will bring them near together: you will think that they ought to attract each other; but now what happens? It does not attract; on the contrary, it very strongly *repels,* and I can thus drive it round to any extent. These, therefore, repel each other, although they are so strongly attractive—repel each other to the extent of driving this heavy piece of shellac round and round in this way. But if I excite this piece of shellac as before, and take this piece of glass and rub it with silk, and then bring them near,

what think you will happen? [The lecturer held the excited glass near the excited shellac, when they attracted each other strongly.] You see, therefore, what a difference there is between these two attractions; they are actually two *kinds* of attraction concerned in this case, quite different to any thing we have met with before, but the *force* is the same. We have here, then, a double attraction—a dual attraction or force—one attracting and the other repelling.

Again, to show you another experiment which will help to make this clear to you: Suppose I set up this rough indicator again [the

FIG. 34

excited shellac suspended in the stirrup]: it is rough, but delicate enough for my purpose; and suppose I take this other piece of shellac, and take away the power, which I can do by drawing it gently through the hand; and suppose I take a piece of flannel (FIG. 34), which I have shaped into a cap for it and made dry. I will put this shellac into the flannel, and here comes out a very beautiful result. I will rub this shellac and the flannel together (which I can do by twisting the shellac round), and leave them in contact; and then if I ask, by bringing them near our indicator, what is the attractive force? it is nothing; but if I take them apart, and then ask what will they do when they are separated? why, the shellac is strongly repelled, as it was before, but the cap is strongly attractive; and yet, if I bring them both together again, there is no attraction; it has all disappeared [the experiment was repeated].

Those two bodies, therefore, still contain this attractive power; when they were parted, it was evident to your senses that they had it, though they do not attract when they are together.

This, then, is sufficient, in the outset, to give you an idea of the nature of the force which we call ELECTRICITY. There is no

FIG. 35

end to the things from which you can evolve this power. When you go home, take a stick of sealing-wax—I have rather a large stick, but a smaller one will do—and make an indicator of this sort (FIG. 35). Take a watch-glass (or your watch itself will do; you only want something which shall have a round face); and now, if you place a piece of flat glass upon that, you have a very easily moved centre; and if I take this lath and put it on the flat glass (you see I am searching for the centre of gravity of this lath; I want to balance it upon the watch-glass), it is very easily moved round; and if I take this piece of sealing-wax and rub it against my coat, and then try whether it is attractive [holding it near the lath], you see how strong the attraction is; I can even draw it about. Here, then, you have a very beautiful indicator, for I have, with a small piece of sealing-wax

FIG. 36

and my coat, pulled round a plank of that kind, so you need be in no want of indicators to discover the presence of this attraction. There is scarcely a substance which we may not use. Here are some indicators (FIG. 36). I bend round a strip of paper into a hoop, and we have as good an indicator as can be required. See how it rolls along, traveling after the sealing-wax! If I make them smaller, of course we have them running faster, and sometimes they are actually attracted up into the air. Here, also, is a little collodion balloon. It is so electrical that it will scarcely leave my hand unless to go to the

other. See how curiously electrical it is; it is hardly possible for me to touch it without making it electrical; and here is a piece which clings to any thing it is brought near, and which it is not easy to lay down. And here is another substance, gutta-percha, in thin strips: it is astonishing how, by rubbing this in your hands, you make it electrical; but our time forbids us to go farther into this subject at present; you see clearly there are two kinds of electricities which may be obtained by rubbing shellac with flannel or glass with silk.

Now there are some curious bodies in nature (of which I have two specimens on the table) which are called *magnets* or *loadstones;* ores of iron, of which there is a great deal sent from Sweden. They have the attraction of gravitation, and attraction of cohesion, and certain chemical attraction; but they also have a great attractive power, for this little key is held up by this stone. Now that is not chemical attraction; it is not the attraction of chemical affinity, or of aggregation of particles, or of cohesion, or of electricity (for it will not attract this ball if I bring it near it), but it is a separate and dual attraction, and, what is more, one which is not readily removed from the substance, for it has existed in it for ages and ages in the bowels of the earth. Now we can make artificial magnets (you will see me to-morrow make artificial magnets of extraordinary power). And let us take one of these artificial magnets and examine it, and see where the power is in the mass, and whether it is a dual power. You see it attracts these keys, two or three in succession, and it will attract a very large piece of iron. That, then, is a very different thing indeed to what you saw in the case of the shellac, for *that* only attracted a light ball, but here I have several ounces of iron held up. And if we come to examine this attraction a little more closely, we shall find it presents some other remarkable differences; first of all, one end of this bar (Fig. 37) attracts this key, but the middle does not attract. It is not, then, the *whole* of the substance which attracts. If I place this little key in the middle it does not adhere; but if I place it *there,* a little nearer the end, it does, though feebly. Is it not, then, very curious to find that there is an attractive power at the extremities which is not in the middle—to have thus in one bar two places in which this force of attraction resides? If I take this bar and balance it carefully on a point, so that it will be

free to move round, I can try what action this piece of iron has on it. Well, it attracts one end, and it also attracts the other end, just as you saw the shellac and the glass did, with the exception of its not attracting in the middle. But if now, instead of a piece of iron, I take a *magnet,* and examine it in a similar way, you see that one of its ends *repels* the suspended magnet; the force, then, is no longer attraction, but repulsion; but, if I take the other end of the magnet and bring it near, it shows attraction again.

You will see this better, perhaps, by another kind of experiment. Here (Fig. 38) is a little magnet, and I have colored the ends differ-

FIG. 37 FIG. 38

ently, so that you may distinguish one from the other. Now this end (S) of the magnet (Fig. 37) attracts the *uncolored* end of the little magnet. You see it pulls toward it with great power; and, as I carry it round, the uncolored end still follows. But now, if I gradually bring the middle of the bar magnet opposite the uncolored end of the needle, it has no effect upon it, either of attraction or repulsion, until, as I come to the opposite extremity (N), you see that it is the *colored* end of the needle which is pulled toward it. We are now, therefore, dealing with two kinds of power, attracting different ends of the magnet—a double power, already existing in these bodies, which takes up the form of attraction and repulsion. And now, when I put up this label with the word MAGNETISM, you will understand that it is to express this double power.

Now with this loadstone you may make magnets artificially. Here is an artificial magnet (Fig. 39) in which both ends have been brought together in order to increase the attraction. This mass will lift that lump of iron, and, what is more, by placing this *keeper,* as it is called, on the top of the magnet, and taking hold of the

handle, it will adhere sufficiently strongly to allow itself to be lifted
up, so wonderful is its power of attraction. If you take a needle,
and just draw one of its ends along one extremity of the magnet,
and then draw the other end along the other extremity, and then
gently place it on the surface of some water (the needle
will generally float on the surface, owing to the slight
greasiness communicated to it by the fingers), you will
be able to get all the phenomena of attraction and repul-
sion by bringing another magnetized needle near to it.

I want you now to observe that, although I have shown
you in these magnets that this double power becomes evi-
dent principally at the extremities, yet the *whole* of the
magnet is concerned in giving the power. That will at
first seem rather strange; and I must therefore show you

Fig. 39

an experiment to prove that this is not an accidental matter, but that
the whole of the mass is really concerned in this force, just as in
falling the whole of the mass is acted upon by the force of gravita-
tion. I have here (Fig. 40) a steel bar, and I am going to make it a
magnet by rubbing it on the large magnet (Fig. 39). I have now
made the two ends magnetic in opposite ways. I do not at present
know one from the other, but we can soon find out. You see, when
I bring it near our magnetic needle (Fig. 38), one end repels and
the other attracts; and the middle will neither attract nor repel—it
can not, because it is *half way between the two ends.* But now, if I
break out that piece (*n, s*), and then examine it, see how strongly
one end (*n*) pulls at this end (S, Fig. 38), and how it repels the
other end (N). And so it can be shown that every part of the magnet

N *sn sn* S
contains this power of attraction and repul-
sion, but that the power is only rendered evi-
dent at the end of the mass. You will

Fig. 40

understand all this in a little while; but what
you have now to consider is that every part of this steel is in itself a
magnet. Here is a little fragment which I have broken out of the
very centre of the bar, and you will still see that one end is attrac-
tive and the other is repulsive. Now is not this power a most won-
derful thing? And very strange, the means of taking it from one
substance and bringing it to other matters. I can not make a piece

of iron or any thing else heavier or lighter than it is; its cohesive power it must and does have; but, as you have seen by these experiments, we can add or subtract this power of magnetism, and almost do as we like with it.

And now we will return for a short time to the subject treated of at the commencement of this lecture. You see here (FIG. 41) a large machine arranged for the purpose of rubbing glass with silk, and

FIG. 41

for obtaining the power called *electricity;* and the moment the handle of the machine is turned a certain amount of electricity is evolved, as you will see by the rise of the little straw indicator (at A). Now I know, from the appearance of repulsion of the pith ball at the end of the straw, that electricity is present in those brass conductors (BB), and I want you to see the manner in which that electricity can pass away [touching the conductor (B) with his finger, the lecturer drew a spark from it, and the straw electrometer immediately fell]. There, it has all gone; and that I have really taken it away you shall see by an experiment of this sort. If I hold this cylinder of brass by the glass handle, and touch the conductor with it, I take away a little of the electricity. You see the spark in which it passes, and observe that the pith-ball indicator has fallen a little, which seems to imply that so much electricity is lost; but it is not lost; it is here in this brass, and I can take it away and carry it about, not because it has any substance of its own, but by some

strange property which we have not before met with as belonging to any other force. Let us see whether we have it here or not. [The lecturer brought the charged cylinder to a jet from which gas was issuing; the spark was seen to pass from the cylinder to the jet, but the gas did not light.] Ah! the gas did not light, but you saw the spark; there is, perhaps, some draught in the room which blew the gas on one side, or else it would light; we will try this experiment afterward. You see from the spark that I can transfer the power from the machine to this cylinder, and then carry it away and give it to some other body.

You know very well, as a matter of experiment, that we can transfer the power of heat from one thing to another; for if I put my hand near the fire it becomes hot. I can show you this by placing before us this ball, which has just been brought red-hot from the fire. If I press this wire to it some of the heat will be transferred from the ball, and I have only now to touch this piece of gun-cotton with the hot wire, and you see how I can transfer the heat from the ball to the wire, and from the wire to the cotton. So you see that some powers are transferable, and others are not. Observe how long the heat stops in this ball. I might touch it with the wire or with my finger, and if I did so quickly I should merely burn the surface of the skin; whereas, if I touch that cylinder, however rapidly, with my finger, the electricity is gone at once—dispersed on the instant, in a manner wonderful to think of.

I must now take up a little of your time in showing you the manner in which these powers are transferred from one thing to another; for the manner in which *force* may be conducted or transmitted is extraordinary, and most essential for us to understand. Let us see in what manner these powers travel from place to place. Both heat and electricity can be conducted; and here is an arrangement I have made to show how the former can travel. It consists of a bar of copper (FIG. 42); and if I take a spirit lamp (this is one way of obtaining the power of heat) and place it under that little chimney, the flame will strike against the bar of copper and keep it hot. Now you are aware that power is being transferred from the flame of that lamp to the copper, and you will see by-and-by that it is being conducted along the copper from particle to particle; for, inasmuch

as I have fastened these wooden balls by a little wax at particular distances from the point where the copper is first heated, first one ball will fall and then the more distant ones, as the heat travels along, and thus you will learn that the heat travels gradually through the copper. You will see that this is a very slow conduction of power as compared with electricity. If I take cylinders of wood and metal, joined together at the ends, and wrap a piece of paper round, and then apply the heat of this lamp to the place where the metal and wood join, you will see how the heat will accumulate where the

FIG. 42

wood is, and burn the paper with which I have covered it; but where the metal is beneath, the heat is conducted away too fast for the paper to be burned. And so, if I take a piece of wood and a piece of metal joined together, and put it so that the flame shall play equally both upon one and the other, we shall soon find that the metal will become hot before the wood; for if I put a piece of phosphorus on the wood and another piece on the copper, you will find that the phosphorus on the copper will take fire before that on the wood is melted; and this shows you how badly the wood conducts heat. But with regard to the traveling of electricity from place to place, its rapidity is astonishing. I will, first of all, take these pieces of glass and metal, and you will soon understand how it is that the glass does not lose the power which it acquired when it is rubbed by the silk; by one or two experiments I will show you. If I take this piece of brass and bring it near the machine, you see how the electricity leaves the latter and passes to the brass cylinder. And again: if I take a rod of metal and touch the machine with it, I lower the indicator; but when I touch it with a rod of glass, no

power is drawn away, showing you that the electricity is conducted by the glass and the metal in a manner entirely different; and, to make you see that more clearly, we will take one of our Leyden jars. Now I must not embarrass your minds with this subject too much, but if I take a piece of metal and bring it against the knob at the top and the metallic coating at the bottom, you will see the electricity passing through the air as a brilliant spark. It takes no sensible time to pass through this; and if I were to take a long metallic wire, no matter what the length, at least as far as we are concerned, and if I make one end of it touch the outside, and the

other touch the knob at the top, see how the electricity passes! It has flashed instantaneously through the whole length of this wire. Is not this different from the transmission of heat through this copper bar (Fig. 42) which has taken a quarter of an hour or more to reach the first ball?

Here is another experiment for the purpose of showing the conductibility of this power through some bodies and not through others. Why do I have this arrangement made of brass? [pointing to the brass work of the electrical machine, Fig. 41]. Because it conducts electricity. And why do I have these columns made of glass? Because they obstruct the passage of electricity. And why do I put that paper tassel (Fig. 43) at the top of the pole, upon a glass rod, and connect it with this machine by means of a wire? You see at once that as soon as the handle of the machine is

Fig. 43

turned, the electricity which is evolved travels along this wire and up the wooden rod, and goes to the tassel at the top, and you see the power of repulsion with which it has endowed these strips of paper, each spreading outward to the ceiling and sides of the room. The out-

side of that wire is covered with gutta-percha; it would not serve to keep the force from you when touching it with your hands, because it would burst through; but it answers our purpose for the present. And so you perceive how easily I can manage to send this power of electricity from place to place by choosing the materials which can conduct the power. Suppose I want to fire a portion of gunpowder, I can readily do it by this transferable power of electricity. I will take a Leyden jar, or any other arrangement which gives us this power, and arrange wires so that they may carry the power to the place I wish; and then placing a little gunpowder on the extremities of the wires, the moment I make the connection by this discharging rod I shall fire the gunpowder [the connection was made and the gunpowder ignited]. And if I were to show you a stool like this, and were to explain to you its construction, you could easily understand that we use glass legs because these are capable of preventing the electricity from going away to the earth. If, therefore, I were to stand on this stool, and receive the electricity through this conductor, I could give it to anything that I touched. [The lecturer stood upon the insulating stool, and placed himself in connection with the conductor of the machine.] Now I am electrified; I can feel my hair rising up, as the paper tassel did just now. Let us see whether I can succeed in lighting gas by touching the jet with my finger. [The lecturer brought his finger near a jet from which gas was issuing, when, after one or two attempts, the spark which came from his finger to the jet set fire to the gas.] You now see how it is that this power of electricity can be transferred from the matter in which it is generated, and conducted along wires and other bodies, and thus be made to serve new purposes, utterly unattainable by the powers we have spoken of on previous days; and you will not now be at a loss to bring this power of electricity into comparison with those which we have previously examined, and to-morrow we shall be able to go farther into the consideration of these transferable powers.

LECTURE VI

THE CORRELATION OF THE PHYSICAL FORCES

WE have frequently seen, during the course of these lectures, that one of those powers or forces of matter, of which I have written the names on that board, has produced results which are due to the action of some other force. Thus you have seen the force of electricity acting in other ways than in attracting; you have also seen it combine matters together or disunite them by means of its action on the chemical force; and in this case, therefore, you have an instance in which these two powers are related. But we have other and deeper relations than these; we have not merely to see how it is that one power affects another—how the force of heat affects chemical affinity, and so forth, but we must try and comprehend what relation they bear to each other, and how these powers may be changed one into the other; and it will to-day require all my care, and your care too, to make this clear to your minds. I shall be obliged to confine myself to one or two instances, because to take in the whole extent of this mutual relation and conversion of forces would surpass the human intellect.

In the first place, then, here is a piece of fine zinc foil, and if I cut it into narrow strips and apply to it the power of heat, admitting the contact of air at the same time, you will find that it burns; and then, seeing that it burns, you will be prepared to say that there is chemical action taking place. You see all I have to do is to hold the piece of zinc at the side of the flame, so as to let it get heated, and yet to allow the air which is flowing into the flame from all sides to have access to it; there is the piece of zinc burning just like a piece of wood, only brighter. A part of the zinc is going up into the air in the form of that white smoke, and part is falling down on to the table. This, then, is the action of chemical affinity exerted between the zinc and the oxygen of the air. I will show you what a curious kind of affinity this is by an experiment which is rather striking

when seen for the first time. I have here some iron filings and gun-powder, and will mix them carefully together, with as little rough handling as possible; now we will compare the combustibility, so to speak, of the two. I will pour some spirit of wine into a basin and set it on fire; and, having our flame, I will drop this mixture of iron filings and gunpowder through it, so that both sets of particles will have an equal chance of burning. And now tell me which of them it is that burns? You see a plentiful combustion of the iron filings; but I want you to observe that, though they have equal chances of burning, we shall find that by far the greater part of the gunpowder remains untouched; I have only to drain off this spirit of wine, and let the powder which has gone through the flame dry, which it will do in a few minutes, and I will then test it with a lighted match. So ready is the iron to burn, that it takes, under certain circumstances, even less time to catch fire than gunpowder. [As soon as the gunpowder was dry, Mr. Anderson handed it to the lecturer, who applied a lighted match to it, when a sudden flash showed how large a proportion of gunpowder had escaped com-bustion when falling through the flame of alcohol.]

These are all cases of chemical affinity, and I show them to make you understand that we are about to enter upon the consideration of a strange kind of chemical affinity, and then to see how far we are enabled to convert this force of affinity into electricity or magnetism, or any other of the forces which we have discussed. Here is some zinc (I keep to the metal zinc, as it is very useful for our purpose), and I can produce hydrogen gas by putting the zinc and sulphuric acid together, as they are in that retort; there you see the mixture which gives us hydrogen—the zinc is pulling the water to pieces and setting free hydrogen gas. Now we have learned by experience that if a little mercury is spread over that zinc, it does not *take away* its power of decomposing the water, but *modifies* it most curiously. See how that mixture is now boiling; but when I add a little mercury to it the gas ceases to come off. We have now scarcely a bubble of hydrogen set free, so that the action is suspended for the time. We have not *destroyed* the power of chemical affinity, but modified it in a wonderful and beautiful manner. Here are some pieces of zinc covered with mercury exactly in the same way as the zinc in that

retort is covered; and if I put this plate into sulphuric acid I get no gas, but this most extraordinary thing occurs, that if I introduce along with the zinc another metal which is *not* so combustible, then I reproduce all the action. I am now going to put to the amalgamated zinc in this retort some portions of copper wire (copper not being so combustible a metal as the zinc), and observe how I get hydrogen again, as in the first instance; there, the bubbles are coming over through the pneumatic trough, and ascending faster and faster in the jar; the zinc *now* is acting by reason of its contact with the copper.

Every step we are now taking brings us to a knowledge of new phenomena. That hydrogen which you now see coming off so abundantly does not come from the zinc, as it did before, *but from the copper*. Here is a jar containing a solution of copper. If I put a piece of this amalgamated zinc into it, and leave it there, it has scarcely any action; and here is a plate of platinum which I will immerse in the same solution, and might leave it there for hours, days, months, or even years, and no action would take place; but, by putting them both together, and allowing them to touch (Fig. 44), you see what a coating of copper there is immediately thrown down on the platinum. Why is this? The platinum has no power of itself to reduce that metal from that fluid, but it has, in some mysterious way, received this power by its contact with the metal zinc. Here, then, you see a strange transfer of chemical force from one metal to another; the chemical force from the zinc is transferred and made over to the platinum by the mere association of the two metals. I might take, instead of the platinum, a piece of copper or of silver, and it would have no action of its own on this solution, but the moment the zinc was introduced and touched the other metal, then the action would take place, and it would become covered with copper. Now is not this most wonderful and beautiful to see? We still have the identical chemical force of the particles of zinc acting, and yet, in some strange manner, we have power to make that chemical force, or something it produces, travel from one place to another; for we do make the chemical force travel from the zinc to the platinum by this very curious experiment of using the two metals in the same fluid in contact with each other.

Let us now examine these phenomena a little more closely. Here is a drawing (Fig. 45) in which I have represented a vessel containing the acid liquid and the slips of zinc and platinum or copper, and I have shown them touching each other *outside* by means of a wire coming from each of them (for it matters not whether they touch in the fluid or outside; by pieces of metal attached, they still, by that communication between them, have this power transferred from one to the other). Now if, instead of only using one vessel, as I have shown there, I take another, and another, and put in zinc

Fig. 44

Fig. 45

and platinum, zinc and platinum, zinc and platinum, and connect the platinum of one vessel with the zinc of another, the platinum of this vessel with the zinc of that, and so on, we should only be using a series of these vessels instead of one. This we have done in that arrangement which you see behind me. I am using what we call a Grove's voltaic battery, in which one metal is zinc and the other platinum; and I have as many as forty pairs of these plates all exercising their force at once in sending the whole amount of chemical power there evolved through these wires under the floor and up to these two rods coming through the table. We need do no more than just bring these two ends in contact, when the spark shows us what power is present; and what a strange thing it is to see that this force is brought away from the battery behind me, and carried along through these wires! I have here an apparatus (Fig. 46) which Sir Humphry Davy constructed many years ago, in order to see whether this power from the voltaic battery caused bodies to attract each other in the same manner as the ordinary electricity did. He made it in order to experiment with his large voltaic battery, which was the most power-

ful then in existence. You see there are in this glass jar two leaves of gold, which I can cause to move to and fro by this rack-work. I will connect each of these gold leaves with separate ends of this battery, and if I have a sufficient number of plates in the battery, I shall be able to show you that there will be some attraction between those leaves even before they come in contact; if I bring them sufficiently near when they are in communication with the ends of the battery, they will be drawn gently together; and you will know when this takes place, because the power will cause the gold leaves to burn away, which they could only do when they touched each other. Now I am going to cause these two leaves of gold to approach gradually, and I have no doubt that some of you will see that they approach before they burn, and those who are too far off to see them approach will see by their burning that they have come together. Now they are attract-

Fig. 46

ing each other, long before the connection is complete, and there they go! burnt up in that brilliant flash, so strong is the force. You thus see, from the attractive force at the two ends of this battery, that these are really and truly electrical phenomena.

Now let us consider what is this spark. I take these two ends and bring them together, and there I get this glorious spark like the sunlight in the heavens above us. What is this? It is the same thing which you saw when I discharged the large electrical machine, when you saw one single bright flash; it is the same thing, only *continued,* because here we have a more effective arrangement. Instead of having a machine which we are obliged to turn for a long time together, we have here a *chemical* power which sends forth the spark; and it is wonderful and beautiful to see how this spark is carried about through these wires. I want you to perceive, if possible, that this very spark and the heat it produces (for there is heat) is neither more nor less than the chemical force of the zinc—its *very* force carried along wires and conveyed to this place. I am about to take a portion of the zinc and burn it in oxygen gas for the sake of show-ing you the kind of light produced by the actual combustion in

oxygen gas of some of this metal. [A tassel of zinc-foil was ignited at a spirit lamp and introduced into a jar of oxygen, when it burnt with a brilliant light.] That shows you what the affinity is when we come to consider it in its energy and power. And the zinc is being burned in the battery behind me at a much more rapid rate than you see in that jar, because the zinc is there dissolving and *burning*, and produces here this great electric light. That very same power which in that jar you saw evolved from the actual combustion of the zinc in oxygen, is carried along these wires and made evident here; and you may, if you please, consider that the zinc is burning in those cells, and that *this* is the light of that burning [bringing the two poles in contact and showing the electric light]; and we might so arrange our apparatus as to show that the amounts of power evolved in either case are identical. Having thus obtained power over the chemical force, how wonderfully we are able to convey it from place to place! When we use gunpowder for explosive pur-

FIG. 47

poses, we can send into the mine chemical affinity by means of this electricity; not having provided fire beforehand, we can send it in at the moment we require it. Now here (FIG. 47) is a vessel containing two charcoal points, and I bring it forward as an illustration of the wonderful power of conveying this force from place to place. I have merely to connect these by means of wires to the opposite ends of the battery, and bring the points in contact. See what an exhibition of force we have! We have exhausted the air so that the charcoal can not burn, and therefore the light you see is really the burning of the zinc in the cells behind me; there is no disappearance of the carbon, although we have that glorious electric light; and the moment I cut off the connection it stops. Here is a better instance to enable some of you to see the certainty with which we can convey this force, where under ordinary circumstances, chemical affinity would not act. We may absolutely take these two charcoal poles down under water,

and get our electric light there. There they are in the water, and you observe, when I bring them into connection, we have the same light as we had in that glass vessel.

Now besides this production of light, we have all the other effects and powers of burning zinc. I have a few wires here which are not combustible, and I am going to take one of them, a small platinum wire, and suspend it between these two rods which are connected with the battery, and when contact is made at the battery see what

Fig. 48

heat we get (Fig. 48). Is not that beautiful? It is a complete bridge of power. There is metallic connection all the way round in this arrangement, and where I have inserted the platinum, which offers some resistance to the passage of the force, you see what an amount of heat is evolved; this is the heat which the zinc would give if burnt in oxygen; but, as it is being burnt in the voltaic battery, it is giving it out at this spot. I will now shorten this wire for the sake of showing you that, the shorter the obstructing wire is, the more and more intense is the heat, until at last our platinum is fused and falls down, breaking off the circuit.

Here is another instance. I will take a piece of the metal silver, and place it on charcoal connected with one end of the battery, and lower the other charcoal pole on to it. See how brilliantly it burns! (Fig. 49.) Here is a piece of iron on the charcoal: see what a combustion is going on; and we might go on in this way, burning almost every thing we place between the poles. Now I want to show you that this power is still chemical affinity; that if we call the power which is evolved at this point *heat,* or *electricity,* or any other name referring to its source, or the way in which it travels, we still

shall find it to be chemical action. Here is a colored liquid which can show by its change of color the effects of chemical action; I will pour part of it into this glass, and you will find that these wires have a very strong action. I am not going to show you any effects of com-

FIG. 49

bustion or heat, but I will take these two platinum plates, and fasten one to the one pole and the other to the other end, and place them in this solution, and in a very short time you will see the blue color will be entirely destroyed. See, it is colorless now! I have merely brought the end of the wires into the solution of indigo, and the power of electricity has come through these wires and made itself evident by its chemical action. There is also another curious thing to be noticed now we are dealing with the chemistry of electricity, which is, that the chemical power which destroys the color is only

FIG. 50

due to the action on one side. I will pour some more of this sulphindigotic acid([22]) into a flat dish, and will then make a porous dike of sand separating the two portions of fluid into two parts (FIG. 50), and now we shall be able to see whether there is any difference in the two ends of the battery, and which

it is that possesses this peculiar action. You see it is the one on my right hand which has the power of destroying the blue, for the portion on that side is thoroughly bleached, while nothing has apparently occurred on the other side. I say *apparently,* for you

[22] *Sulphindigotic acid.* A mixture of one part of indigo and fifteen parts of concentrated oil of vitriol. It is bleached on the side at which hydrogen gas is evolved in consequence of the liberated hydrogen withdrawing oxygen from the indigo, thereby forming a colorless deoxidized indigo. In making the experiment, only enough of the sulphindigotic acid must be added to give the water a decided blue color.

must not imagine that because you can not perceive any action none has taken place.

Here we have another instance of chemical action. I take these platinum plates again and immerse them in this solution of copper, from which we formerly precipitated some of the metal, when the platinum and zinc were both put in it together. You see that these two platinum plates have no chemical action of any kind; they might remain in the solution as long as I liked, without having any power of themselves to reduce the copper; but the moment I bring the two poles of the battery in contact with them, the chemical action which is there transformed into electricity and carried along the wires again becomes chemical action at the two platinum poles, and now we shall have the power appearing on the left-hand side, and throwing down the copper in the metallic state on the platinum plate; and in this way I might give you many instances of the extraordinary way in which this chemical action or electricity may be carried about. That strange nugget of gold, of which there is a model in the other room, and which has an interest of its own in the natural history of gold, and which came from Ballarat, and was worth £8,000 or £9,000 when it was melted down last November, was brought together in the bowels of the earth, perhaps ages and ages ago, by some such power as this. And there is also another beautiful result dependent upon chemical affinity in that fine lead-tree([23]), the lead growing and growing by virtue of this power. The lead and the zinc are combined together in a little voltaic arrangement in a manner far more important than the powerful one you see here, because in nature these minute actions are going on forever, and are of great and wonderful importance in the precipitation of metals and formation of mineral veins, and so forth. These actions are not for a limited time, like my battery here, but they act forever in small degrees, accumulating more and more of the results.

I have here given you all the illustrations that time will permit me

[23] *Lead tree.* To make a lead tree, pass a bundle of brass wires through the cork of a bottle, and fasten a plate of zinc round them just as they issue from the cork, so that the zinc may be in contact with every one of the wires. Make the wires to diverge so as to form a sort of cone, and, having filled the bottle quite full of a solution of sugar of lead, insert the wires and cork, and seal it down, so as to perfectly exclude the air. In a short time the metallic lead will begin to crystallize around the divergent wires, and form a beautiful object.

to show you of chemical affinity producing electricity, and electricity again becoming chemical affinity. Let that suffice for the present; and now let us go a little deeper into the subject of this chemical force, or this electricity—which shall I name first?—the one producing the other in a variety of ways. These forces are also wonderful in their power of producing another of the forces we have been considering, namely, that of magnetism; and you know that it is only of late years, and long since I was born, that the discovery of the relations of these two forces of electricity and chemical affinity to produce magnetism has become known. Philosophers had been suspecting this affinity for a long time, and had long had great hopes of success; for in the pursuit of science we first start with hopes and expectations; these we realize and establish, never again to be lost, and upon them we found new expectations of farther discoveries, and so go on pursuing, realizing, establishing, and founding new hopes again and again.

Now observe this: here is a piece of wire which I am about to make into a bridge of force, that is to say, a communicator between

FIG. 51

the two ends of the battery. It is copper wire only, and is therefore not magnetic of itself. We will examine this wire with our magnetic needle (FIG. 51), and, though connected with one extreme end of the battery, you see that before the circuit is completed it has no power over the magnet. But observe it when I make contact; watch the needle; see how it is swung round; and notice how indifferent it becomes if I break contact again; so, you see, we have this wire evidently affecting the magnetic needle under these circumstances. Let me show you that a little more strongly. I have here a quantity of wire which has been wound into a spiral, and this will affect the

magnetic needle in a very curious manner, because, owing to its shape, it will act very like a real magnet. The copper spiral has no power over that magnetic needle at present; but if I cause the electric current to circulate through it, by bringing the two ends of the battery in contact with the ends of the wire which forms the spiral, what will happen? Why, one end of the needle is most powerfully drawn to it; and if I take the other end of the needle, it is repelled; so, you see, I have produced exactly the same phenomena as I had with the bar magnet, one end attracting and the other repelling. Is not this, then, curious to see, that we can construct a magnet of copper? Furthermore, if I take an iron bar, and put it inside the coil, so long as there is no electric current circulating round, it has no attraction, as you will observe if I bring a little iron filings or nails near the iron. But now, if I make contact with the battery, they are attracted at once. It becomes at once a powerful magnet, so much so that I should not wonder if these magnetic needles on different parts of the table pointed to it. And I will show you, by another experiment, what an attraction it has. This piece

and that piece of iron, and many other pieces, are now strongly attracted (FIG. 52); but, as soon as I break contact, the power is all gone, and they fall.

FIG. 52

What, then, can be a better or a stronger proof than this of the relation of the powers of magnetism and electricity? Again: here is a little piece of iron which is not magnetized. It will not, at present, take up any one of these nails; but I will take a piece of wire and coil it round the iron (the wire being covered with cotton in every part it does not touch the iron), so that the current must go round in this spiral coil; I am, in fact, preparing an *electro-magnet* (we are obliged to use such terms to express our meaning, because it is a magnet made by electricity—because we produce by the force of electricity a magnet of far greater power than a permanent steel one). It is now completed, and I will repeat the experiment which

you saw the other day, of building up a bridge of iron nails: the contact is now made and the current is going through; it is now a powerful magnet; here are the iron nails which we had the other day, and now I have brought this magnet near them they are

clinging so hard that I can scarcely move them with my hand (FIG. 53). But when the contact is broken, see how they fall. What can show you better than such an experiment as this the magnetic attraction with which we have endowed these portions of iron? Here, again, is a fine illustration of this strong power of magnetism. It is a magnet of the same sort as the one you have just seen. I am about to make the current of electricity pass through the wires which are round this iron for the purpose of showing you what

FIG. 53

powerful effects we get. Here are the poles of the magnet; and let us place on one of them this long bar of iron. You see, as soon as contact is made, how it rises in position (FIG. 54); and if I take such a piece as this cylinder, and place it on, woe be to me if I get my finger

FIG. 54

between; I can roll it over, but if I try to pull it off, I might lift up the whole magnet, but I have no power to overcome the magnetic power which is here evident. I might give you an infinity of illustrations of this high magnetic power. There is that long bar of iron held out, and I have no doubt that if I were to examine the

other end I should find that it was a magnet. See what power it must have to support not only these nails, but all those lumps of iron hanging on to the end. What, then, can surpass these evidences of the change of chemical force into electricity, and electricity into magnetism? I might show you many other experiments whereby I could obtain electricity and chemical action, heat and light from a magnet, but what more need I show you to prove the universal correlation of the physical forces of matter, and their mutual conversion one into another?

And now let us give place as juveniles to the respect we owe to our elders, and for a time let me address myself to those of our seniors who have honored me with their presence during these lectures. I wish to claim this moment for the purpose of tendering our thanks to them, and my thanks to you all for the way in which you have borne the inconvenience that I at first subjected you to. I hope that the insight which you have here gained into some of the laws by which the universe is governed, may be the occasion of some among you turning your attention to these subjects; for what study is there more fitted to the mind of man than that of the physical sciences? And what is there more capable of giving him an insight into the actions of those laws, a knowledge of which gives interest to the most trifling phenomenon of nature, and makes the observing student find

> "Tongues in trees, books in the running brooks,
> Sermons in stones, and good in every thing?"

THE CHEMICAL HISTORY
OF A CANDLE

A COURSE OF LECTURES DELIVERED BEFORE A
JUVENILE AUDIENCE AT THE ROYAL
INSTITUTION

LECTURE I

A CANDLE: THE FLAME—ITS SOURCES—STRUCTURE—
MOBILITY—BRIGHTNESS

I PURPOSE, in return for the honor you do us by coming to see
what are our proceedings here, to bring before you, in the course
of these lectures, the Chemical History of a Candle. I have
taken this subject on a former occasion, and, were it left to my own
will, I should prefer to repeat it almost every year, so abundant is
the interest that attaches itself to the subject, so wonderful are the
varieties of outlet which it offers into the various departments of
philosophy. There is not a law under which any part of this uni-
verse is governed which does not come into play and is touched upon
in these phenomena. There is no better, there is no more open door
by which you can enter into the study of natural philosophy than by
considering the physical phenomena of a candle. I trust, therefore, I
shall not disappoint you in choosing this for my subject rather than
any newer topic, which could not be better, were it even so good.

And, before proceeding, let me say this also: that, though our
subject be so great, and our intention that of treating it honestly,
seriously, and philosophically, yet I mean to pass away from all those
who are seniors among us. I claim the privilege of speaking to juve-
niles as a juvenile myself. I have done so on former occasions, and,
if you please, I shall do so again. And, though I stand here with the
knowledge of having the words I utter given to the world, yet that

shall not deter me from speaking in the same familiar way to those whom I esteem nearest to me on this occasion.

And now, my boys and girls, I must first tell you of what candles are made. Some are great curiosities. I have here some bits of timber, branches of trees particularly famous for their burning. And here you see a piece of that very curious substance, taken out of some of the bogs in Ireland, called *candle-wood;* a hard, strong, excellent wood, evidently fitted for good work as a register of force, and yet, withal, burning so well that where it is found they make splinters of it, and torches, since it burns like a candle, and gives a very good light indeed. And in this wood we have one of the most beautiful illustrations of the general nature of a candle that I can possibly give. The fuel provided, the means of bringing that fuel to the place of chemical action, the regular and gradual supply of air to that place of action—heat and light—all produced by a little piece of wood of this kind, forming, in fact, a natural candle.

But we must speak of candles as they are in commerce. Here are a couple of candles commonly called dips. They are made of lengths of cotton cut off, hung up by a loop, dipped into melted tallow, taken out again and cooled, then redipped, until there is an accumulation of tallow round the cotton. In order that you may have an idea of the various characters of these candles, you see these which I hold in my hand—they are very small and very curious. They are, or were, the candles used by the miners in coal mines. In olden times the miner had to find his own candles, and it was supposed that a small candle would not so soon set fire to the fire-damp in the coal mines as a large one; and for that reason, as well as for economy's sake, he had candles made of this sort—20, 30, 40, or 60 to the pound. They have been replaced since then by the steel-mill, and then by the Davy lamp, and other safety lamps of various kinds. I have here a candle that was taken out of the *Royal George*([1]), it is said, by Colonel Pasley. It has been sunk in the sea for many years, subject to the action of salt water. It shows you how well candles may be preserved; for, though it is cracked about and broken a great deal,

[1] The *Royal George* sunk at Spithead on the 29th of August, 1782. Colonel Pasley commenced operations for the removal of the wreck by the explosion of gunpowder, in August, 1839. The candle which Professor Faraday exhibited must therefore have been exposed to the action of salt water for upward of fifty-seven years.

yet when lighted it goes on burning regularly, and the tallow resumes its natural condition as soon as it is fused.

Mr. Field, of Lambeth, has supplied me abundantly with beautiful illustrations of the candle and its materials; I shall therefore now refer to them. And, first, there is the suet—the fat of the ox—Russian tallow, I believe, employed in the manufacture of these dips, which Gay-Lussac, or some one who intrusted him with his knowledge, converted into that beautiful substance, stearin, which you see lying beside it. A candle, you know, is not now a greasy thing like an ordinary tallow candle, but a clean thing, and you may almost scrape off and pulverize the drops which fall from it without soiling any thing. This is the process he adopted([2]): The fat or tallow is first boiled with quick-lime, and made into a soap, and then the soap is decomposed by sulphuric acid, which takes away the lime, and leaves the fat rearranged as stearic acid, while a quantity of glycerin is produced at the same time. Glycerin—absolutely a sugar, or a substance similar to sugar—comes out of the tallow in this chemical change. The oil is then pressed out of it; and you see here this series of pressed cakes, showing how beautifully the impurities are carried out by the oily part as the pressure goes on increasing, and at last you have left that substance, which is melted, and cast into candles as here represented. The candle I have in my hand is a stearin candle, made of stearin from tallow in the way I have told you. Then here is a sperm candle, which comes from the purified oil of the spermaceti whale. Here, also, are yellow beeswax and refined beeswax, from which candles are made. Here, too, is that curious substance called paraffine, and some paraffine candles, made of paraffine obtained from the bogs of Ireland. I have here also a substance brought from Japan since we have forced an entrance into

[2] The fat or tallow consists of a chemical combination of fatty acids with glycerin. The lime unites with the palmitic, oleic, and stearic acids, and separates the glycerin. After washing, the insoluble lime soap is decomposed with hot dilute sulphuric acid. The melted fatty acids thus rise as an oil to the surface, when they are decanted. They are again washed and cast into thin plates, which, when cold, are placed between layers of cocoanut matting and submitted to intense hydraulic pressure. In this way the soft oleic acid is squeezed out, while the hard palmitic and stearic acids remain. These are farther purified by pressure at a higher temperature and washing in warm dilute sulphuric acid, when they are ready to be made into candles. These acids are harder and whiter than the fats from which they were obtained, while at the same time they are cleaner and more combustible.

that out-of-the-way place—a sort of wax which a kind friend has sent me, and which forms a new material for the manufacture of candles.

And how are these candles made? I have told you about dips, and I will show you how moulds are made. Let us imagine any of these candles to be made of materials which can be cast. "Cast!" you say. "Why, a candle is a thing that melts, and surely if you can melt it you can cast it." Not so. It is wonderful, in the progress of manufacture, and in the consideration of the means best fitted to produce the required result, how things turn up which one would not expect beforehand. Candles can not always be cast. A wax candle can never be cast. It is made by a particular process which I can illustrate in a minute or two, but I must not spend much time on it. Wax is a thing which, burning so well, and melting so easily in a candle, can not be cast. However, let us take a material that can be cast. Here is a frame, with a number of moulds fastened in it. The first thing to be done is to put a wick through them. Here is one—a plaited wick, which does not require snuffing([3])—supported by a little wire. It goes to the bottom, where it is pegged in—the little peg holding the cotton tight, and stopping the aperture so that nothing fluid shall run out. At the upper part there is a little bar placed across, which stretches the cotton and holds it in the mould. The tallow is then melted, and the moulds are filled. After a certain time, when the moulds are cool, the excess of tallow is poured off at one corner, and then cleaned off altogether, and the ends of the wick cut away. The candles alone then remain in the mould, and you have only to upset them, as I am doing, when out they tumble, for the candles are made in the form of cones, being narrower at the top than at the bottom; so that, what with their form and their own shrinking, they only need a little shaking, and out they fall. In the same way are made these candles of stearin and of paraffine. It is a curious thing to see how wax candles are made. A lot of cottons are hung upon frames, as you see here, and covered with metal tags at the ends to keep the wax from covering the cotton in those places. These are carried to a heater, where the wax is melted.

[3] A little borax or phosphorus salt is sometimes added in order to make the ash fusible.

As you see, the frames can turn round; and, as they turn, a man takes a vessel of wax and pours it first down one, and then the next, and the next, and so on. When he has gone once round. if it is sufficiently cool, he gives the first a second coat, and so on until they are all of the required thickness. When they have been thus clothed, or fed, or made up to that thickness, they are taken off and placed elsewhere. I have here, by the kindness of Mr. Field, several specimens of these candles. Here is one only half finished. They are then taken down and well rolled upon a fine stone slab, and the conical top is moulded by properly shaped tubes, and the bottoms cut off and trimmed. This is done so beautifully that they can make candles in this way weighing exactly four or six to the pound, or any number they please.

We must not, however, take up more time about the mere manufacture, but go a little farther into the matter. I have not yet referred you to luxuries in candles (for there is such a thing as luxury in candles). See how beautifully these are colored; you see here mauve, magenta, and all the chemical colors recently introduced, applied to candles. You observe, also, different forms employed. Here is a fluted pillar most beautifully shaped; and I have also here some candles sent me by Mr. Pearsall, which are ornamented with designs upon them, so that, as they burn, you have, as it were, a glowing sun above, and bouquet of flowers beneath. All, however, that is fine and beautiful is not useful. These fluted candles, pretty as they are, are bad candles; they are bad because of their external shape. Nevertheless, I show you these specimens, sent to me from kind friends on all sides, that you may see what is done and what may be done in this or that direction; although, as I have said, when we come to these refinements, we are obliged to sacrifice a little in utility.

Now as to the light of the candle. We will light one or two, and set them at work in the performance of their proper functions. You observe a candle is a very different thing from a lamp. With a lamp you take a little oil, fill your vessel, put in a little moss or some cotton prepared by artificial means, and then light the top of the wick. When the flame runs down the cotton to the oil, it gets extinguished, but it goes on burning in the part above. Now I have no doubt you will ask how it is that the oil which will not burn of itself gets up to

the top of the cotton, where it will burn. We shall presently examine that; but there is a much more wonderful thing about the burning of a candle than this. You have here a solid substance with no vessel to contain it; and how is it that this solid substance can get up to the place where the flame is? How is it that this solid gets there, it not being a fluid? or, when it is made a fluid, then how is it that it keeps together? This is a wonderful thing about a candle.

We have here a good deal of wind, which will help us in some of our illustrations, but tease us in others; for the sake, therefore, of a little regularity, and to simplify the matter, I shall make a quiet flame, for who can study a subject when there are difficulties in the way not belonging to it? Here is a clever invention of some costermonger or street-stander in the market-place for the shading of their candles on Saturday nights, when they are selling their greens, or potatoes, or fish. I have very often admired it. They put a lamp-glass round the candle, supported on a kind of gallery, which clasps it, and it can be slipped up and down as required. By the use of this lamp-glass, employed in the same way, you have a steady flame, which you can look at, and carefully examine, as I hope you will do, at home.

You see, then, in the first instance, that a beautiful cup is formed. As the air comes to the candle, it moves upward by the force of the current which the heat of the candle produces, and it so cools all the sides of the wax, tallow, or fuel as to keep the edge much cooler than the part within; the part within melts by the flame that runs down the wick as far as it can go before it is extinguished, but the part on the outside does not melt. If I made a current in one direction, my cup would be lop-sided, and the fluid would consequently run over; for the same force of gravity which holds worlds together holds this fluid in a horizontal position, and if the cup be not horizontal, of course the fluid will run away in guttering. You see, therefore, that the cup is formed by this beautifully regular ascending current of air playing upon all sides, which keeps the exterior of the candle cool. No fuel would serve for a candle which has not the property of giving this cup, except such fuel as the Irish bogwood, where the material itself is like a sponge and holds its own fuel. You see now why you would have had such a bad result if you were to burn these beautiful candles that I have shown you, which are irregular, inter-

mittent in their shape, and can not, therefore, have that nicely-formed edge to the cup which is the great beauty in a candle. I hope you will now see that the perfection of a process—that is, its utility—is the better point of beauty about it. It is not the best looking thing, but the best acting thing, which is the most advantageous to us. This good-looking candle is a bad-burning one. There will be a guttering round about it because of the irregularity of the stream of air and the badness of the cup which is formed thereby. You may see some pretty examples (and I trust you will notice these instances) of the action of the ascending current when you have a little gutter run down the side of a candle, making it thicker there than it is elsewhere. As the candle goes on burning, that keeps its place and forms a little pillar sticking up by the side, because, as it rises higher above the rest of the wax or fuel, the air gets better round it, and it is more cooled and better able to resist the action of the heat at a little distance. Now the greatest mistakes and faults with regard to candles, as in many other things, often bring with them instruction which we should not receive if they had not occurred. We come here to be philosophers, and I hope you will always remember that whenever a result happens, especially if it be new, you should say, "What is the cause? Why does it occur?" and you will, in the course of time, find out the reason.

Then there is another point about these candles which will answer a question—that is, as to the way in which this fluid gets out of the cup, up the wick, and into the place of combustion. You know that the flames on these burning wicks in candles made of beeswax, stearin, or spermaceti, do not run down to the wax or other matter, and melt it all away, but keep to their own right place. They are fenced off from the fluid below, and do not encroach on the cup at the sides. I can not imagine a more beautiful example than the condition of adjustment under which a candle makes one part subserve to the other to the very end of its action. A combustible thing like that, burning away gradually, never being intruded upon by the flame, is a very beautiful sight, especially when you come to learn what a vigorous thing flame is—what power it has of destroying the wax itself when it gets hold of it, and of disturbing its proper form if it come only too near.

But how does the flame get hold of the fuel? There is a beautiful point about that—*capillary attraction*.([4]) "Capillary attraction!" you say—"the attraction of hairs." Well, never mind the name; it was given in old times, before we had a good understanding of what the real power was. It is by what is called capillary attraction that the fuel is conveyed to the part where combustion goes on, and is deposited there, not in a careless way, but very beautifully in the very midst of the centre of action, which takes place around it. Now I am going to give you one or two instances of capillary attraction. It is that kind of action or attraction which makes two things that do not dissolve in each other still hold together. When you wash your hands, you wet them thoroughly; you take a little soap to make the adhesion better, and you find your hands remain wet. This is by that kind of attraction of which I am about to speak. And, what is more, if your hands are not soiled (as they almost always are by the usages of life), if you put your finger into a little warm water, the water will creep a little way up the finger, though you may not stop to examine it. I have here a substance which is rather porous—a column of salt—and I will pour into the plate at the bottom, not water, as it appears, but a saturated solution of salt which can not absorb more, so that the action which you see will not be due to its dissolving any thing. We may consider the plate to be the candle, and the salt the wick, and this solution the melted tallow. (I have colored the fluid, that you may see the action better.) You observe that, now

FIG. 55

I pour in the fluid, it rises and gradually creeps up the salt higher and higher (Fig. 55); and provided the column does not tumble over, it will go to the top. If this blue solution were combustible, and we were to place a wick at the top of the salt, it would burn as it entered into

[4] Capillary attraction or repulsion is the cause which determines the ascent or descent of a fluid in a capillary tube. If a piece of thermometer tubing, open at each end, be plunged into water, the latter will instantly rise in the tube considerably above its external level. If, on the other hand, the tube be plunged into mercury, a repulsion instead of attraction will be exhibited, and the level of the mercury will be lower in the tube than it is outside.

the wick. It is a most curious thing to see this kind of action taking place, and to observe how singular some of the circumstances are about it. When you wash your hands, you take a towel to wipe off the water; and it is by that kind of wetting, or that kind of attraction which makes the towel become wet with water, that the wick is made wet with the tallow. I have known some careless boys and girls (indeed, I have known it happen to careful people as well) who, having washed their hands and wiped them with a towel, have thrown the towel over the side of the basin, and before long it has drawn all the water out of the basin and conveyed it to the floor, because it happened to be thrown over the side in such a way as to serve the purpose of a siphon.(⁵) That you may the better see the way in which the substances act one upon another, I have here a vessel made of wire gauze filled with water, and you may compare it in its action to the cotton in one respect, or to a piece of calico in the other. In fact, wicks are sometimes made of a kind of wire gauze. You will observe that this vessel is a porous thing; for if I pour a little water on to the top, it will run out at the bottom. You would be puzzled for a good while if I asked you what the state of this vessel is, what is inside it, and why it is there? The vessel is full of water, and yet you see the water goes in and runs out as if it were empty. In order to prove this to you, I have only to empty it. The reason is this: the wire, being once wetted, remains wet; the meshes are so small that the fluid is attracted so strongly from the one side to the other, as to remain in the vessel, although it is porous. In like manner, the particles of melted tallow ascend the cotton and get to the top; other particles then follow by their mutual attraction for each other, and as they reach the flame they are gradually burned.

Here is another application of the same principle. You see this bit of cane. I have seen boys about the streets, who are very anxious to appear like men, take a piece of cane, and light it, and smoke it, as an imitation of a cigar. They are enabled to do so by the permeability

⁵ The late Duke of Sussex was, we believe, the first to show that a prawn might be washed upon this principle. If the tail, after pulling off the fan part, be placed in a tumbler of water, and the head be allowed to hang over the outside, the water will be sucked up the tail by capillary attraction, and will continue to run out through the head until the water in the glass has sunk so low that the tail ceases to dip into it.

of the cane in one direction, and by its capillarity. If I place this piece of cane on a plate containing some camphene (which is very much like paraffine in its general character), exactly in the same manner as the blue fluid rose through the salt will this fluid rise through the piece of cane. There being no pores at the side, the fluid can not go in that direction, but must pass through its length. Already the fluid is at the top of the cane; now I can light it and make it serve as a candle. The fluid has risen by the capillary attraction of the piece of cane, just as it does through the cotton in the candle.

Now the only reason why the candle does not burn all down the side of the wick is that the melted tallow extinguishes the flame. You know that a candle, if turned upside down, so as to allow the fuel to run upon the wick, will be put out. The reason is, that the flame has not had time to make the fuel hot enough to burn, as it does above, where it is carried in small quantities into the wick, and has all the effect of the heat exercised upon it.

FIG. 56

There is another condition which you must learn as regards the candle, without which you would not be able fully to understand the philosophy of it, and that is the vaporous condition of the fuel. In order that you may understand that, let me show you a very pretty but very commonplace experiment. If you blow a candle out cleverly, you will see the vapor rise from it. You have, I know, often smelt the vapor of a blown-out candle, and a very bad smell it is; but if you blow it out cleverly you will be able to see pretty well the vapor into which this solid matter is transformed. I will blow out one of these candles in such a way as not to disturb the air around it by the continuing action of my breath; and now, if I hold a lighted taper two or three inches from the wick, you will observe a train of fire going through the air till it reaches the candle (FIG. 56). I am obliged to be quick and ready, because if I allow the vapor time to cool, it becomes condensed into a liquid or solid, or the stream of combustible matter gets disturbed.

Now as to the shape or form of the flame. It concerns us much to

know about the condition which the matter of the candle finally assumes at the top of the wick, where you have such beauty and brightness as nothing but combustion or flame can produce. You have the glittering beauty of gold and silver, and the still higher lustre of jewels like the ruby and diamond; but none of these rival the brilliancy and beauty of flame. What diamond can shine like

FIG. 57

flame? It owes its lustre at nighttime to the very flame shining upon it. The flame shines in darkness, but the light which the diamond has is as nothing until the flame shines upon it, when it is brilliant again. The candle alone shines by itself and for itself, or for those who have arranged the materials. Now let us look a little at the form of the flame as you see it under the glass shade. It is steady and equal, and its general form is that which is represented in the diagram (FIG. 57), varying with atmospheric disturbances, and also varying according to the size of the candle. It is a bright oblong, brighter at the top than toward the bottom, with the wick in the middle, and, besides the wick in the middle, certain darker parts towards the bottom, where the ignition is not so perfect as in the part above. I have a drawing here, sketched many years ago by Hooker, when he made his investigations. It is the drawing of the flame of a lamp, but it will apply to the flame of a candle. The cup of the candle is the vessel or lamp; the melted spermaceti is the oil; and the wick is common to both. Upon that he sets this little flame, and then he represents what is true, a certain quantity of matter rising about it which you do not see, and which, if you have not been here before, or are not familiar with the subject, you will not know of. He has here represented the parts of the surrounding atmosphere that are very essential to the flame, and that are always present with it. There is a current formed, which draws the flame out; for the flame which you see is really drawn out by the current, and drawn upward to a great height, just as Hooker has here shown you by that prolongation of the current in the diagram. You may see this by taking a lighted candle, and putting it in the sun so as to get its shadow thrown on a piece of paper. How remarkable it is that that thing which is light enough to produce shadows of other objects can be made to throw its own shadow on a piece

of white paper or card, so that you can actually see streaming round the flame something which is not part of the flame, but is ascending and drawing the flame upward. Now I am going to imitate the sunlight by applying the voltaic battery to the electric lamp. You now see our sun and its great luminosity; and by placing a candle between it and the screen, we get the shadow of the flame. You observe the shadow of the candle and of the wick; then there is a darkish part, as represented in the diagram (FIG. 58), and then a part which is more distinct. Curiously enough, however, what we see in the shadow as the darkest part of the flame is, in reality, the brightest part; and here you see streaming upward the ascending current of hot air, as shown by Hooker, which draws out the flame, supplies it with air, and cools the sides of the cup of melted fuel.

FIG. 58

I can give you here a little farther illustration, for the purpose of showing you how flame goes up or down according to the current. I have here a flame—it is not a candle flame—but you can, no doubt, by this time generalize enough to be able to compare one thing with another. What I am about to do is to change the ascending current that takes the flame upward into a descending current. This I can easily do by the little apparatus you see before me. The flame, as I have said, is not a candle flame, but it is produced by alcohol, so that it shall not smoke too much. I will also color the flame with another substance([6]), so that you may trace its course; for, with the spirit alone, you could hardly see well enough to have the opportunity of tracing its direction. By lighting this spirit of wine we have then a flame produced, and you observe that when held in the air it naturally goes upward. You understand now, easily enough, why flames go up under ordinary circumstances: it is because of the draught of air by which the combustion is formed. But now, by blowing the flame down, you see I am enabled to make it go downward into this little chimney, the direction of the current being changed (FIG. 59). Before we have concluded this course of lectures

[6] The alcohol had chloride of copper dissolved in it: this produces a beautiful green flame.

we shall show you a lamp in which the flame goes up and the smoke goes down, or the flame goes down and the smoke goes up. You see, then, that we have the power in this way of varying the flame in different directions.

There are now some other points that I must bring before you. Many of the flames you see here vary very much in their shape by

FIG. 59

the currents of air blowing around them in different directions; but we can, if we like, make flames so that they will look like fixtures, and we can photograph them —indeed, we have to photograph them— so that they become fixed to us, if we wish to find out every thing concerning them. That, however, is not the only thing I wish to mention. If I take a flame sufficiently large, it does not keep that homogeneous, that uniform condition of shape, but it breaks out with a power of life which is quite wonderful. I am about to use another kind of fuel, but one which is truly and fairly a representative of the wax or tallow of a candle. I have here a large ball of cotton, which will serve as a wick. And, now that I have immersed it in spirit and applied a light to it, in what way does it differ from an ordinary candle? Why, it differs very much in one respect, that we have a vivacity and power about it, a beauty and a life entirely different from the light presented by a candle. You see those fine tongues of flame rising up. You have the same general disposition of the mass of the flame from below upward; but, in addition to that, you have this remarkable breaking out into tongues which you do not perceive in the case of a candle. Now, why is this? I must explain it to you, because, when you understand that perfectly, you will be able to follow me better in what I have to say hereafter. I suppose some here will have made for themselves the experiment I am going to show you. Am I right in supposing that any body here has played at snapdragon? I do not know a more beautiful illustration of the philosophy of flame, as to a certain part of its history, than the game of snapdragon. First, here is the dish; and let me say, that

when you play snapdragon properly you ought to have the dish well warmed; you ought also to have warm plums, and warm brandy, which, however, I have not got. When you have put the spirit into the dish, you have the cup and the fuel; and are not the raisins acting like the wicks? I now throw the plums into the dish, and light the spirit, and you see those beautiful tongues of flame that I refer to. You have the air creeping in over the edge of the dish forming these

FIG. 60

tongues. Why? Because, through the force of the current and the irregularity of the action of the flame, it can not flow in one uniform stream. The air flows in so irregularly that you have what would otherwise be a single image broken up into a variety of forms, and each of these little tongues has an independent existence of its own. Indeed, I might say, you have here a multitude of independent candles. You must not imagine, because you see these tongues all at once, that the flame is of this particular shape. A flame of that shape is never so at any one time. Never is a body of flame, like that which you just saw rising from the ball, of the shape it appears to you. It consists of a multitude of different shapes, succeeding each other so fast that the eye is only able to take cognizance of them all at once. In former times I purposely analyzed a flame of that general character, and the diagram shows you the different parts of which it is composed (FIG. 60). They do not occur all at once; it is only because we see these shapes in such rapid succession that they seem to us to exist all at one time.

It is too bad that we have not got farther than my game of snap-dragon; but we must not, under any circumstances, keep you beyond your time. It will be a lesson to me in future to hold you more strictly to the philosophy of the thing than to take up your time so much with these illustrations.

LECTURE II

A CANDLE: BRIGHTNESS OF THE FLAME—AIR NECESSARY FOR COMBUSTION—PRODUCTION OF WATER

WE were occupied the last time we met in considering the general character and arrangement as regards the fluid portion of a candle, and the way in which that fluid got into the place of combustion. You see, when we have a candle burning fairly in a regular, steady atmosphere, it will have a shape something like the one shown in the diagram, and will look pretty uniform, although very curious in its character. And now I have to ask your attention to the means by which we are enabled to ascertain what happens in any particular part of the flame; why it happens; what it does in happening; and where, after all, the whole candle goes to; because, as you know very well, a candle being brought before us and burned, disappears, if burned properly, without the least trace of dirt in the candle stick; and this is a very curious circumstance. In order, then, to examine this candle carefully, I have arranged certain apparatus, the use of which you will see as I go on. Here is a candle; I am about to put the end of this glass tube into the middle of the flame—into that part which old Hooker has represented in the diagram as being rather dark, and which you can see at any time if you will look at a candle carefully, without blowing it about. We will examine this dark part first.

Now I take this bent glass tube, and introduce one end into that part of the flame, and you see at once that something is coming from the flame, out at the other end of the tube; and if I put a flask there, and leave it for a little while, you will see that something from the middle part of the flame is gradually drawn out, and goes through the tube, and into that flask, and there behaves very differently from what it does in the open air. It not only escapes from the end of the tube, but falls down to the bottom of the flask like a

heavy substance, as indeed it is (FIG. 61). We find that this is the wax of the candle made into a vaporous fluid—not a gas. (You must learn the difference between a gas and a vapor: a gas remains permanent; a vapor is something that will condense.) If you blow out a candle, you perceive a very nasty smell, resulting from the condensation of this vapor. That is very different from what you have outside the flame; and, in order to make that more clear to you, I am about to produce and set fire to a larger portion of this vapor; for

FIG. 61

what we have in the small way in a candle, to understand thoroughly, we must, as philosophers, produce in a larger way, if needful, that we may examine the different parts. And now Mr. Anderson will give me a source of heat, and I am about to show you what that vapor is. Here is some wax in a glass flask, and I am going to make it hot, as the inside of that candle flame is hot, and the matter about the wick is hot. [The lecturer placed some wax in a glass flask, and heated it over a lamp.] Now I dare say that is hot enough for me. You see that the wax I put in it has become fluid, and there is a little smoke coming from it. We shall very soon have the vapor rising up. I will make it still hotter, and now we get more of it, so that I can actually pour the vapor out of the flask into that basin, and set it on fire there. This, then, is exactly the same kind of vapor as

we have in the middle of the candle; and that you may be sure this is the case, let us try whether we have not got here, in this flask, a real combustible vapor out of the middle of the candle. [Taking the flask into which the tube from the candle proceeded, and introducing a lighted taper (Fig. 62).] See how it burns. Now this is the vapor from the middle of the candle, produced by its own heat; and that is one of the first things you have to consider with respect to the progress of the wax in the course of its combustion, and as regards the changes it undergoes. I will arrange another tube carefully in the flame, and I should not wonder if we were able, by a little care, to get that vapor to pass through the tube to the other extremity, where we will light it, and obtain absolutely the flame of the candle at a place distant from it. Now, look at that. Is not that a very pretty experiment? Talk about laying on gas—why, we can actually lay on a candle! And you see from this that there are clearly two different kinds of action—one the *production* of the vapor, and the other the *combustion* of it—both of which take place in particular parts of the candle.

FIG. 62

I shall get no vapor from that part which is already burnt. If I raise the tube (Fig. 61) to the upper part of the flame, so soon as the vapor has been swept out what comes away will be no longer combustible; it is already burned. How burned? Why, burned thus: In the middle of the flame, where the wick is, there is this combustible vapor; on the outside of the flame is the air which we shall find necessary for the burning of the candle; between the two, intense chemical action takes place, whereby the air and the fuel act upon each other, and at the very same time that we obtain light the vapor inside is destroyed. If you examine where the heat of a candle is, you will find it very curiously arranged. Suppose I take this candle, and hold a piece of paper close upon the flame, where is the heat of that flame? Do you not see that it is *not* in the inside? It is in a ring, exactly in the place where I told you the chemical action was; and even in my irregular mode of making the experiment, if there is not too much disturbance, there will always be a ring. This is a good experiment for you to make at home. Take a strip of paper,

have the air in the room quiet, and put the piece of paper right across the middle of the flame—(I must not talk while I make the experiment)—and you will find that it is burnt in two places, and that it is not burnt, or very little so, in the middle; and when you have tried the experiment once or twice, so as to make it nicely, you will be very interested to see where the heat is, and to find that it is where the air and the fuel come together.

This is most important for us as we proceed with our subject. Air is absolutely necessary for combustion; and, what is more, I must have you understand that *fresh* air is necessary, or else we should be imperfect in our reasoning and our experiments. Here is a jar of air; I place it over a candle, and it burns very nicely in it at first, showing that what I have said about it is true; but there will soon be a change. See how the flame is drawing upward, presently fading, and at last going out. And going out, why? Not because it wants air merely, for the jar is as full now as it was before; but it wants pure, fresh air. The jar is full of air, partly changed, partly not changed; but it does not contain sufficient of the fresh air which is necessary for the combustion of a candle. These are all points which we, as young chemists, have to gather up; and if we look a little more closely into this kind of action, we shall find certain steps of reasoning extremely interesting. For instance, here is the oil-lamp I showed you—an excellent lamp for our experiments—the old Argand lamp. I now make it like a candle [obstructing the passage of air into the centre of the flame]; there is the cotton; there is the oil rising up in it, and there is the conical flame. It burns poorly because there is a partial restraint of air. I have allowed no air to get to it save around the outside of the flame, and it does not burn well. I can not admit more air from the outside, because the wick is large; but if, as Argand did so cleverly, I open a passage to the middle of the flame, and so let air come in there, you will see how much more beautifully it burns. If I shut the air off, look how it smokes; and why? We have now some very interesting points to study: we have the case of the combustion of a candle; we have the case of a candle being put out by the want of air; and we have now the case of imperfect combustion, and this is to us so interesting that I want you to understand it as thoroughly as you do the case of a candle

burning in its best possible manner. I will now make a great flame, because we need the largest possible illustrations. Here is a larger wick [burning turpentine on a ball of cotton]. All these things are the same as candles, after all. If we have larger wicks, we must have a larger supply of air, or we shall have less perfect combustion. Look, now, at this black substance going up into the atmosphere; there is a regular stream of it. I have provided means to carry off the imperfectly burned part, lest it should annoy you. Look at the soots that fly off from the flame; see what an imperfect combustion it is, because it can not get enough air. What, then, is happening? Why, certain things which are necessary to the combustion of a candle are absent, and very bad results are accordingly produced; but we see what happens to a candle when it is burnt in a pure and proper state of air. At the time when I showed you this charring by the ring of flame on the one side of the paper, I might have also shown you, by turning to the other side, that the burning of a candle produces the same kind of soot—charcoal, or carbon.

But, before I show that, let me explain to you, as it is quite necessary for our purpose, that, though I take a candle, and give you, as the general result, its combustion in the form of a flame, we must see whether combustion is always in this condition, or whether there are other conditions of flame; and we shall soon discover that there are, and that they are most important to us. I think, perhaps, the best illustration of such a point to us, as juveniles, is to show the result of strong contrast. Here is a little gunpowder. You know that gunpowder burns with flame; we may fairly call it flame. It contains carbon and other materials, which altogether cause it to burn with a flame. And here is some pulverized iron, or iron filings. Now I purpose burning these two things together. I have a little mortar in which I will mix them. (Before I go into these experiments, let me hope that none of you, by trying to repeat them for fun's sake, will do any harm. These things may all be very properly used if you take care, but without that much mischief will be done.) Well, then, here is a little gunpowder, which I put at the bottom of that little wooden vessel, and mix the iron filings up with it, my object being to make the gunpowder set fire to the filings and burn them in the air, and thereby show the difference between substances burn-

ing with flame and not with flame. Here is the mixture; and when I set fire to it you must watch the combustion, and you will see that it is of two kinds. You will see the gunpowder burning with a flame and the filings thrown up. You will see them burning, too, but without the production of flame. They will each burn separately. [The lecturer then ignited the mixture.] There is the gunpowder, which burns with a flame, and there are the filings: they burn with a different kind of combustion. You see, then, these two great distinctions; and upon these differences depend all the utility and all the beauty of flame which we use for the purpose of giving out light. When we use oil, or gas, or candle for the purpose of illumination, their fitness all depends upon these different kinds of combustion.

There are such curious conditions of flame that it requires some cleverness and nicety of discrimination to distinguish the kinds of combustion one from another. For instance, here is a powder which is very combustible, consisting, as you see, of separate little particles. It is called *lycopodium*,([7]) and each of these particles can produce a vapor, and produce its own flame; but, to see them burning, you would imagine it was all one flame. I will now set fire to a quantity, and you will see the effect. We saw a cloud of flame, apparently in one body; but that rushing noise [referring to the sound produced by the burning] was a proof that the combustion was not a continuous or regular one. This is the lightning of the pantomimes, and a very good imitation. [The experiment was twice repeated by blowing lycopodium from a glass tube through a spirit flame.] This is not an example of combustion like that of the filings I have been speaking of, to which we must now return.

Suppose I take a candle and examine that part of it which appears brightest to our eyes. Why, there I get these black particles, which already you have seen many times evolved from the flame, and which I am now about to evolve in a different way. I will take this candle and clear away the gutterage, which occurs by reason of the currents of air; and if I now arrange the glass tube so as just to dip into this luminous part, as in our first experiment, only higher, you see the

[7] Lycopodium is a yellowish powder found in the fruit of the club moss (*Lycopodium clavatum*). It is used in fireworks.

result. In place of having the same white vapor that you had before, you will now have a black vapor. There it goes, as black as ink. It is certainly very different from the white vapor; and when we put a light to it we shall find that it does not burn, but that it puts the light out. Well, these particles, as I said before, are just the smoke of the candle; and this brings to mind that old employment which Dean Swift recommended to servants for their amusement, namely, writing on the ceiling of a room with a candle. But what is that black substance? Why, it is the same carbon which exists in the candle. How comes it out of the candle? It evidently existed in the candle, or else we should not have had it here. And now I want you to follow me in this explanation. You would hardly think that all those substances which fly about London, in the form of soots and blacks, are the very beauty and life of the flame, and which are burned in it as those iron filings were burned here. Here is a piece of wire gauze, which will not let the flame go through it; and I think you will see, almost immediately, that when I bring it low enough to touch that part of the flame which is otherwise so bright, it quells and quenches it at once, and allows a volume of smoke to rise up.

I want you now to follow me in this point—that whenever a substance burns, as the iron filings burnt in the flame of gunpowder, without assuming the vaporous state (whether it becomes liquid or remains solid), it becomes exceedingly luminous. I have here taken three or four examples apart from the candle on purpose to illustrate this point to you, because what I have to say is applicable to all substances, whether they burn or whether they do not burn—that they are exceedingly bright if they retain their solid state, and that it is to this presence of solid particles in the candle flame that it owes its brilliancy.

Here is a platinum wire, a body which does not change by heat. If I heat it in this flame, see how exceedingly luminous it becomes. I will make the flame dim for the purpose of giving a little light only, and yet you will see that the heat which it can give to that platinum wire, though far less than the heat it has itself, is able to raise the platinum wire to a far higher state of effulgence. This flame

has carbon in it; but I will take one that has no carbon in it. There is a material, a kind of fuel—a vapor, or gas, whichever you like to call it—in that vessel, and it has no solid particles in it; so I take that because it is an example of flame itself burning without any solid matter whatever; and if I now put this solid substance in it, you see what an intense heat it has, and how brightly it causes the solid body to glow. This is the pipe through which we convey this particular gas, which we call hydrogen, and which you shall know all about the next time we meet. And here is a substance called oxygen, by means of which this hydrogen can burn; and although we produce, by their mixture, far greater heat ([8]) than you can obtain from the candle, yet there is very little light. If, however, I take a solid substance, and put that into it, we produce an intense light. If I take a piece of lime, a substance which will not burn, and which will not vaporize by the heat (and because it does not vaporize remains solid, and remains heated), you will soon observe what happens as to its glowing. I have here a most intense heat produced by the burning of hydrogen in contact with the oxygen; but there is as yet very little light—not for want of heat, but for want of particles which can retain their solid state; but when I hold this piece of lime in the flame of the hydrogen as it burns in the oxygen, see how it glows! This is the glorious lime light, which rivals the voltaic light, and which is almost equal to sunlight. I have here a piece of carbon or charcoal, which will burn and give us light exactly in the same manner as if it were burnt as part of a candle. The heat that is in the flame of a candle decomposes the vapor of the wax, and sets free the carbon particles; they rise up heated and glowing as this now glows, and then enter into the air. But the particles, when burnt, never pass off from a candle in the form of carbon. They go off into the air as a perfectly invisible substance, about which we shall know hereafter.

Is it not beautiful to think that such a process is going on, and that such a dirty thing as charcoal can become so incandescent? You see it comes to this—that all bright flames contain these solid particles; all things that burn and produce solid particles, either during the time they are burning, as in the candle, or immediately after

[8] Bunsen has calculated that the temperature of the oxyhydrogen blowpipe is 8061° Centigrade. Hydrogen burning in air has a temperature of 3259° C., and coal gas in air, 2350° C.

being burnt, as in the case of the gunpowder and iron filings—all these things give us this glorious and beautiful light.

I will give you a few illustrations. Here is a piece of phosphorus, which burns with a bright flame. Very well; we may now conclude that phosphorus will produce, either at the moment that it is burning or afterwards, these solid particles. Here is the phosphorus lighted, and I cover it over with this glass for the purpose of keeping in what is produced. What is all that smoke? (FIG. 63.) That smoke consists of those very particles which are produced by the combustion of the phosphorus. Here, again, are two substances. This is chlorate of potassa, and this other sulphuret of antimony. I shall mix these together a little, and then they may

Fig. 63

be burnt in many ways. I shall touch them with a drop of sulphuric acid, for the purpose of giving you an illustration of chemical action, and they will instantly burn.([9]) [The lecturer then ignited the mixture by means of sulphuric acid.] Now, from the appearance of things, you can judge for yourselves whether they produce solid matter in burning. I have given you the train of reasoning which will enable you to say whether they do or do not; for what is this bright flame but the solid particles passing off?

Mr. Anderson has in the furnace a very hot crucible. I am about to throw into it some zinc filings, and they will burn with a flame like gunpowder. I make this experiment because you can make it well at home. Now I want you to see what will be the result of the combustion of this zinc. Here it is burning—burning beautifully like a candle, I may say. But what is all that smoke, and what are those little clouds of wool which will come to you if you can not come to them, and make themselves sensible to you in the form of the old philosophic wool, as it was called? We shall have left in that crucible, also, a quantity of this woolly matter. But I will take a piece of this

[9] The following is the action of the sulphuric in inflaming the mixture of sulphuret of antimony and chlorate of potassa. A portion of the latter is decomposed by the sulphuric acid into oxide of chlorine, bisulphate of potassa, and perchlorate of potassa. The oxide of chlorine inflames the sulphuret of antimony, which is a combustible body, and the whole mass instantly bursts into flame.

same zinc, and make an experiment a little more closely at home, as it were. You will have here the same thing happening. Here is the piece of zinc; there [pointing to a jet of hydrogen] is the furnace, and we will set to work and try and burn the metal. It glows, you see; there is the combustion; and there is the white substance into which it burns. And so, if I take that flame of hydrogen as the representative of a candle, and show you a substance like zinc burning in the flame, you will see that it was merely during the action of combustion that this substance glowed—while it was kept hot; and if I take a flame of hydrogen and put this white substance from the zinc into it, look how beautifully it glows, and just because it is a solid substance.

I will now take such a flame as I had a moment since, and set free from it the particles of carbon. Here is some camphene, which will burn with a smoke; but if I send these particles of smoke through this pipe into the hydrogen flame you will see they will burn and become luminous, because we heat them a second time. There they are. Those are the particles of carbon reignited a second time. They are those particles which you can easily see by holding a piece of paper behind them, and which, while they are in the flame, are ignited by the heat produced, and, when so ignited, produce this brightness. When the particles are not separated you get no brightness. The flame of coal gas owes its brightness to the separation, during combustion, of these particles of carbon, which are equally in that as in a candle. I can very quickly alter that arrangement. Here, for instance, is a bright flame of gas. Supposing I add so much air to the flame as to cause it all to burn before those particles are set free, I shall not have this brightness; and I can do that in this way: If I place over the jet this wire-gauze cap, as you see, and then light the gas over it, it burns with a non-luminous flame, owing to its having plenty of air mixed with it before it burns; and if I raise the gauze, you see it does not burn below([10]). There is plenty of carbon

[10] The "air-burner," which is of such value in the laboratory, owes its advantage to this principle. It consists of a cylindrical metal chimney, covered at the top with a piece of rather coarse iron wire gauze. This is supported over an Argand burner in such a manner that the gas may mix in the chimney with an amount of air sufficient to burn the carbon and hydrogen simultaneously, so that there may be no separation of carbon in the flame with consequent deposition of soot. The flame, being unable to pass through the wire gauze, burns in a steady, nearly invisible manner above.

in the gas; but, because the atmosphere can get to it, and mix with it before it burns, you see how pale and blue the flame is. And if I blow upon a bright gas flame, so as to consume all this carbon before it gets heated to the glowing point, it will also burn blue. [The lecturer illustrated his remarks by blowing on the gas light.] The only reason why I have not the same bright light when I thus blow upon the flame is that the carbon meets with sufficient air to burn it before it gets separated in the flame in a free state. The difference is solely due to the solid particles not being separated before the gas is burnt.

You observe that there are certain products as the result of the combustion of a candle, and that of these products one portion may be considered as charcoal, or soot; that charcoal, when afterward burnt, produces some other product; and it concerns us very much now to ascertain what that other product is. We showed that something was going away; and I want you now to understand how much is going up into the air; and for that purpose we will have combustion on a little larger scale. From that candle ascends heated air, and two or three experiments will show you the ascending current; but, in order to give you a notion of the quantity of matter which ascends in this way, I will make an experiment by which I shall try to imprison some of the products of this combustion. For this purpose I have here what boys call a fire-balloon; I use this fire-balloon merely as a sort of measure of the result of the combustion we are considering; and I am about to make a flame in such an easy and simple manner as shall best serve my present purpose. This plate shall be the "cup," we will so say, of the candle; this spirit shall be our fuel; and I am about to place this chimney over it, because it is better for me to do so than to let things proceed at random. Mr. Anderson will now light the fuel, and here at the top we shall get the results of the combustion. What we get at the top of that tube is exactly the same, generally speaking, as you get from the combustion of a candle; but we do not get a luminous flame here, because we use a substance which is feeble in carbon. I am about to put this balloon— not into action, because that is not my object—but to show you the effect which results from the action of those products which arise from the candle, as they arise here from the furnace. [The balloon

was held over the chimney (Fig. 64), when it immediately com-
menced to fill.] You see how it is disposed to ascend; but we must
not let it up; because it might come in contact with those upper
gaslights, and that would be very inconvenient. [The upper gas-

lights were turned out at the request of the
lecturer, and the balloon was allowed to
ascend.] Does not that show you what a
large bulk of matter is being evolved? Now
there is going through this tube [placing a
large glass tube over a candle] all the prod-
ucts of that candle, and you will presently
see that the tube will become quite opaque.
Suppose I take another candle, and place it
under a jar, and then put a light on the other
side, just to show you what is going on. You
see that the sides of the jar become cloudy,
and the light begins to burn feebly. It is the
products, you see, which make the light so
dim, and this is the same thing which makes
the sides of the jar so opaque. If you go
home, and take a spoon that has been in the
cold air, and hold it over a candle—not so as

Fig. 64 to soot it—you will find that it becomes dim

just as that jar is dim. If you can get a silver dish, or something of
that kind, you will make the experiment still better; and now, just
to carry your thoughts forward to the time we shall next meet, let
me tell you that it is *water* which causes the dimness, and when we
next meet I will show you that we can make it, without difficulty,
assume the form of a liquid.

LECTURE III

PRODUCTS: WATER FROM THE COMBUSTION—
NATURE OF WATER—A COMPOUND—
HYDROGEN

I DARE say you well remember that when we parted we had just mentioned the word "products" from the candle; for when a candle burns we found we were able, by nice adjustment, to get various products from it. There was one substance which was not obtained when the candle was burning properly, which was charcoal or smoke, and there was some other substance that went upward from the flame which did not appear as smoke, but took some other form, and made part of that general current which, ascending from the candle upward, becomes invisible, and escapes. There were also other products to mention. You remember that in that rising current having its origin at the candle we found that one part was condensable against a cold spoon, or against a clean plate, or any other cold thing, and another part was incondensable.

We will first take the condensable part, and examine it, and, strange to say, we find that that part of the product is just water— nothing but water. On the last occasion I spoke of it incidentally, merely saying that water was produced among the condensable products of the candle; but to-day I wish to draw your attention to water, that we may examine it carefully, especially in relation to this subject, and also with respect to its general existence on the surface of the globe.

Now, having previously arranged an experiment for the purpose of condensing water from the products of the candle, my next point will be to show you this water; and perhaps one of the best means that I can adopt for showing its presence to so many at once is to exhibit a very visible action of water, and then to apply that test to what is collected as a drop at the bottom of that vessel. I have here a chemical substance, discovered by Sir Humphry Davy, which

has a very energetic action upon water, which I shall use as a test
of the presence of water. If I take a little piece of it—it is called
potassium, as coming from potash—if I take a little piece of it, and
throw it into that basin, you see how it shows the presence of water
by lighting up and floating about, burning with a violet flame. I
am now going to take away the candle which has been burning
beneath the vessel containing ice and salt, and you see a drop of
water—a condensed product of the candle—hanging

from the under surface of the dish (FIG. 65). I will
show you that potassium has the same action upon it
as upon the water in that basin in the experiment we
have just tried. See! it takes fire, and burns in just
the same manner. I will take another drop upon this
glass slab, and when I put the potassium on to it, you
see at once, from its taking fire, that there is water
present. Now that water was produced by the candle.
In the same manner, if I put this spirit lamp under
that jar, you will soon see the latter become damp
from the dew which is deposited upon it—that dew
being the result of combustion; and I have no doubt
you will shortly see, by the drops of water which fall
upon the paper below, that there is a good deal of

FIG. 65

water produced from the combustion of the lamp. I will let it remain,
and you can afterward see how much water has been collected. So, if
I take a gas lamp, and put any cooling arrangement over it, I shall
get water—water being likewise produced from the combustion of
gas. Here, in this bottle, is a quantity of water—perfectly pure,
distilled water, produced from the combustion of a gas lamp—in no
point different from the water that you distill from the river, or
ocean, or spring, but exactly the same thing. Water is one individual
thing; it never changes. We can add to it by careful adjustment for
a little while, or we can take it apart and get other things from it;
but water, as water, remains always the same, either in a solid, liquid,
or fluid state. Here again [holding another bottle] is some water
produced by the combustion of an oil lamp. A pint of oil, when
burnt fairly and properly, produces rather more than a pint of
water. Here, again, is some water, produced by a rather long experi-

ment, from a wax candle. And so we can go on with almost all combustible substances, and find that if they burn with a flame, as a candle, they produce water. You may make these experiments yourselves: the head of a poker is a very good thing to try with, and if it remains cold long enough over the candle, you may get water condensed in drops on it; or a spoon, or ladle, or any thing else may be used, provided it be clean, and can carry off the heat, and so condense the water.

And now—to go into the history of this wonderful production of water from combustibles, and by combustion—I must first of all tell you that this water may exist in different conditions; and although you may now be acquainted with all its forms, they still require us to give a little attention to them for the present; so that we may perceive how the water, while it goes through its Protean changes, is entirely and absolutely the same thing, whether it is produced from a candle, by combustion, or from the rivers or ocean.

First of all, water, when at the coldest, is ice. Now we philosophers —I hope that I may class you and myself together in this case— speak of water as water, whether it be in its solid, or liquid, or gaseous state—we speak of it chemically as water. Water is a thing compounded of two substances, one of which we have derived from the candle, and the other we shall find elsewhere. Water may occur as ice; and you have had most excellent opportunities lately of seeing this. Ice changes back into water—for we had on our last Sabbath a strong instance of this change by the sad catastrophe which occurred in our own house, as well as in the houses of many of our friends—ice changes back into water when the temperature is raised; water also changes into steam when it is warmed enough. The water which we have here before us is in its densest state[11]; and, although it changes in weight, in condition, in form, and in many other qualities, it still is water; and whether we alter it into ice by cooling, or whether we change it into steam by heat, it increases in volume—in the one case very strangely and powerfully, and in the other case very largely and wonderfully. For instance, I will now take this tin cylinder, and pour a little water into it, and, seeing how much water I pour in, you may easily estimate for yourselves how

[11] Water is in its densest state at a temperature of 39.1° Fahrenheit.

high it will rise in the vessel: it will cover the bottom about two inches. I am now about to convert the water into steam for the purpose of showing to you the different volumes which water occupies in its different states of water and steam.

Let us now take the case of water changing into ice: we can effect that by cooling it in a mixture of salt and pounded ice([12])—and I shall do so to show you the expansion of water into a thing of larger bulk when it is so changed. These bottles [holding one] are made of strong cast iron, very strong and very thick—I suppose they are the third of an inch in thickness; they are very carefully filled with water, so as to exclude all air, and then they are screwed down tight. We shall see that when we freeze the water in these iron vessels, they will not be able to hold the ice, and the expansion within them will break them in pieces as these [pointing to some fragments] are broken, which have been bottles of exactly the same kind. I am about to put these two bottles into that mixture of ice and salt for the purpose of showing that when water becomes ice it changes in volume in this extraordinary way.

In the mean time, look at the change which has taken place in the water to which we have applied heat; it is losing its fluid state. You may tell this by two or three circumstances. I have covered the mouth of this glass flask, in which water is boiling, with a watch-glass. Do you see what happens? It rattles away like a valve chattering, because the steam rising from the boiling water sends the valve up and down, and forces itself out, and so makes it clatter. You can very easily perceive that the flask is quite full of steam, or else it would not force its way out. You see, also, that the flask contains a substance very much larger than the water, for it fills the whole of the flask over and over again, and there it is blowing away into the air; and yet you can not observe any great diminution in the bulk of the water, which shows you that its change of bulk is very great when it becomes steam.

I have put our iron bottles containing water into this freezing mixture, that you may see what happens. No communication will take place, you observe, between the water in the bottles and the ice in

[12] A mixture of salt and pounded ice reduces the temperature from 32° F. to zero, the ice at the same time becoming fluid.

the outer vessel. But there will be a conveyance of heat from the one to the other, and if we are successful—we are making our experiment in very great haste—I expect you will by-and-by, so soon as the cold has taken possession of the bottles and their contents, hear a pop on the occasion of the bursting of the one bottle or the other, and, when we come to examine the bottles, we shall find their contents masses of ice, partly inclosed by the covering of iron which is too small for them, because the ice is larger in bulk than the

FIG. 66

water. You know very well that ice floats upon water; if a boy falls through a hole into the water, he tries to get on the ice again to float him up. Why does the ice float? Think of that, and philosophize. Because the ice is larger than the quantity of water which can produce it, and therefore the ice weighs the lighter and the water is the heavier.

To return now to the action of heat on water. See what a stream of vapor is issuing from this tin vessel! You observe, we must have made it quite full of steam to have it sent out in that great quantity. And now, as we can convert the water into steam by heat, we convert it back into liquid water by the application of cold. And if we

take a glass, or any other cold thing, and hold it over this steam, see how soon it gets damp with water: it will condense it until the glass is warm—it condenses the water which is now running down the sides of it. I have here another experiment to show the condensation of water from a vaporous state back into a liquid state, in the same way as the vapor, one of the products of the candle, was condensed against the bottom of the dish and obtained in the form of water; and to show you how truly and thoroughly these changes take place, I will take this tin flask, which is now full of steam, and close the top. We shall see what takes place when we cause this water or steam to return back to the fluid state by pouring some cold water on the outside. [The lecturer poured the cold water over the vessel, when it immediately collapsed (Fig. 66).] You see what has happened. If I had closed the stopper, and still kept the heat applied to it, it would have burst the vessel; yet, when the steam returns to the state of water, the vessel collapses, there being a vacuum produced inside by the condensation of the steam. I show you these experiments for the purpose of pointing out that in all these occurrences there is nothing that changes the water into any other thing; it still remains water; and so the vessel is obliged to give way, and is crushed inward, as in the other case, by the farther application of heat, it would have been blown outward.

And what do you think the bulk of that water is when it assumes the vaporous condition? You see that cube [pointing to a cubic foot]. There, by its side, is a cubic inch (Fig. 67), exactly the same shape as the cubic foot, and that bulk of water [the cubic inch] is sufficient to expand into that bulk [the cubic foot] of steam; and, on the contrary, the application of cold will contract that large quantity of steam into this small quantity of water. [One of the iron bottles burst at that moment.] Ah! There is one of our bottles burst, and here, you see, is a crack down one side an eighth of an inch in width. [The other now exploded, sending the freezing mixture in all directions.] This other bottle is also broken; although

Fig. 67

the iron was nearly half an inch thick, the ice has burst it asunder. These changes always take place in water; they do not require to be always produced by artificial means; we only use them here because we want to produce a small winter round that little bottle instead of a long and severe one. But if you go to Canada, or to the North, you will find the temperature there out of doors will do the same thing as has been done here by the freezing mixture.

To return to our quiet philosophy. We shall not in future be deceived, therefore, by any changes that are produced in water. Water is the same every where, whether produced from the ocean or from the flame of the candle. Where, then, is this water which we get from a candle? I must anticipate a little, and tell you. It evidently comes, as to part of it, from the candle, but is it within the candle beforehand? No, it is not in the candle; and it is not in the air around about the candle which is necessary for its combustion. It is neither in one nor the other, but it comes from their conjoint action, a part from the candle, a part from the air; and this we have now to trace, so that we may understand thoroughly what is the chemical history of a candle when we have it burning on our table. How shall we get at this? I myself know plenty of ways, but I want *you* to get at it from the association in your own minds of what I have already told you.

I think you can see a little in this way. We had just now the case of a substance which acted upon the water in the way that Sir Humphry Davy showed us([13]), and which I am now going to recall to your minds by making again an experiment upon that dish. It is a thing which we have to handle very carefully; for you see, if I allow a little splash of water to come upon this mass, it sets fire to part of it; and if there were free access of air, it would quickly set fire to the whole. Now this is a metal—a beautiful and bright metal—which rapidly changes in the air, and, as you know, rapidly changes in water. I will put a piece on the water, and you see it burns beautifully, making a floating lamp, using the water in the place of air. Again, if we take a few iron filings or turnings and

[13] Potassium, the metallic basis of potash, was discovered by Sir Humphry Davy in 1807, who succeeded in separating it from potash by means of a powerful voltaic battery. Its great affinity for oxygen causes it to decompose water with evolution of hydrogen, which takes fire with the heat produced.

put them in water, we find that they likewise undergo an alteration. They do not change so much as this potassium does, but they change somewhat in the same way; they become rusty, and show an action upon the water, though in a different degree of intensity to what this beautiful metal does; but they act upon the water in the same manner generally as this potassium. I want you to put these different facts together in your minds. I have another metal here [zinc], and when we examined it with regard to the solid substance produced by its combustion, we had an opportunity of seeing that it burned; and I suppose, if I take a little strip of this zinc and put it over the candle, you will see something half way, as it were, between the combustion of potassium on the water and the action of iron—you see there is a sort of combustion. It has burned, leaving a white ash or residuum; and here also we find that the metal has a certain amount of action upon water.

By degrees we have learned how to modify the action of these different substances, and to make them tell us what we want to know. And now, first of all, I take iron. It is a common thing in all chemical reactions, where we get any result of this kind, to find that it is increased by the action of heat; and if we want to examine minutely and carefully the action of bodies one upon another, we often have to refer to the action of heat. You are aware, I believe, that iron filings burn beautifully in the air; but I am about to show you an experiment of this kind, because it will impress upon you what I am going to say about iron in its action on water. If I take a flame and make it hollow—you know why, because I want to get air to it and into it, and therefore I make it hollow—and then take a few iron filings and drop them into the flame, you see how well they burn. That combustion results from the chemical action which is going on when we ignite those particles. And so we proceed to consider these different effects, and ascertain what iron will do when it meets with water. It will tell us the story so beautifully, so gradually and regularly, that I think it will please you very much.

I have here a furnace with a pipe going through it like an iron gun barrel (FIG. 68), and I have stuffed that barrel full of bright iron turnings, and placed it across the fire to be made red-hot. We can either send air through the barrel to come in contact with the

iron, or we can send steam from this little boiler at the end of the barrel. Here is a stop-cock which shuts off the steam from the barrel until we wish to admit it. There is some water in these glass jars, which I have colored blue, so that you may see what happens. Now you know very well that any steam I might send through that barrel, if it went through into the water, would be condensed; for you have seen that steam can not retain its gaseous form if it be cooled down; you saw it here [pointing to the tin flask] crushing itself into a small bulk, and causing the flask holding it to collapse;

FIG. 68

so that if I were to send steam through that barrel it would be condensed, supposing the barrel were cold; it is, therefore, heated to perform the experiment I am now about to show you. I am going to send the steam through the barrel in small quantities, and you shall judge for yourselves, when you see it issue from the other end, whether it still remains steam. Steam is condensible into water, and when you lower the temperature of steam you convert it back into fluid water; but I have lowered the temperature of the gas which I have collected in this jar by passing it through water after it has traversed the iron barrel, and still it does not change back into water. I will take another test and apply to this gas. (I hold the jar in an inverted position, or my substance would escape.) If I now apply a light to the mouth of the jar, it ignites with a slight noise. That tells you that it is not steam; steam puts out a fire: it does not burn; but you saw that what I had in that jar burnt. We may obtain this

substance equally from water produced from the candle flame as from any other source. When it is obtained by the action of the iron upon the aqueous vapor, it leaves the iron in a state very similar to that in which these filings were after they were burnt. It makes the iron heavier than it was before. So long as the iron remains in the tube and is heated, and is cooled again without the access of air or water, it does not change in its weight; but after having had this current of steam passed over it, it then comes out heavier than it was before, having taken something out of the steam, and having allowed something else to pass forth, which we see here. And now, as we have another jar full, I will show you something most interesting. It is a combustible gas; and I might at once take this jar and set fire to the contents, and show you that it is combustible; but I intend to show you more, if I can. It is also a very light substance. Steam will condense; this body will rise in the air, and not condense. Suppose I take another glass jar, empty of all but air: if I examine it with a taper I shall find that it contains nothing but air. I will now take this jar full of the gas that I am speaking of, and deal with it as though it were a light body;

FIG. 69

I will hold both upside down, and turn the one up under the other (FIG. 69); and that which did contain the gas procured from the steam, what does it contain now? You will find it now only contains air. But look! Here is the combustible substance [taking the other jar] which I have poured out of the one jar into the other. It still preserves its quality, and condition, and independence, and therefore is the more worthy of our consideration, as belonging to the products of a candle.

Now this substance which we have just prepared by the action of iron on the steam or water, we can also get by means of those other things which you have already seen act so well upon the water. If I take a piece of potassium, and make the necessary arrangements, it will produce this gas; and if, instead, a piece of zinc, I find, when I come to examine it very carefully, that the main reason why this zinc can not act upon the water continuously as

the other metal does, is because the result of the action of the water envelops the zinc in a kind of protecting coat. We have learned in consequence, that if we put into our vessel only the zinc and water, they, by themselves, do not give rise to much action, and we get no result. But suppose I proceed to dissolve off this varnish—this encumbering substance—which I can do by a little acid; the moment I do this I find the zinc acting upon the water exactly as the iron did, but at the common temperature. The acid in no way is altered, except in its combination with the oxide of zinc which is produced. I have now poured the acid into the glass, and the effect is as though I were applying heat to cause this boiling up. There is something coming off from the zinc very abundantly, which is not steam. There is a jar full of it; and you will find that I have exactly the same combustible substance remaining in the vessel, when I hold it upside down, that I produced during the experiment with the iron barrel. This is what we get from water, the same substance which is contained in the candle.

Let us now trace distinctly the connection between these two points. This is hydrogen—a body classed among those things which

Fig. 70

in chemistry we call elements, because we can get nothing else out of them. A candle is not an elementary body, because we can get carbon out of it; we can get this hydrogen out of it, or at least out of the water which it supplies. And this gas has been so named hydrogen, because it is that element which, in association with another, generates water.* Mr. Anderson having now been able to get two or three jars of gas, we shall have a few experiments to make, and I want to show you the best way of making these experi-

*Ὕδωρ, "water," and γεννάω, "I generate."

ments. I am not afraid to show you, for I wish you to make experiments, if you will only make them with care and attention, and the assent of those around you. As we advance in chemistry we are obliged to deal with substances which are rather injurious if in their wrong places; the acids, and heat, and combustible things we use, might do harm if carelessly employed. If you want to make hydrogen, you can make it easily from bits of zinc, and sulphuric or muriatic acid. Here is what in former times was called the "philosopher's candle." It is a little phial with a cork and a tube or pipe passing through it. And I am now putting a few little pieces of zinc into it. This little instrument I am going to apply to a useful purpose in our demonstrations, for I want to show you that you can prepare hydrogen, and make some experiments with it as you please, at your own homes. Let me here tell you why I am so careful to fill this phial nearly, and yet not quite full. I do it because the evolved gas, which, as you have seen, is very combustible, is explosive to a considerable extent when mixed with air, and might lead to harm if you were to apply a light to the end of that pipe before all the air had been swept out of the space above the water. I am now about to pour in the sulphuric acid. I have used very little zinc and more sulphuric acid and water, because I want to keep it at work for some time. I therefore take care in this way to modify the proportions of the ingredients so that I may have a regular supply—not too quick and not too slow. Supposing I now take a glass and put it upside down over the end of the tube, because the hydrogen is light I expect that it will remain in that vessel a little while. We will now test the contents of our glass to see if there be hydrogen in it; I think I am safe in saying we have caught some [applying a light]. There it is, you see. I will now apply a light to the top of the tube. There is the hydrogen burning (FIG. 71). There is our philosophical candle. It is a foolish, feeble sort of a flame, you may say, but it is so hot that scarcely any common flame gives out so much heat. It goes on burning regularly, and I am now about to put that flame to burn under a certain arrangement, in order that we may examine its results and make use of the information which we may thereby acquire. Inas-

FIG. 71

much as the candle produces water, and this gas comes out of the water, let us see what this gives us by the same process of combustion that the candle went through when it burnt in the atmosphere; and for that purpose I am going to put the lamp under this apparatus (FIG. 72), in order to condense whatever may arise from the com-

FIG. 72

bustion within it. In the course of a short time you will see moisture appearing in the cylinder, and you will get the water running down the side, and the water from this hydrogen flame will have absolutely the same effect upon all our tests, being obtained by the same general process as in the former case. This hydrogen is a very beautiful substance. It is so light that it carries things up; it is far lighter than the atmosphere; and I dare say I can show you this by an experiment which, if you are very clever, some of you may even have skill enough to repeat. Here is our generator of hydrogen, and here are some soapsuds. I have an India-rubber tube connected with the hydrogen generator, and at the end of the tube is a tobacco pipe. I can thus put the pipe into the suds and blow bubbles by means of the hydrogen. You observe how the bubbles fall downward when I blow them with my warm breath; but notice the difference when I blow them with hydrogen. [The lecturer here blew bubbles with hydrogen, which rose to the roof of the theatre.] It shows you how light this gas must be in order to carry with it not merely the ordinary soap bubble, but the larger portion of a drop hanging to the bottom of it. I can show its lightness in a better way than this; larger bubbles than these may be so lifted up; indeed, in former times balloons used to be filled with this gas. Mr. Anderson will fasten this tube on to our generator, and we shall have a stream of hydrogen here with which we can charge this balloon made of collodion. I need not even be very careful to get all the air out, for I know the power of this gas to carry it up. [Two collodion balloons were inflated and sent up, one being held by a string.] Here is another larger one, made of thin membrane, which we will fill and allow to ascend; you will see they will all remain floating about until the gas escapes.

What, then, are the comparative weights of these substances? I have a table here which will show you the proportion which their weights bear to each other. I have taken a pint and a cubic foot as the measures, and have placed opposite to them the respective figures. A pint measure of this hydrogen weighs three-quarters of our smallest weight, a grain, and a cubic foot weighs one-twelfth of an ounce; whereas a pint of water weighs 8,750 grains, and a cubic foot of water weighs almost 1,000 ounces. You see, therefore, what a vast difference there is between the weight of a cubic foot of water and a cubic foot of hydrogen.

Hydrogen gives rise to no substance that can become solid, either during combustion or afterward as a product of its combustion; but when it burns it produces water only; and if we take a cold glass and put it over the flame, it becomes damp, and you have water produced immediately in appreciable quantity; and nothing is produced by its combustion but the same water which you have seen the flame of the candle produce. It is important to remember that this hydrogen is the only thing in nature which furnishes water as the sole product of combustion.

And now we must endeavor to find some additional proof of the general character and composition of water, and for this purpose I will keep you a little longer, so that at our next meeting we may be better prepared for the subject. We have the power of arranging the zinc which you have seen acting upon the water by the assistance of an acid, in such a manner as to cause all the power to be evolved in the place where we require it. I have behind me a voltaic pile, and I am just about to show you, at the end of this lecture, its character and power, that you may see what we shall have to deal with when next we meet. I hold here the extremities of the wires which transport the power from behind me, and which I shall cause to act on the water.

We have previously seen what a power of combustion is possessed by the potassium, or the zinc, or the iron filings; but none of them show such energy as this. [The lecturer here made contact between the two terminal wires of the battery, when a brilliant flash of light was produced.] This light is, in fact, produced by a forty-zinc power of burning; it is a power that I can carry about in my hands

through these wires at pleasure, although if I applied it wrongly to myself, it would destroy me in an instant, for it is a most intense thing, and the power you see here put forth while you count five [bringing the poles in contact and exhibiting the electric light] is equivalent to the power of several thunder-storms, so great is its force([14]). And that you may see what intense energy it has, I will take the ends of the wires which convey the power from the battery, and with it I dare say I can burn this iron file. Now this is a chemical power, and one which, when we next meet, I shall apply to water, and show you what results we are able to produce.

[14] Professor Faraday has calculated that there is as much electricity required to decompose one grain of water as there is in a very powerful flash of lightning.

LECTURE IV

HYDROGEN IN THE CANDLE—BURNS INTO
WATER—THE OTHER PART OF
WATER—OXYGEN

I SEE you are not tired of the candle yet, or I am sure you would not be interested in the subject in the way you are. When our candle was burning we found it produced water exactly like the water we have around us; and by farther examination of this water we found in it that curious body, hydrogen—that light substance of which there is some in this jar. We afterward saw the burning powers of that hydrogen, and that it produced water. And I think I introduced to your notice an apparatus which I very briefly said was an arrangement of chemical force, or power, or energy, so adjusted as to convey its power to us in these wires; and I said I should use that force to pull the water to pieces, to see what else there was in the water besides hydrogen; because, you remember, when we passed the water through the iron tube, we by no means got the weight of water back which we put in in the form of steam, though we had a very large quantity of gas evolved. We have now to see what is the other substance present. That you may understand the character and use of this instrument, let us make an experiment or two. Let us put together, first of all, some substances, knowing what they are, and then see what that instrument does to them. There is some copper (observe the various changes which it can undergo), and here is some nitric acid, and you will find that this, being a strong chemical agent, will act very powerfully when I add it to the copper. It is now sending forth a beautiful red vapor; but as we do not want that vapor, Mr. Anderson will hold it near the chimney for a short time, that we may have the use and beauty of the experiment without the annoyance. The copper which I have put into the flask will dissolve it: it will change the acid and the water into a blue fluid containing copper and other

128

things, and I purpose then showing you how this voltaic battery deals with it; and in the mean time we will arrange another kind of experiment for you to see what power it has. This is a substance which is to us like water—that is to say, it contains bodies which we do not know of as yet, as water contains a body which we do not know as yet. Now this solution of a salt([15]) I will put upon paper, and spread about, and apply the power of the battery to it, and observe what will happen. Three or four important things will happen which we shall take advantage of. I place this wetted paper upon a sheet of tin foil, which is convenient for keeping all clean, and also for the advantageous application of the power; and this solution, you see, is not at all affected by being put upon the paper or tin foil, nor by any thing else I have brought in contact with it yet, and which, therefore, is free to us to use as regards that instrument. But first let us see that our instrument is in order. Here are our wires. Let us see whether it is in the state in which it was last time. We can soon tell. As yet, when I bring them together, we have no power, because the conveyers—what we call the electrodes—the passages or ways for the electricity—are stopped; but now Mr. Anderson by that [referring to a sudden flash at the ends of the wires] has given me a telegram to say that it is ready. Before I begin our experiment I will get Mr. Anderson to break contact again at the battery behind me, and we will put a platinum wire across to connect the poles, and then if I find I can ignite a pretty good length of this wire we shall be safe in our experiment. Now you will see the power. [The connection was established, and the intermediate wire became red-hot.] There is the power running beautifully through the wire, which I have made thin on purpose to show you that we have those powerful forces; and now, having that power, we will proceed with it to the examination of water.

I have here two pieces of platinum, and if I lay them down upon this piece of paper [the moistened paper on the tin foil] you will see no action; and if I take them up there is no change that you can see, but the arrangement remains just as it was before. But, now,

[15] A solution of acetate of lead submitted to the action of the voltaic current yields lead at the negative pole, and brown peroxide of lead at the positive pole. A solution of nitrate of silver, under the same circumstances, yields silver at the negative pole, and peroxide of silver at the positive pole.

see what happens: if I take these two poles and put either one or the other of them down separately on the platinum plates, they do nothing for me; both are perfectly without action; but if I let them both be in contact at the same moment, see what happens [a brown spot appeared under each pole of the battery]. Look here at the effect that takes place, and see how I have pulled something apart from the white—something brown; and I have no doubt, if I were to arrange it thus, and were to put one of the poles to the tin foil on the other side of the paper—why, I get such a beautiful action upon the paper that I am going to see whether I can not write with it—a telegram, if you please. [The lecturer here traced the word "juvenile" on the paper with one of the terminal wires.] See there how beautifully we can get our results!

You see we have here drawn something which we have not known about before out of this solution. Let us now take that flask from Mr. Anderson's hands, and see what we can draw out of that. This, you know, is a liquid which we have just made up from copper and nitric acid while our other experiments were in hand; and though I am making this experiment very hastily, and may bungle a little, yet I prefer to let you see what I do rather than prepare it beforehand.

Now see what happens. These two platinum plates are the two ends (or I will make them so immediately) of this apparatus; and I am about to put them in contact with that solution, just as we did a moment ago on the paper. It does not matter to us whether the solution be on the paper or whether it be in the jar, so long as we bring the ends of the apparatus to it. If I put the two platinums in by themselves they come out as clean and as white as they go in [inserting them into the fluid without connecting them with the battery]; but when we take the power and lay that on [the platinums were connected with the battery and again dipped into the solution], this, you see [exhibiting one of the platinums], is at once turned into copper, as it were; it has become like a plate of copper; and that [exhibiting the other piece of platinum] has come out quite clean. If I take this coppered piece and change sides, the copper will leave the right-hand side and come over to the left side; what was before the coppered plate comes out clean, and the plate which was clean

comes out coated with copper; and thus you see that the same copper we put into this solution we can also take out of it by means of this instrument.

Putting that solution aside, let us now see what effect this instrument will have upon water (FIG. 73). Here are two little platinum plates which I intend to make the ends of the battery, and this (C)

FIG. 73

is a little vessel so shaped as to enable me to take it to pieces, and show you its construction. In these two cups (A and B) I pour mercury, which touches the ends of the wires connected with the platinum plates. In the vessel (C) I pour some water containing a little acid (but which is put in only for the purpose of facilitating the action; it undergoes no change in the process), and connected with the top of the vessel is a bent glass tube (D), which may remind you of the pipe which was connected with the gun barrel in our furnace experiment, and which now passes under the jar (F). I have now adjusted this apparatus, and we will proceed to affect the water in some way or other. In the other case I sent the water through a tube which was made red-hot; I am now going to pass the electricity through the contents of this vessel. Perhaps I may boil the water; if I do boil the water, I shall get steam; and you know that steam condenses when it gets cold, and you will therefore see by that whether I do boil the water or not. Perhaps, however, I shall not boil the water, but produce some other effect. You shall have the experiment and see. There is one wire which I will

put to this side (A), and here is the other wire which I will put to the other side (B), and you will soon see whether any disturbance takes place. Here it is seeming to boil up famously; but does it boil? Let us see whether that which goes out is steam or not. I think you will soon see the jar (F) will be filled with vapor, if that which rises from the water is steam. But can it be steam? Why, certainly not; because there it remains, you see, unchanged. There it is standing over the water, and it can not therefore be steam, but must be a permanent gas of some sort. What is it? Is it hydrogen? Is it anything else? Well, we will examine it. If it is hydrogen it will burn. [The lecturer then ignited a portion of the gas collected, which burnt with an explosion.] It is certainly something combustible, but not combustible in the way that hydrogen is. Hydrogen would not have given you that noise; but the color of that light, when the thing did burn, was like that of hydrogen; it will, however, burn without contact with the air. That is why I have chosen this other form of apparatus, for the purpose of pointing out to you what are the particular circumstances of this experiment. In place of an open vessel, I have taken one that is closed (our battery is so beautifully active that we are even boiling the mercury, and getting all things right—not wrong, but vigorously right); and I am going to show you that that gas, whatever it may be, can burn without air, and in that respect differs from a candle, which can not burn without the air. And our manner of doing this is as follows: I have here a glass vessel (G) which is fitted with two platinum wires (I K) through which I can apply electricity; and we can put the vessel on the air pump and exhaust the air; and when we have taken the air out we can bring it here and fasten it on to this jar (F), and let into the vessel that gas which was formed by the action of the voltaic battery upon the water, and which we have produced by changing the water into it; for I may go as far as this, and say we have really, by that experiment, changed the water into that gas. We have not only altered its condition, but we have changed it really and truly into that gaseous substance, and all the water is there which was decomposed by the experiment. As I screw this vessel (G H) on here (H), and make the tubes well connected, and when I open the stop-cocks (H H H), if you watch the level of the water

(in F), you will see that the gas will rise. I will now close the stop-cocks, as I have drawn up as much as the vessel can hold, and being safely conveyed into that chamber, I will pass into it an electric spark from this Leyden jar (L), when the vessel, which is now quite clear and bright, will become dim. There will be no sound, for the vessel is strong enough to confine the explosion. [A spark was then passed through the jar, when the explosive mixture was ignited.] Did you see that brilliant light? If I again screw the vessel on to the jar, and open these stop-cocks, you will see that the gas will rise a second time. [The stop-cocks were then opened.] Those gases [referring to the gases first collected in the jar, and which had just been ignited by the electric spark] have disappeared, as you see; their place is vacant, and fresh gas has gone in. Water has been formed from them; and if we repeat our operation [repeating the last experiment], I shall have another vacancy, as you will see by the water rising. I always have an empty vessel after the explosion, because the vapor or gas into which that water has been resolved by the battery explodes under the influence of the spark, and changes into water; and by-and-by you will see in this upper vessel some drops of water trickling down the sides and collecting at the bottom.

We are here dealing with water entirely, without reference to the atmosphere. The water of the candle had the atmosphere helping to produce it; but in this way it can be produced independently of the air. Water, therefore, ought to contain that other substance which the candle takes from the air, and which, combining with the hydrogen, produces water.

Just now you saw that one end of this battery took hold of the copper, extracting it from the vessel which contained the blue solution. It was effected by this wire; and surely we may say, if the battery has such power with a metallic solution which we made and unmade, may we not find that it is possible to split asunder the component parts of the water, and put them into this place and that place? Suppose I take the poles—the metallic ends of this battery—and see what will happen with the water in this apparatus (FIG. 74), where we have separated the two ends far apart. I place one here (at A), and the other there (at B); and I have little shelves with holes which I can put upon each pole, and so arrange them that

whatever escapes from the two ends of the battery will appear as separate gases; for you saw that the water did not become vaporous, but gaseous. The wires are now in perfect and proper connection with the vessel containing the water, and you see the bubbles rising; let us collect these bubbles and see what they are. Here is a glass

FIG. 74

cylinder (O); I fill it with water and put it over one end (A) of the pile, and I will take another (H), and put it over the other end (B) of the pile. And so now we have a double apparatus, with both places delivering gas. Both these jars will fill with gas. There they go, that to the right (H) filling very rapidly; the one to the left (O) filling not so rapidly; and, though I have allowed some bubbles to escape, yet still the action is going on pretty regularly; and were it not that one is rather smaller than the other, you would see that I should have twice as much in this (H) as I have in that (O). Both these gases are colorless; they stand over the water without condensing; they are alike in all things—I mean in all *apparent* things; and we have here an opportunity of examining these bodies and ascertaining what they are. Their bulk is large, and we can easily apply experiments to them. I will take this jar (H) first, and will ask you to be prepared to recognize hydrogen.

Think of all its qualities—the light gas which stood well in inverted vessels, burning with a pale flame at the mouth of the jar, and see whether this gas does not satisfy all these conditions. If it be hydrogen it will remain here while I hold this jar inverted. [A light was then applied, when the hydrogen burnt.] What is there now in the other jar? You know that the two together made an explosive mixture. But what can this be which we find as the other constituent in water, and which must therefore be that substance which made the hydrogen burn? We know that the water we put into the vessel consisted of the two things together. We find one of these is hydrogen: what must that other be which was in the water before the experiment, and which we now have by itself? I am about to put

this lighted splinter of wood into the gas. The gas itself will not burn, but it will make the splinter of wood burn. [The lecturer ignited the end of the wood and introduced it into the jar of gas.] See how it invigorates the combustion of the wood, and how it makes it burn far better than the air would make it burn; and now you see by itself that every other substance which is contained in the water, and which, when the water was formed by the burning of the candle, must have been taken from the atmosphere. What shall we call it, A, B, or C? Let us call it O—call it "Oxygen"; it is a very good, distinct-sounding name. This, then, is the oxygen which was present in the water, forming so large a part of it.

We shall now begin to understand more clearly our experiments and researches, because when we have examined these things once or twice we shall soon see why a candle burns in the air. When we have in this way analyzed the water—that is to say, separated or electrolyzed its parts out of it, we get two volumes of hydrogen and one of the body that burns it. And these two are represented to us on the following diagram, with their weights also stated; and we shall find that the oxygen is a very heavy body by comparison with the hydrogen. It is the other element in water.

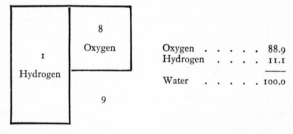

Oxygen 88.9
Hydrogen 11.1

Water 100.0

I had better, perhaps, tell you now how we get this oxygen abundantly, having shown you how we can separate it from the water. Oxygen, as you will immediately imagine, exists in the atmosphere; for how should the candle burn to produce water without it? Such a thing would be absolutely impossible, and chemically impossible, without oxygen. Can we get it from the air? Well, there are some very complicated and difficult processes by which we can get it from the air; but we have better processes. There is a substance called

the black oxide of manganese; it is a very black-looking mineral, but very useful, and when made red-hot it gives out oxygen. Here is an iron bottle which has had some of this substance put into it, and there is a tube fixed to it (Fig. 75), and a fire ready made, and Mr. Anderson will put that retort into the fire, for it is made of iron, and can stand the heat. Here is a salt called chlorate of potassa, which is now made in large quantities for bleaching, and chemical and medical uses, and for pyrotechnic and other purposes. I will take some and mix it with some of the oxide of manganese (oxide of copper, or oxide of iron would do as well); and if I put these together in a retort, far less than a red heat is sufficient to evolve this oxygen from the mixture. I am not preparing to make much, because we only want sufficient for our experiments; only, as you will see immediately, if I use too small a charge, the first portion of the gas will be mixed with the air already in the retort, and I should be obliged to sacrifice the first portion of the gas because it would be so much diluted with air; the first portion must therefore be thrown away. You will find in this case that a common spirit lamp is quite sufficient for me to get the oxygen, and so we shall have two processes going on for its preparation. See how freely the gas is coming over from that small portion of the mixture. We will examine it and see what are its properties. Now in this way we are producing, as you will observe, a gas just like the one we had in the experiment with the battery, transparent, undissolved by water, and presenting the ordinary visible properties of the atmosphere. (As this first jar contains the air, together with the first portions of the oxygen set free during the preparation, we will carry it out of the way, and be prepared to make our experiments in a regular, dignified manner.) And inasmuch as that power of making wood, wax, or other things burn, was so marked in the oxygen we obtained by means of the voltaic battery from water, we may expect to find the same property here. We will try it. You see there is the combustion of a lighted taper in air, and here is its combustion in this gas [lowering the taper into the jar]. See how brightly and how

Fig. 75

beautifully it burns! You can also see more than this: you will per-
ceive it is a heavy gas, while the hydrogen would go up like a
balloon, or even faster than a balloon, when not encumbered with
the weight of the envelope. You may easily see that although we
obtained from water twice as much in volume of the hydrogen as of
oxygen, it does not follow that we have twice as much in weight,
because one is heavy and the other a very light gas. We have means
of weighing gases or air; but, without stopping to explain that, let
me just tell you what their respective weights are. The weight
of a pint of hydrogen is three-quarters of a grain; the weight of
the same quantity of oxygen is nearly twelve grains. This is a
very great difference. The weight of a cubic foot of hydrogen
is one-twelfth of an ounce; and the weight of a cubic foot of
oxygen is one ounce and a third. And so on we might come
to masses of matter which may be weighed in the balance, and
which we can take account of as to hundred-weights and as to
tons, as you will see almost immediately.

Now, as regards this very property of oxygen supporting
combustion, which we may compare to air, I will take a piece
of candle to show it you in a rough way—and the result will be
rough. There is our candle burning in the air: how will it burn
in oxygen? I have here a jar of this gas, and I am about to put it over
the candle for you to compare the action of this gas with that of the
air. Why, look at it; it looks something like the light you saw at the
poles of the voltaic battery. Think how vigorous that action must be.
And yet, during all that action, nothing more is produced than what
is produced by the burning of the candle in air. We have the same
production of water, and the same phenomena exactly, when we use
this gas instead of air, as we have when the candle is burnt in air.

But now we have got a knowledge of this new substance, we can
look at it a little more distinctly, in order to satisfy ourselves that
we have got a good general understanding of this part of the product
of a candle. It is wonderful how great the supporting powers of this
substance are as regards combustion. For instance, here is a lamp
which, simple though it be, is the original, I may say, of a great
variety of lamps which are constructed for divers purposes—for
lighthouses, microscopic illuminations, and other uses; and if it was

Fig.
76

proposed to make it burn very brightly, you would say, "If a candle burnt better in oxygen, will not a lamp do the same?" Why, it will do so. Mr. Anderson will give me a tube coming from our oxygen reservoir, and I am about to apply it to this flame, which I will previously make burn badly on purpose. There comes the oxygen: what a combustion that makes! But if I shut it off, what becomes of the lamp? [The flow of oxygen was stopped, and the lamp

relapsed to its former dimness.] It is wonderful how, by means of oxygen, we get combustion accelerated. But it does not affect merely the combustion of hydrogen, or carbon, or the candle, but it exalts all combustions of the common kind. We will take one which relates to iron, for instance, as you have already seen iron burn a little in the atmosphere. Here is a jar of oxygen, and this is a piece of iron wire; but if it were a bar as thick as my wrist,

Fig. 77

it would burn the same. I first attach a little piece of wood to the iron; I then set the wood on fire, and let them both down together into the jar (Fig. 77). The wood is now alight, and there it burns as wood should burn in oxygen; but it will soon communicate its combustion to the iron. The iron is now burning brilliantly, and will continue so for a long time. As long as we supply oxygen, so long can we carry on the combustion of the iron, until the latter is consumed.

We will now put that on one side, and take some other substance; but we must limit our experiments, for we have not time to spare for all the illustrations you would have a right to if we had more time. We will take a piece of sulphur: you know how sulphur burns in the air; well, we put it into the oxygen, and you will see that whatever can burn in air can burn with a far greater intensity in oxygen, leading you to think that perhaps the atmosphere itself owes all its power of com-

Fig. 78

bustion to this gas. The sulphur is now burning very quietly in the oxygen; but you can not for a moment mistake the very high and increased action which takes place when it is so burnt, instead of being burnt merely in common air.

I am now about to show you the combustion of another sub-

stance—phosphorus. I can do it better for you here than you can do it at home. This is a very combustible substance; and if it be so combustible in air, what might you expect it would be in oxygen? I am about to show it to you not in its fullest intensity, for if I did so we should almost blow the apparatus up; I may even now crack the jar, though I do not want to break things carelessly. You see how it burns in the air. But what a glorious light it gives out when I introduce it into oxygen! [Introducing the lighted phosphorus into the jar of oxygen.] There you see the solid particles going off which cause that combustion to be so brilliantly luminous.

Thus far we have tested this power of oxygen, and the high combustion it produces, by means of other substances. We must now, for a little while longer, look at it as respects the hydrogen. You know, when we allowed the oxygen and the hydrogen derived from the water to mix and burn together, we had a little explosion. You remember also that when I burnt the oxygen and the hydrogen in a jet together, we got very little light, but great heat; I am now about to set fire to oxygen and hydrogen mixed in the proportion in which they occur in water. Here is a vessel containing one volume of oxygen and two volumes of hydrogen. This mixture is exactly of the same nature as the gas we just now obtained from the voltaic battery; it would be far too much to burn at once; I have therefore arranged to blow soap bubbles with it and burn those bubbles, that we may see by a general experiment or two how this oxygen supports the combustion of the hydrogen. First of all, we will see whether we can blow a bubble. Well, there goes the gas [causing it to issue through a tobacco-pipe into some soapsuds]. Here I have a bubble. I am receiving them on my hand, and you will perhaps think I am acting oddly in this experiment, but it is to show you that we must not always trust to noise and sounds, but rather to real facts. [Exploding a bubble on the palm of his hand.] I am afraid to fire a bubble from the end of the pipe, because the explosion would pass up into the jar and blow it to pieces. This oxygen, then, will unite with the hydrogen, as you see by the phenomena, and hear by the sound, with the utmost readiness of action, and all its powers are then taken up in its neutralization of the qualities of the hydrogen.

So now I think you will perceive the whole history of water with reference to oxygen and the air from what we have before said. Why does a piece of potassium decompose water? Because it finds oxygen in the water. What is set free when I put it in the water, as I am about to do again? It sets free hydrogen, and the hydrogen burns; but the potassium itself combines with oxygen; and this piece of potassium, in taking the water apart—the water, you may say, derived from the combustion of the candle—takes away the oxygen which the candle took from the air, and so sets the hydrogen free; and even if I take a piece of ice, and put a piece of potassium upon it, the beautiful affinities by which the oxygen and the hydrogen are related are such that the ice will absolutely set fire to the potassium. I show this to you to-day, in order to enlarge your ideas of these things, and that you may see how greatly results are modified by circumstances. There is the potassium on the ice, producing a sort of volcanic action.

It will be my place when next we meet, having pointed out these anomalous actions, to show you that none of these extra and strange effects are met with by us—that none of these strange and injurious actions take place when we are burning, not merely a candle, but gas in our streets, or fuel in our fireplaces, so long as we confine ourselves within the laws that Nature has made for our guidance.

LECTURE V

OXYGEN PRESENT IN THE AIR—NATURE OF THE
ATMOSPHERE—ITS PROPERTIES—OTHER PROD-
UCTS FROM THE CANDLE—CARBONIC
ACID—ITS PROPERTIES

WE have now seen that we can produce hydrogen and
oxygen from the water that we obtained from the candle.
Hydrogen, you know, comes from the candle, and oxygen,
you believe, comes from the air. But then you have a right to ask me,
"How is it that the air and the oxygen do not equally well burn;
the candle?" If you remember what happened when I put a jar of
oxygen over a piece of candle, you recollect there was a very dif-
ferent kind of combustion to that which took place in the air. Now,
why is this? It is a very important question, and one I shall endeavor
to make you understand; it relates most intimately to the nature of
the atmosphere, and is most important to us.

We have several tests for oxygen besides the mere burning of
bodies; you have seen a candle burnt in oxygen or in the air; you
have seen phosphorus burnt in the air or in oxygen, and you have
seen iron filings burnt in oxygen. But we have other tests besides
these, and I am about to refer to one or two of them for the purpose
of carrying your conviction and your experience farther. Here we
have a vessel of oxygen. I will show its presence to you: if I take a
little spark and put it into that oxygen, you know by the experience
you gained the last time we met what will happen—if I put that
spark into the jar, it will tell you whether we have oxygen here or
not. Yes! We have proved it by combustion; and now here is an-
other test for oxygen, which is a very curious and useful one. I have
here two jars full of gas, with a plate between them to prevent their
mixing; I take the plate away, and the gases are creeping one into
the other. "What happens?" say you; "they together produce no
such combustion as was seen in the case of the candle." But see how

the presence of oxygen is told by its association with this other sub-stance.([16]) What a beautifully colored gas I have obtained in this way, showing me the presence of the oxygen! In the same way we can try this experiment by mixing common air with this test-gas. Here is a jar containing air—such air as the candle would burn in—and here is a jar or bottle containing the test-gas. I let them come together over water, and you see the result: the contents of the test-bottle are flowing into the jar of air, and you see I obtain exactly the same kind of action as before, and that shows me that there is oxygen in the air—the very same substance that has been already obtained by us from the water produced by the candle. But then, beyond that, how is it that the candle does not burn in air as well as in oxygen? We will come to that point at once. I have here two jars; they are filled to the same height with gas, and the appearance to the eye is alike in both, and I really do not know at present which of these jars contains oxygen and which contains air, although I know they have previously been filled with these gases. But here is our test-gas, and I am going to work with the two jars, in order to examine whether there is any difference between them in the quality of reddening this gas. I am now going to turn this test-gas into one of the jars, and observe what happens. There is reddening, you see; there is, then, oxygen present. We will now test the other jar; but you see this is not so distinctly red as the first, and, farther, this curious thing happens: if I take these two gases and shake them well together with water, we shall absorb the red gas; and then, if I put in more of this test-gas and shake again, we shall absorb more; and I can go on as long as there be any oxygen present to produce that effect. If I let in air, it will not matter; but the moment I intro-duce water, the red gas disappears; and I may go on in this way, put-ting in more and more of the test-gas, until I come to something left behind which will not redden any longer by the use of that particular body that rendered the air and the oxygen red. Why is that? You see in a moment it is because there is, besides oxygen, something else present which is left behind. I will let a little more air into the jar, and if it turns red you will know that some of that reddening gas

[16] The gas which is thus employed as a test for the presence of oxygen is the binoxide of nitrogen, or nitrous oxide. It is a colorless gas, which, when brought in contact with oxygen, unites with it, forming hyponitric acid, the red gas referred to.

is still present, and that, consequently, it was not for the want of this producing body that that air was left behind.

Now you will begin to understand what I am about to say. You saw that when I burnt phosphorus in a jar, as the smoke produced by the phosphorus and the oxygen of the air condensed, it left a good deal of gas unburnt, just as this red gas left something untouched; there was, in fact, this gas left behind, which the phosphorus can not touch, which the reddening gas can not touch, and this something is not oxygen, and yet is part of the atmosphere.

So that is one way of opening out air into the two things of which it is composed—oxygen, which burns our candles, our phosphorus, or any thing else, and this other substance—nitrogen—which will not burn them. This other part of the air is by far the larger proportion, and it is a very curious body when we come to examine it; it is re-markably curious, and yet you say, perhaps, that it is very uninterest-ing. It is uninteresting in some respects because of this, that it shows no brilliant effects of combustion. If I test it with a taper as I do oxygen and hydrogen, it does not burn like hydrogen, nor does it make the taper burn like oxygen. Try it in any way I will, it does neither the one thing nor the other; it will not take fire; it will not let the taper burn; it puts out the combustion of every thing. There is nothing that will burn in it in common circumstances. It has no smell; it is not sour; it does not dissolve in water; it is neither an acid nor an alkali; it is as indifferent to all our organs as it is possible for a thing to be. And you might say, "It is nothing; it is not worth chemical attention; what does it do in the air?" Ah! then come our beautiful and fine results shown us by an observant philosophy. Sup-pose, in place of having nitrogen, or nitrogen and oxygen, we had pure oxygen as our atmosphere; what would become of us? You know very well that a piece of iron lit in a jar of oxygen goes on burn-ing to the end. When you see a fire in an iron grate, imagine where the grate would go to if the whole of the atmosphere were oxygen. The grate would burn up more powerfully than the coals; for the iron of the grate itself is even more combustible than the coals which we burn in it. A fire put into the middle of a locomotive would be a fire in a magazine of fuel, if the atmosphere were oxygen. The ni-trogen lowers it down and makes it moderate and useful for us,

and then, with all that, it takes away with it the fumes that you have
seen produced from the candle, disperses them throughout the whole
of the atmosphere, and carries them away to places where they are
wanted to perform a great and glorious purpose of good to man, for
the sustenance of vegetation, and thus does a most wonderful work,
although you say, on examining it, "Why, it is a perfectly indifferent
thing." This nitrogen in its ordinary state is an inactive element; no
action short of the most intense electric force, and then in the most
infinitely small degree, can cause the nitrogen to combine directly
with the other element of the atmosphere, or with other things round
about it; it is a perfectly indifferent, and therefore to say, a safe sub-
stance.

But, before I take you to that result, I must tell you about the atmos-
phere itself. I have written on this diagram the composition of one
hundred parts of atmospheric air:

	Bulk.	Weight.
Oxygen	20	23.3
Nitrogen	80	77.7
	100	100.0

It is a true analysis of the atmosphere so far as regards the quantity
of oxygen and the quantity of nitrogen present. By our analysis, we
find that 5 pints of the atmosphere contain only 1 pint of oxygen,
and 4 pints, or 4 parts, of nitrogen by bulk. That is our analysis
of the atmosphere. It requires all that quantity of nitrogen to reduce
the oxygen down, so as to be able to supply the candle properly with
fuel, so as to supply us with an atmosphere which our lungs can
healthily and safely breathe; for it is just as important to make the
oxygen right for us to breathe, as it is to make the atmosphere right
for the burning of the fire and the candle.

But now for this atmosphere. First of all, let me tell you the weight
of these gases. A pint of nitrogen weighs 10 4-10 grains, or a cubic
foot weighs 1 1-6 ounces. That is the weight of the nitrogen. The
oxygen is heavier: a pint of it weighs 11 9-10 grs., and a cubic foot
weighs 1 3-4 oz. A pint of air weighs about 10 7-10 grs., and a cubic
foot 1 1-5 oz.

You have asked me several times, and I am very glad you have,
"How do you weigh gases?" I will show you: it is very simple, and

easily done. Here is a balance, and here a copper bottle, made as light as we can consistent with due strength, turned very nicely in the lathe, and made perfectly air-tight, with a stop-cock, which we can open and shut, which at present is open, and, therefore, allows the bottle to be full of air. I have here a nicely-adjusted balance in which I think the bottle, in its present condition, will be balanced by the weight on the other side. And here is a pump by which we can force the air into this bottle, and with it we will force in a certain number of volumes of air as measured by the pump. [Twenty measures were pumped in.] We will shut that in and put it in the balance. See how it sinks; it is much heavier than it was. By what? By the air that we have forced into it by the pump. There is not a greater *bulk* of air, but there is the same bulk of *heavier* air, because we have forced in air upon it. And that you may have a fair notion in your mind as to how much this air measures, here is a jar full of water. We will open that copper vessel into this jar, and let the air return to its former state. All I have to do now is to screw them tightly together, and to turn the taps, when there, you see, is the bulk of the twenty pumps of air which I forced into the bottle; and to make sure that we have been quite correct in what we

FIG. 79

have been doing, we will take the bottle again to the balance, and, if it is now counterpoised by the original weight, we shall be quite sure we have made our experiment correctly. It is balanced; so, you see, we can find out the weight of the extra volumes of air forced in in that way, and by that means we are able to ascertain that a cubic foot of air weighs 1 1-5 oz. But that small experiment will by no means convey to your mind the whole literal truth of this matter. It is wonderful how it accumulates when you come to larger volumes. This bulk of air [a cubic foot] weighs 1 1-5 oz. What do you think of the contents of that box above there which I have had made for the purpose? The air which is within that box weighs one pound—a full pound; and I have calculated the weight of the air in this room: you would hardly imagine it, but it is above a ton. So rapidly do the weights rise up, and so important is the presence of the atmosphere,

and of the oxygen and the nitrogen in it, and the use it performs in conveying things to and fro from place to place, and carrying bad vapors to places where they will do good instead of harm.

Having given you that little illustration with respect to the weight of the air, let me show you certain consequences of it. You have a

right to them, because you would not understand so much without it. Do you remember this kind of experiment? Have you ever seen it? Suppose I take a pump somewhat similar to the one I had a little while ago to force air into the bottle, and suppose I place it in such a manner that by certain arrangements I can apply my hand to it. My hand moves about in the air so easily that it seems to feel nothing, and I can hardly get velocity enough by any motion of my own in the atmosphere to make sure that there is much resistance to it. But when I put my hand here [on the air-pump receiver, which was afterward exhausted] you see what happens. Why is my hand fastened to this place, and why am I able to pull this pump about? And see! how is it that I can hardly get my hand

FIG. 80

away? Why is this? It is the weight of the air—the weight of the air that is above. I have another experiment here, which I think will explain to you more about it. When the air is pumped from underneath the bladder which is stretched over this glass, you will see the effect in another shape: the top is quite flat at present, but I will make a very little motion with the pump, and now look at it; see how it has gone down, see how it is bent in; you will see the bladder go in more and more, until, at last, I expect it will be driven in and broken by the force of the atmosphere pressing upon it. [The bladder at last broke with a loud report.] Now that was done entirely by the weight of the air pressing on it, and you can easily understand how that is. The particles that are piled up in the atmosphere stand upon each other, as these five cubes do; you can easily conceive that four of

these five cubes are resting upon the bottom one, and if I take that away the others will all sink down. So it is with the atmosphere; the air that is above is sustained by the air that is beneath, and when the air is pumped away from beneath them, the change occurs which you

FIG. 81

saw when I placed my hand on the air-pump, and which you saw in the case of the bladder, and which you shall see better here. I have tied over this jar a piece of sheet India-rubber, and I am now about to take away the air from the inside of the jar; and if you will watch the India-rubber—which acts as a partition between the air below and the air above—you will see, when I pump, how the pressure shows itself. See where it is going to: I can actually put my hand into the jar; and yet this result is only caused by the great and powerful action of the air above. How beautifully it shows this curious circumstance!

Here is something that you can have a pull at when I have finished to-day. It is a little apparatus of two hollow brass hemispheres, closely fitted together, and having connected with it a pipe and a cock, through which we can exhaust the air from the inside; and although the two halves are so easily taken apart, while the air is left within, yet you will

FIG. 82

see, when we exhaust it by-and-by, no power of any two of you will be able to pull them apart. Every square inch of surface that is contained in the area of that vessel sustains fifteen pounds by weight, or nearly so, when the air is taken out, and you may try your strength

presently in seeing whether you can overcome that pressure of the atmosphere.

Here is another very pretty thing—the boys' sucker, only refined by the philosopher. We young ones have a perfect right to take toys, and make them into philosophy, inasmuch as nowadays we are turning philosophy into toys. Here is a sucker, only it is made of India-rubber. If I clap it upon the table, you see at once it holds. Why does it hold? I can slip it about, and yet if I try to pull it up, it seems as if it would pull the table with it. I can easily make it slip about from place to place, but only when I bring it to the edge of the table can I get it off. It is only kept down by the pressure of the atmosphere above; we have a couple of them, and if you take these two and press them together, you will see how firmly they stick. And, indeed, we may use them as they are proposed to be used, to stick against windows, or against walls, where they will adhere for an evening, and serve to hang any thing on that you want. I think, however, that you boys ought to be shown experiments that you can make at home; and so here is a very pretty experiment in illustration of the pressure of the atmosphere. Here is a tumbler of water. Suppose I were to ask you to turn that tumbler upside down so that the water should not fall out, and yet not be kept in by your hand, but merely by using the pressure of the atmosphere; could you do that? Take a wine-glass, either quite full or half full of water, and put a flat card on the top; turn it upside down, and then see what becomes of the card and of the water. The air can not get in because the water, by its capillary attraction round the edge, keeps it out.

I think this will give you a correct notion of what you may call the materiality of the air; and when I tell you that that box holds a pound of it, and this room more than a ton, you will begin to think that air is something very serious. I will make another experiment to convince you of this positive resistance. There is that beautiful experiment of the popgun, made so well and so easily, you know, out of a quill, or a tube, or any thing of that kind,—where we take a slice of potato, for instance, or an apple, and take the tube and cut out a pellet, as I have now done, and push it to one end. I have made that end tight; and now I take another piece and put it in: it will confine the air that is within the tube perfectly and completely for

our purpose; and I shall now find it absolutely impossible by any force of mine to drive that little pellet close up to the other. It can not be done; I may press the air to a certain extent, but if I go on pressing, long before it comes to the second, the confined air will drive the front one out with a force something like that of gunpowder; for gunpowder is in part dependent upon the same action that you see here exemplified.

I saw the other day an experiment which pleased me much, as I thought it would serve our purpose here. (I ought to have held my tongue for four or five minutes before beginning this experiment, because it depends upon my lungs for success.) By the proper application of air, I expect to be able to drive this egg out of one cup into the other by the force of my breath; but if I fail it is in a good cause, and I do not promise success, because I have been talking more than I ought to do to make the experiment succeed.

[The lecturer here tried the experiment, and succeeded in blowing the egg from one egg cup to the other.]

You see that the air which I blow goes downward between the egg and the cup, and makes a blast under the egg, and is thus able to lift a heavy thing; for a full egg is a very heavy thing for air to lift. If you want to make the experiment, you had better boil the egg quite hard first, and then you may very safely try to blow it from one cup to the other, with a little care.

I have now kept you long enough upon this property of the weight of the air, but there is another thing I should like to mention. You saw the way in which, in this popgun, I was able to drive the second piece of potato half or two-thirds of an inch before the first piece started, by virtue of the elasticity of the air, just as I pressed into the copper bottle the particles of air by means of the pump. Now this depends upon a wonderful property in the air, namely, its elasticity, and I should like to give you a good illustration of this. If I take any thing that confines the air properly, as this membrane, which also is able to contract and expand so as to give us a measure of the elasticity of the air, and confine in this bladder a certain portion of air; and then, if we take the atmosphere off from the outside of it, just as in these cases we put the pressure on—if we take the pressure off, you will see how it will then go on expanding and expanding,

larger and larger, until it will fill the whole of this bell jar, showing you that wonderful property of the air, its elasticity, its compressibility, and expansibility, to an exceedingly large extent, and which is very essential for the purposes and services it performs in the economy of creation.

We will now turn to another very important part of our subject, remembering that we have examined the candle in its burning, and have found that it gives rise to various products. We have the products, you know, of soot, of water, and of something else, which you have not yet examined. We have collected the water, but have allowed the other things to go into the air. Let us now examine some of these other products.

Here is an experiment which I think will help you in part in this way. We will put our candle there, and place over it a chimney,

Fig. 83

thus. I think my candle will go on burning, because the air passage is open at the bottom and the top. In the first place, you see the moisture appearing—that you know about. It is water produced from the candle by the action of the air upon its hydrogen. But, besides that, something is going out at the top: it is not moisture—it is not water—it is not condensible; and yet, after all, it has very singular properties. You will find that the air coming out of the top of

our chimney is nearly sufficient to blow the light out I am holding to it; and if I put the light fairly opposed to the current, it will blow it quite out. You will say, that is as it should be, and I am supposing that you think it ought to do so, because the nitrogen does not support combustion, and ought to put the candle out, since the candle will not burn in nitrogen. But is there nothing else there than nitrogen? I must now anticipate—that is to say, I must use my own knowledge to supply you with the means that we adopt for the purpose of ascertaining these things, and examining such gases as these. I will take an empty bottle—here is one—and if I hold it over this chimney, I shall get the combustion of the candle below sending its results into the bottle above; and we shall soon find that this bottle contains, not merely an air that is bad as regards the combustion of a taper put into it, but having other properties.

Let me take a little quick-lime and pour some common water on to it—the commonest water will do. I will stir it a moment, then pour it upon a piece of filtering paper in a funnel, and we shall very quickly have a clear water proceeding to the bottle below, as I have here. I have plenty of this water in another bottle, but nevertheless I should like to use the lime-water that was prepared before you, so that you may see what its uses are. If I take some of this beautiful clear lime-water, and pour it into this jar which has collected the air from the candle, you will see a change coming about. Do you see that the water has become quite milky? Observe, that will not happen with air merely. Here is a bottle filled with air; and if I put a little lime-water into it, neither the oxygen nor the nitrogen, nor any thing else that is in that quantity of air, will make any change in the lime-water. It remains perfectly clear, and no shaking of that quantity of lime-water with that quantity of air in its common state will cause any change; but if I take this bottle with the lime-water and hold it so as to get the general products of the candle in contact with it, in a very short time we shall have it milky. There is the chalk, consisting of the lime which we used in making the lime-water, combined with something that came from the candle —that other product which we are in search of, and which I want to tell you about today. This is a substance made visible to us by its action, which is not the action of the lime-water either upon the

oxygen or upon the nitrogen, nor upon the water itself, but it is something new to us from the candle. And then we find this white powder, produced by the lime-water and the vapor from the candle, appears to us very much like whitening or chalk, and when examined it does prove to be exactly the same substance as whitening or chalk. So we are led, or have been led, to observe upon the various circumstances of this experiment, and to trace this production of chalk to its various causes, to give us the true knowledge of the nature of this combustion of the candle—to find that this substance issuing from the candle is exactly the same as that substance which would issue from a retort if I were to put some chalk into it with a little moisture and make it red-hot; you would then find that exactly the same substance would issue from it as from the candle.

But we have a better means of getting this substance, and in greater quantity, so as to ascertain what its general characters are. We find this substance in very great abundance in a multitude of cases where you would least expect it. All limestones contain a great deal of this gas which issues from the candle, and which we call *carbonic acid*. All chalks, all shells, all corals, contain a great quantity of this curious air. We find it fixed in these stones, for which reason Dr. Black called it "fixed air"—finding it in these fixed things like marble and chalk—he called it fixed air because it lost its quality of air, and assumed the condition of a solid body. We can easily get this air from marble. Here is a jar containing a little muriatic acid, and here is a taper which, if I put it into that jar, will show only the presence of common air. There is, you see, pure air down to the bottom; the jar is full of it. Here is a substance—marble ([17]), a very beautiful and superior marble—and if I put these pieces of marble into the jar, a great boiling apparently goes on. That, however, is not steam; it is a gas that is rising up; and if I now search the jar by a candle, I shall have exactly the same effect produced upon the taper as I had from the air which issued from the end of the chimney over the burning candle. It is exactly the same action, and caused by the very same substance that issued from the candle; and in this way we can get carbonic acid in great abundance

[17] *Marble* is a compound of carbonic acid and lime. The muriatic acid, being the stronger of the two, takes the place of the carbonic acid, which escapes as a gas, the residue forming muriate of lime or chloride of calcium.

—we have already nearly filled the jar. We also find that this gas is not merely contained in marble. Here is a vessel in which I have put some common whitening—chalk which has been washed in water and deprived of its coarser particles, and so supplied to the plasterer as whitening—here is a large jar containing this whitening and water; and I have here some strong sulphuric acid, which is the acid you might have to use if you were to make these experiments (only, in using this acid with limestone, the body that is produced is an insoluble substance, whereas the muriatic acid produces a soluble substance that does not so much thicken the water). And you will seek out a reason why I take this kind of apparatus for the purpose of showing this experiment. I do it because you may repeat in a small way what I am about to do in a large one. You will have here just the same kind of action; and I am evolving in this large jar carbonic acid exactly the same in its nature and properties as the gas which we obtained from the combustion of the candle in the atmosphere. And, no matter how different the two methods by which we prepare this carbonic acid, you will see, when we get to the end of our subject, that it is all exactly the same, whether prepared in the one way or in the other.

We will now proceed to the next experiment with regard to this gas. What is its nature? Here is one of the vessels full, and we will try it as we have done so many other gases—by combustion. You see it is not combustible, nor does it support combustion. Neither, as we know, does it dissolve much in water, because we collect it over water very easily. Then you know that it has an effect, and becomes white in contact with lime-water; and when it does become white in that way, it becomes one of the constituents to make carbonate of lime or limestone.

The next thing I must show you is that it really does dissolve a little in water, and therefore that it is unlike oxygen and hydrogen in that respect. I have here an apparatus by which we can produce this solution. In the lower part of this apparatus is marble and acid, and in the upper part cold water. The valves are so arranged that the gas can get from one to the other. I will set it in action now, and you can see the gas bubbling up through the water, as it has been doing all night long, and by this time we shall find that we have

this substance dissolved in the water. If I take a glass and draw off some of the water, I find that it tastes a little acid to the mouth; it is impregnated with carbonic acid; and if I now apply a little lime-water to it, that will give us a test of its presence. This water will make the lime-water turbid and white, which is proof of the presence of carbonic acid.

Then it is a very weighty gas; it is heavier than the atmosphere. I have put their respective weights at the lower part of this table, along with, for comparison, the weights of the other gases we have been examining:

	Pint.	Cubic Foot.
Hydrogen	$\frac{3}{4}$ grs.	$\frac{1}{12}$ oz.
Oxygen	$11\frac{9}{10}$,,	$1\frac{1}{3}$,,
Nitrogen	$10\frac{4}{10}$,,	$1\frac{1}{8}$,,
Air	$10\frac{4}{10}$,,	$1\frac{1}{5}$,,
Carbonic acid	$16\frac{1}{3}$,,	$1\frac{9}{10}$,,

A pint of it weighs 16 1-3 grains, and a cubic foot weighs 1 9-10 ounce, almost two ounces. You can see by many experiments that this is a heavy gas. Suppose I take a glass containing nothing else but air, and from this vessel containing the carbonic acid I attempt

to pour a little of this gas into that glass—I wonder whether any has gone in or not. I can not tell by the appearance, but I can in this way [introducing the taper]. Yes, there it is, you see; and if I were to examine it by lime-water, I should find it by that test also. I will take this little bucket, and put it down into the well of carbonic acid—indeed, we too often have real wells of carbonic acid—and now, if there is any carbonic acid, I must have got to it by this time, and it will be in this bucket, which we will examine with a taper. There it is, you see; it is full of carbonic acid.

Fig. 84

There is another experiment by which I will show you its weight. I have here a jar suspended at one end of a balance—it is now equipoised; but when I pour this carbonic acid into the jar on the one side which now contains air, you will see it sink down at once

because of the carbonic acid that I pour into it. And now, if I examine this jar with the lighted taper, I shall find that the carbonic acid has fallen into it, and it no longer has any power of supporting the combustion. If I blow a soap bubble, which of course will be filled with air, and let it fall into this jar of carbonic acid, it will float. But I shall first of all take one of these little balloons filled with air. I am not quite sure where the carbonic acid is; we will just try

Fig. 85

the depth, and see whereabouts is its level. There, you see, we have this bladder floating on the carbonic acid; and if I evolve some more of the carbonic acid, the bladder will be lifted up higher. There it goes; the jar is nearly full, and now I will see whether I can blow a soap bubble on that and float it in the same way. [The lecturer here blew a soap bubble and allowed it to fall into the jar of carbonic acid, when it floated in it midway.] It is floating, as the balloon floated, by virtue of the greater weight of the carbonic acid than of the air. And now, having so far given you the history of the carbonic acid, as to its sources in the candle, as to its physical properties and weight, when we next meet I shall show you of what it is composed, and where it gets its elements from.

LECTURE VI

CARBON OR CHARCOAL—COAL GAS—RESPIRATION AND ITS ANALOGY TO THE BURNING OF A CANDLE—CONCLUSION

A LADY who honors me by her presence at these lectures has conferred a still farther obligation by sending me these two candles, which are from Japan, and, I presume, are made of that substance to which I referred in a former lecture. You see that they are even far more highly ornamented than the French candles, and, I suppose, are candles of luxury, judging from their appearance. They have a remarkable peculiarity about them,—namely, a hollow wick,—that beautiful peculiarity which Argand introduced into the lamp and made so valuable. To those who receive such presents from the East, I may just say that this and such like materials gradually undergo a change which gives them on the surface a dull and dead appearance; but they may easily be restored to their original beauty if the surface be rubbed with a clean cloth or silk handkerchief, so as to polish the little rugosity or roughness: this will restore the beauty of the colors. I have so rubbed one of these candles, and you see the difference between it and the other which has not been polished, but which may be restored by the same process. Observe, also, that these moulded candles from Japan are made more conical than the moulded candles in this part of the world.

I told you, when we last met, a good deal about carbonic acid. We found by the lime-water test that when the vapor from the top of the candle or lamp was received into bottles and tested by this solution of lime-water (the composition of which I explained to you, and which you can make for yourselves), we had that white opacity which was in fact calcareous matter, like shells and corals, and many of the rocks and minerals in the earth. But I have not yet told you fully and clearly the chemical history of this substance, carbonic acid, as we have it from the candle, and I must now resume that

subject. We have seen the products, and the nature of them, as they issue from the candle. We have traced the water to its elements, and now we have to see where are the elements of the carbonic acid supplied by the candle. A few experiments will show this. You remember that when a candle burns badly it produces smoke; but if it is burning well there is no smoke. And you know that the brightness of the candle is due to this smoke, which becomes ignited. Here is an experiment to prove this: so long as the smoke remains in the flame of the candle and becomes ignited, it gives a beautiful light, and never appears to us in the form of black particles. I will light some fuel which is extravagant in its burning. This will serve our purpose—a little turpentine on a sponge. You see the smoke rising from it, and floating into the air in large quantities; and re-member now, the carbonic acid that we have from the candle is from such smoke as that. To make that evident to you, I will intro-duce this turpentine burning on the sponge into a flask where I have plenty of oxygen, the rich part of the atmosphere, and you now see that the smoke is all consumed. This is the first part of our experi-ment; and now, what follows? The carbon which you saw flying off from the turpentine flame in the air is now entirely burned in this oxygen, and we shall find that it will, by this rough and tem-porary experiment, give us exactly the same conclusion and result as we had from the combustion of the candle. The reason why I make the experiment in this manner is solely that I may cause the steps of our demonstration to be so simple that you can never for a moment lose the train of reasoning, if you only pay attention. All the carbon which is burned in oxygen, or air, comes out as carbonic acid, while those particles which are not so burned show you the second substance in the carbonic acid,—namely, the carbon— that body which made the flame so bright while there was plenty of air, but which was thrown off in excess when there was not oxygen enough to burn it.

I have also to show you a little more distinctly the history of car-bon and oxygen in their union to make carbonic acid. You are now better able to understand this than before, and I have prepared three or four experiments by way of illustration. This jar is filled with oxygen, and here is some carbon which has been placed in a crucible

for the purpose of being made red-hot. I keep my jar dry, and venture to give you a result imperfect in some degree, in order that I may make the experiment brighter. I am about to put the oxygen and the carbon together. That this is carbon (common charcoal pulverized) you will see by the way in which it burns in the air [letting some of the red-hot charcoal fall out of the crucible]. I am now about to burn it in oxygen gas, and look at the difference. It may appear to you at a distance as if it were burning with a flame; but it is not so. Every little piece of charcoal is burning as a spark, and while it so burns it is producing carbonic acid. I specially want these two or three experiments to point out what I shall dwell upon more distinctly by-and-by—that carbon burns in this way, and not as a flame.

Instead of taking many particles of carbon to burn, I will take a rather large piece, which will enable you to see the form and size, and to trace the effects very decidedly. Here is the jar of oxygen, and here is the piece of charcoal, to which I have fastened a little piece of wood, which I can set fire to, and so commence the combustion, which I could not conveniently do without. You now see the charcoal burning, but not as a flame (or if there be a flame it is the smallest possible one, which I know the cause of, namely, the formation of a little carbonic oxide close upon the surface of the carbon). It goes on burning, you see, slowly producing carbonic acid by the union of this carbon or charcoal (they are equivalent terms) with the oxygen. I have here another piece of charcoal, a piece of bark, which has the quality of being blown to pieces—exploding—as it burns. By the effect of the heat we shall reduce the lump of carbon into particles that will fly off; still every particle, equally with the whole mass, burns in this peculiar way—it burns as a coal and not like a flame. You observe a multitude of little combustions going on, but no flame. I do not know a finer experiment than this to show that carbon burns with a spark.

Here, then, is carbonic acid formed from its elements. It is produced at once; and if we examined it by lime-water you will see that we have the same substance which I have previously described to you. By putting together 6 parts of carbon by weight (whether it comes from the flame of a candle or from powdered charcoal)

and 16 parts of oxygen by weight, we have 22 parts of carbonic acid; and, as we saw last time, the 22 parts of carbonic acid combined with 28 parts of lime, produced common carbonate of lime. If you were to examine an oyster-shell and weigh the component parts, you would find that every 50 parts would give 6 of carbon and 16 of oxygen combined with 28 of lime. However, I do not want to trouble you with these minutiæ; it is only the general philosophy of the matter that we can now go into. See how finely the carbon is dissolving away [pointing to the lump of charcoal burning quietly in the jar of oxygen]. You may say that the charcoal is actually dissolving in the air round about; and if that were perfectly pure charcoal, which we can easily prepare, there would be no residue whatever. When we have a perfectly cleansed and purified piece of carbon, there is no ash left. The carbon burns as a solid dense body, that heat alone can not change as to its solidity, and yet it passes away into vapor that never condenses into solid or liquid under ordinary circumstances; and what is more curious still is the fact that the oxygen does not change in its bulk by the solution of the carbon in it. Just as the bulk is at first, so it is at last, only it has become carbonic acid.

There is another experiment which I must give you before you are fully acquainted with the general nature of carbonic acid. Being a compound body, consisting of carbon and oxygen, carbonic acid is a body that we ought to be able to take asunder. And so we can. As we did with water, so we can with carbonic acid—take the two parts asunder. The simplest and quickest way is to act upon the carbonic acid by a substance that can attract the oxygen from it, and leave the carbon behind. You recollect that I took potassium and put it upon water or ice, and you saw that it could take the oxygen from the hydrogen. Now, suppose we do something of the same kind here with this carbonic acid. You know carbonic acid to be a heavy gas. I will not test it with lime-water, as that will interfere with our subsequent experiments, but I think the heaviness of the gas and the power of extinguishing flame will be sufficient for our purpose. I introduce a flame into the gas, and you will see whether it will be put out. You see the light is extinguished. Indeed, the gas may, perhaps, put out phosphorus, which you know has a pretty

strong combustion. Here is a piece of phosphorus heated to a high degree. I introduce it into gas, and you observe the light is put out, but it will take fire again in the air, because there it re-enters into combustion. Now let me take a piece of potassium, a substance which even at common temperatures can act upon carbonic acid, though not sufficiently for our present purpose, because it soon gets covered with a protecting coat; but if we warm it up to the burning point in air, as we have a fair right to do, and as we have done with phosphorus, you will see that it can burn in carbonic acid; and if it burns, it will burn by taking oxygen, so that you will see what is left behind. I am going, then, to burn this potassium in the carbonic acid, as a proof of the existence of oxygen in the carbonic acid. [In the preliminary process of heating the potassium exploded.] Sometimes we get an awkward piece of potassium that explodes, or something like it, when it burns. I will take another piece, and now that it is heated I introduce it into the jar, and you perceive that it burns in the carbonic acid—not so well as in the air, because the carbonic acid contains the oxygen combined; but it does burn, and takes away the oxygen. If I now put this potassium into water, I find that besides the potash formed (which you need not trouble about) there is a quantity of carbon produced. I have here made the experiment in a very rough way, but I assure you that if I were to make it carefully, devoting a day to it instead of five minutes, we should get all the proper amount of charcoal left in the spoon, or in the place where the potassium was burned, so that there could be no doubt as to the result. Here, then, is the carbon obtained from the carbonic acid, as a common black substance; so that you have the entire proof of the nature of carbonic acid as consisting of carbon and oxygen. And now I may tell you, that *whenever* carbon burns under common circumstances it produces carbonic acid.

Suppose I take this piece of wood, and put it into a bottle with lime-water. I might shake that lime-water up with wood and the atmosphere as long as I pleased, it would still remain clear as you see it; but suppose I burn the piece of wood in the air of that bottle. You, of course, know I get water. Do I get carbonic acid? [The experiment was performed.] There it is, you see—that is to say, the carbonate of lime, which results from carbonic acid, and

that carbonic acid must be formed from the carbon which comes from the wood, from the candle, or any other thing. Indeed, you have yourselves frequently tried a very pretty experiment, by which you may see the carbon in wood. If you take a piece of wood, and partly burn it, and then blow it out, you have carbon left. There are things that do not show carbon in this way. A candle does not so show it, but it contains carbon. Here also is a jar of coal gas, which produces carbonic acid abundantly; you do not see the carbon, but we can soon show it to you. I will light it, and as long as there is any gas in the cylinder it will go on burning. You see no carbon, but you see a flame, and because that is bright it will lead you to guess that there is carbon in the flame. But I will show it to you by another process. I have some of the same gas in another vessel, mixed with a body that will burn the hydrogen of the gas, but will not burn the carbon. I will light them with a burning taper, and you perceive the hydrogen is consumed, but not the carbon, which is left behind as a dense black smoke. I hope that by these three or four experiments you will learn to see when carbon is present, and understand what are the products of combustion when gas or other bodies are thoroughly burned in the air.

Before we leave the subject of carbon, let us make a few experiments and remarks upon its wonderful condition as respects ordinary combustion. I have shown you that the carbon, in burning, burns only as a solid body, and yet you perceive that, after it is burned, it ceases to be a solid. There are very few fuels that act like this. It is, in fact, only that great source of fuel, the carbonaceous series, the coals, charcoals, and woods, that can do it. I do not know that there is any other elementary substance besides carbon that burns with these conditions; and if it had not been so, what would happen to us? Suppose all fuel had been like iron, which, when it burns, burns into a solid substance. We could not then have such a combustion as you have in this fireplace. Here also is another kind of fuel which burns very well—as well as, if not better, than carbon—so well, indeed, as to take fire of itself when it is in the air, as you see [breaking a tube full of lead pyrophorus]. This substance is lead, and you see how wonderfully combustible it is. It is very much divided, and is like a heap of coals in the fireplace; the air can get to its surface and inside,

and so it burns. But why does it not burn in that way now, when it is lying in a mass? [emptying the contents of the tube in a heap on to a plate of iron.] Simply because the air can not get to it. Though it can produce a great heat, the great heat which we want in our furnaces and under our boilers, still that which is produced can not get away from the portion which remains unburned underneath, and that portion, therefore, is prevented from coming in contact with the atmosphere, and can not be consumed. How different is that from carbon! Carbon burns just in the same way as this lead does, and so gives an intense fire in the furnace, or wherever you choose to burn it; but then the body produced by its combustion passes away, and the remaining carbon is left clear. I showed you how carbon went on dissolving in the oxygen, leaving no ash, whereas here [pointing to the heap of pyrophorus] we have actually more ash than fuel, for it is heavier by the amount of the oxygen which has united with it. Thus you see the difference between carbon and lead or iron—if we choose iron, which gives so wonderful a result in our applications of this fuel, either as light or heat. If, when the carbon burnt, the product went off as a solid body, you would have had the room filled with an opaque substance, as in the case of the phosphorus; but when carbon burns, every thing passes up into the atmosphere. It is in a fixed, almost unchangeable condition before the combustion; but afterward it is in the form of gas, which it is very difficult (though we have succeeded) to produce in a solid or liquid state.

Now I must take you to a very interesting part of our subject—to the relation between the combustion of a candle and that living kind of combustion which goes on within us. In every one of us there is a living process of combustion going on very similar to that of a candle, and I must try to make that plain to you. For it is not merely true in a poetical sense—the relation of the life of man to a taper; and if you will follow, I think I can make this clear. In order to make the relation very plain, I have devised a little apparatus which we can soon build up before you. Here is a board, and a groove cut in it, and I can close the groove at the top part by a little cover; I can then continue the groove as a channel by a glass tube at each end, there being a free passage through the whole.

Suppose I take a taper or candle (we can now be liberal in our use of the word "candle," since we understand what it means), and place it in one of the tubes; it will go on, you see, burning very well. You observe that the air which feeds the flame passes down the tube at one end, then goes along the horizontal tube, and ascends the tube at the other end in which the taper is placed. If I stop the aperture through which the air enters, I stop combustion, as you perceive. I stop the supply of air, and consequently the candle goes out. But now what will you think of this fact? In a former experiment I

Fig. 86

showed you the air going from one burning candle to a second candle. If I took the air proceeding from another candle, and sent it down by a complicated arrangement into this tube, I should put this burning candle out. But what will you say when I tell you that my breath will put out that candle? I do not mean by blowing at all, but simply that the nature of my breath is such that a candle can not burn in it. I will now hold my mouth over the aperture, and without blowing the flame in any way, let no air enter the tube but what comes from my mouth. You see the result. I did not blow the candle out. I merely let the air which I expired pass into the aperture, and the result was that the light went out for want of oxygen, and for no other reason. Something or other—namely, my lungs—had taken away the oxygen from the air and there was no more to supply the combustion of the candle. It is, I think, very pretty to see the time it takes before the bad air which I throw into this part of the apparatus has reached the candle. The candle at first goes on burning, but so soon as the air has had time to reach it, it

goes out. And now I will show you another experiment, because this is an important part of our philosophy. Here is a jar which contains fresh air, as you can see by the circumstance of a candle or gas light burning it. I make it close for a little time, and by means of a pipe I get my mouth over it so that I can inhale the air. By putting it over water, in the way that you see, I am able to draw up this air

Fig. 87

(supposing the cork to be quite tight), take it into my lungs, and throw it back into the jar: we can then examine it, and see the result. You observe, I first take up the air, and then throw it back, as is evident from the ascent and descent of the water; and now, by putting a taper into the air, you will see the state in which it is, by the light being extinguished. Even one inspiration, you see, has completely spoiled this air, so that it is no use my trying to breathe it a second time. Now you understand the ground of the impropriety of many of the arrangements among the houses of the poorer classes, by which the air is breathed over and over again for the want of a supply, by means of proper ventilation, sufficient to produce a good result. You see how bad the air becomes by a single breathing, so that you can easily understand how essential fresh air is to us.

To pursue this a little farther, let us see what will happen with lime-water. Here is a globe which contains a little lime-water, and it is so arranged as regards the pipes, as to give access to the air within, so that we can ascertain the effect of respired or unrespired air upon it. Of course I can either draw in air (through A), and so make the air that feeds my lungs go through the lime-water, or I can force the air out of my lungs through the tube (B), which goes to the bottom, and so show its effect upon the lime-water. You will observe that however long I draw the external air into the lime-water and then through it to my lungs, I shall produce no effect upon the water—it will not make the lime-water turbid; but if I throw the air *from* my lungs through the lime-water several times in succession, you see how white and milky the water is getting,

showing the effect which expired air has had upon it; and now you begin to know that the atmosphere which we have spoiled by respiration is spoiled by carbonic acid, for you see it here in contact with the lime-water.

B A

FIG. 88

I have here two bottles, one containing lime-water and the other common water, and tubes which pass into the bottles and connect them. The apparatus is very rough, but it is useful notwithstanding. If I take these two bottles, inhaling here and exhaling there, the arrangement of the tubes will prevent the air going backward. The air coming in will go to my mouth and lungs, and in going out will pass through the lime-water, so that I can go on breathing, and making an experiment very refined in its nature and very good in its results. You will observe that the good air has done nothing to the lime-water; in the other case, nothing has come to the lime-water but my respiration, and you see the difference in the two cases.

Let us now go a little farther. What is all this process going on within us which we can not do without, either day or night, which is so provided for by the Author of all things that He has arranged that it shall be independent of all will? If we restrain our respiration, as we can to a certain extent, we should destroy ourselves. When we are asleep the organs of respiration and the parts that are associated with them still go on with their action, so necessary is this process of respiration to us, this contact of the air with the lungs. I must tell you, in the briefest possible

FIG. 89

manner, what this process is. We consume food; the food goes through that strange set of vessels and organs within us, and is brought into various parts of the system, into the digestive parts especially; and alternately the portion which is so changed is

carried through our lungs by one set of vessels, while the air that we inhale and exhale is drawn into and thrown out of the lungs by another set of vessels, so that the air and the food come close together, separated only by an exceedingly thin surface: the air can thus act upon the blood by this process, producing precisely the same results in kind as we have seen in the case of the candle. The candle combines with parts of the air, forming carbonic acid, and evolves heat; so in the lungs there is this curious, wonderful change taking place. The air entering, combines with the carbon (not carbon in a free state, but, as in this case, placed ready for action at the moment), and makes carbonic acid and is so thrown out into the atmosphere, and thus this singular result takes place; we may thus look upon the food as fuel. Let me take that piece of sugar, which will serve my purpose. It is a compound of carbon, hydrogen, and oxygen, similar to a candle, as containing the same elements, though not in the same proportion, the proportions being as shown in this table:

SUGAR.

Carbon ... 72	
Hydrogen ... 11	99
Oxygen ... 88	

This is, indeed, a very curious thing, which you can well remember, for the oxygen and hydrogen are in exactly the proportions which form water, so that sugar may be said to be compounded of 72 parts of carbon and 99 parts of water; and it is the carbon in the sugar that combines with the oxygen carried in by the air in the process of respiration—so making us like candles—producing these actions, warmth, and far more wonderful results besides, for the sustenance of the system, by a most beautiful and simple process. To make this still more striking, I will take a little sugar; or, to hasten the experiment, I will use some sirup, which contains about three-fourths of sugar and a little water. If I put a little oil of vitriol on it, it takes away the water, and leaves the carbon in a black mass. [The lecturer mixed the two together.] You see how the carbon is coming out, and before long we shall have a solid mass of charcoal, all of which has come out of sugar. Sugar, as you know, is food, and here we have absolutely a solid lump of carbon where you would not

have expected it. And if I make arrangements so as to oxidize the carbon of sugar we shall have a much more striking result. Here is sugar, and I have here an oxidizer—a quicker one than the atmosphere; and so we shall oxidize this fuel by a process different from respiration in its form, though not different in its kind. It is the combustion of the carbon by the contact of oxygen which the body has supplied to it. If I set this into action at once, you will see combustion produced. Just what occurs in my lungs—taking in oxygen from another source, namely, the atmosphere—takes place here by a more rapid process.

You will be astonished when I tell you what this curious play of carbon amounts to. A candle will burn some four, five, six, or seven hours. What, then, must be the daily amount of carbon going up into the air in the way of carbonic acid! What a quantity of carbon must go from each of us in respiration! What a wonderful change of carbon must take place under these circumstances of combustion or respiration! A man in twenty-four hours converts as much as seven ounces of carbon into carbonic acid; a milch cow will convert seventy ounces, and a horse seventy-nine ounces, solely by the act of respiration. That is, the horse in twenty-four hours burns seventy-nine ounces of charcoal, or carbon, in his organs of respiration to supply his natural warmth in that time. All the warm-blooded animals get their warmth in this way, by the conversion of carbon, not in a free state, but in a state of combination. And what an extraordinary notion this gives us of the alterations going on in our atmosphere. As much as 5,000,000 pounds, or 548 tons, of carbonic acid is formed by respiration in London alone in twenty-four hours. And where does all this go? Up into the air. If the carbon had been like the lead which I showed you, or the iron which, in burning, produces a solid substance, what would happen? Combustion could not go on. As charcoal burns it becomes a vapor and passes off into the atmosphere, which is the great vehicle, the great carrier for conveying it away to other places. Then what becomes of it? Wonderful is it to find that the change produced by respiration, which seems so injurious to us (for we can not breathe air twice over), is the very life and support of plants and vegetables that grow upon the surface of the earth. It is the same also under the surface,

in the great bodies of water; for fishes and other animals respire
upon the same principle, though not exactly by contact with the
open air.

Such fish as I have here [pointing to a globe of goldfish] respire
by the oxygen which is dissolved from the air by the water, and form
carbonic acid, and they all move about to produce the one great
work of making the animal and vegetable kingdoms subservient to
each other. And all the plants growing upon the surface of the
earth, like that which I have brought here to serve as an illustration,
absorb carbon; these leaves are taking up their carbon from the at-
mosphere to which we have given it in the form of carbonic acid,
and they are growing and prospering. Give them a pure air like
ours, and they could not live in it; give them carbon with other
matters, and they live and rejoice. This piece of wood gets all its
carbon, as the trees and plants get theirs, from the atmosphere,
which, as we have seen, carries away what is bad for us and at the
same time good for them—what is disease to the one being health
to the other. So are we made dependent not merely upon our fellow-
creatures, but upon our fellow-existers, all Nature being tied to-
gether by the laws that make one part conduce to the good of
another.

There is another little point which I must mention before we draw
to a close—a point which concerns the whole of these operations,
and most curious and beautiful it is to see it clustering upon and
associated with the bodies that concern us—oxygen, hydrogen, and
carbon, in different states of their existence. I showed you just now
some powdered lead, which I set burning([18]); and you saw that the
moment the fuel was brought to the air, it acted, even before it
got out of the bottle—the moment the air crept in, it acted. Now
there is a case of chemical affinity by which all our operations pro-
ceed. When we breathe, the same operation is going on within us.
When we burn a candle, the attraction of the different parts one to
the other is going on. Here it is going on in this case of the lead, and
it is a beautiful instance of chemical affinity. If the products of com-

[18] *Lead pyrophorus* is made by heating dry tartrate of lead in a glass tube (closed at
one end, and drawn out to a fine point at the other) until no more vapors are evolved.
The open end of the tube is then to be sealed before the blowpipe. When the tube
is broken and the contents shaken out into the air, they burn with a red flash.

bustion rose off from the surface, the lead would take fire, and go on burning to the end; but you remember that we have this difference between charcoal and lead—that, while the lead can start into action at once if there be access of air to it, the carbon will remain days, weeks, months, or years. The manuscripts of Herculaneum were written with carbonaceous ink, and there they have been for 1,800 years or more, not having been at all changed by the atmosphere, though coming in contact with it under various circumstances. Now, what is the circumstance which makes the lead and carbon differ in this respect? It is a striking thing to see that the matter which is appointed to serve the purpose of fuel *waits* in its action; it does not start off burning, like the lead and many other things that I could show you, but which I have not encumbered the table with; but it waits for action. This waiting is a curious and wonderful thing. Candles—those Japanese candles, for instance—do not start into action at once like the lead or iron (for iron finely divided does the same thing as lead), but there they wait for years, perhaps for ages, without undergoing any alteration. I have here a supply of coal gas. The jet is giving forth the gas, but you see it does not take fire—it comes out into the air, but it waits till it is hot enough before it burns. If I make it hot enough, it takes fire. If I blow it out, the gas that is issuing forth waits till the light is applied to it again. It is curious to see how different substances wait —how some will wait till the temperature is raised a little, and others till it is raised a good deal. I have here a little gunpowder and some guncotton; even these things differ in the conditions under which they will burn. The gunpowder is composed of carbon and other substances, making it highly combustible; and the guncotton is another combustible preparation. They are both waiting, but they will start into activity at different degrees of heat, or under different conditions. By applying a heated wire to them, we shall see which will start first [touching the guncotton with the hot iron]. You see the guncotton has gone off, but not even the hottest part of the wire is now hot enough to fire the gunpowder. How beautifully that shows you the difference in the degree in which bodies act in this way! In the one case the substance will wait any time until the associated bodies are made active by heat; but in the other, as

in the process of respiration, it waits no time. In the lungs, as soon as the air enters, it unites with the carbon; even in the lowest temperature which the body can bear short of being frozen, the action begins at once, producing the carbonic acid of respiration; and so all things go on fitly and properly. Thus you see the analogy between respiration and combustion is rendered still more beautiful and striking. Indeed, all I can say to you at the end of these lectures (for we must come to an end at one time or other) is to express a wish that you may, in your generation, be fit to compare to a candle; that you may, like it, shine as lights to those about you; that, in all your actions, you may justify the beauty of the taper by making your deeds honorable and effectual in the discharge of your duty to your fellow-men.

ON THE CONSERVATION OF FORCE

ICE AND GLACIERS

BY

HERMANN VON HELMHOLTZ

TRANSLATED BY

EDMUND ATKINSON

INTRODUCTORY NOTE

HERMANN LUDWIG FERDINAND VON HELMHOLTZ was born at Potsdam, near Berlin, on August 31, 1821. His father was a man of high culture, a teacher in the gymnasium, whose influence ensured to his son the foundations of a broad general education. His mother was a descendant from William Penn, the English Quaker.

Helmholtz early showed mathematical ability, and wished to devote his life to the study of physics; but practical considerations led him to take up medicine, and he became a surgeon in the Prussian army. He began the publication of original contributions to science in 1842, and for fifty-two years, till his death in 1894, he continued to produce in an unbroken stream. He held a succession of academic positions, teaching physiology at Königsberg, Bonn, and Heidelberg, and for the last twenty-three years of his life filling the chair of physics at Berlin.

The titles of his professorships, however, give a very inadequate idea of his range. His contributions to science cover medicine, physiology, optics, acoustics, mathematics, mechanics, and electricity. His interests in science and art came together in his work on esthetics, and he had a lively appreciation of painting, poetry, and music.

The practice of popular lecturing on scientific subjects was almost unknown in Germany when Helmholtz began, and he did much to give it dignity and to set a standard. His own lectures, as the reader of the following papers will perceive, are masterpieces of their kind. "The matter," says a biographer, "is discussed by a master, who brings to bear upon it all his wealth of learning and research, while there is the ever-enduring interest that attaches to an exposition by one who is giving forth from his own treasury." It is fortunate for the layman when a scientist and thinker of the first order has the skill and the inclination to share with the outside world the rich harvest of his brilliant and laborious research.

ON THE CONSERVATION
OF FORCE

INTRODUCTION TO A SERIES OF LECTURES
DELIVERED AT CARLSRUHE IN THE
WINTER OF 1862–1863

AS I have undertaken to deliver here a series of lectures, I think the best way in which I can discharge that duty will be to bring before you, by means of a suitable example, some view of the special character of those sciences to the study of which I have devoted myself. The natural sciences, partly in consequence of their practical applications, and partly from their intellectual influence on the last four centuries, have so profoundly, and with such increasing rapidity, transformed all the relations of the life of civilised nations; they have given these nations such increase of riches, of enjoyment of life, of the preservation of health, of means of industrial and of social intercourse, and even such increase of political power, that every educated man who tries to understand the forces at work in the world in which he is living, even if he does not wish to enter upon the study of a special science, must have some interest in that peculiar kind of mental labour, which works and acts in the sciences in question.

On a former occasion I have already discussed the characteristic differences which exist between the natural and the mental sciences as regards the kind of scientific work. I then endeavoured to show that it is more especially in the thorough conformity with law which natural phenomena and natural products exhibit, and in the comparative ease with which laws can be stated, that this difference exists. Not that I wish by any means to deny, that the mental life of individuals and peoples is also in conformity with law, as is the object of philosophical, philological, historical, moral, and social sciences to establish. But in mental life, the influences are so inter-

woven, that any definite sequence can but seldom be demonstrated.
In Nature the converse is the case. It has been possible to discover
the law of the origin and progress of many enormously extended
series of natural phenomena with such accuracy and completeness
that we can predict their future occurrence with the greatest cer-
tainty; or in cases in which we have power over the conditions under
which they occur, we can direct them just according to our will.
The greatest of all instances of what the human mind can effect by
means of a well-recognised law of natural phenomena is that
afforded by modern astronomy. The one simple law of gravitation
regulates the motions of the heavenly bodies not only of our own
planetary system, but also of the far more distant double stars; from
which, even the ray of light, the quickest of all messengers, needs
years to reach our eye; and, just on account of this simple con-
formity with law, the motions of the bodies in question can be
accurately predicted and determined both for the past and for future
years and centuries to a fraction of a minute.

On this exact conformity with law depends also the certainty with
which we know how to tame the impetuous force of steam, and to
make it the obedient servant of our wants. On this conformity
depends, moreover, the intellectual fascination which chains the
physicist to his subjects. It is an interest of quite a different kind to
that which mental and moral sciences afford. In the latter it is man
in the various phases of his intellectual activity who chains us.
Every great deed of which history tells us, every mighty passion
which art can represent, every picture of manners, of civic arrange-
ments, of the culture of peoples of distant lands or of remote times,
seizes and interests us, even if there is no exact scientific connection
among them. We continually find points of contact and comparison
in our conceptions and feelings; we get to know the hidden capac-
ities and desires of the mind, which in the ordinary peaceful course
of civilised life remain unawakened.

It is not to be denied that, in the natural sciences, this kind of
interest is wanting. Each individual fact, taken by itself, can indeed
arouse our curiosity or our astonishment, or be useful to us in its
practical applications. But intellectual satisfaction we obtain only
from a connection of the whole, just from its conformity with law.

Reason we call that faculty innate in us of discovering laws and applying them with thought. For the unfolding of the peculiar forces of pure reason in their entire certainty and in their entire bearing, there is no more suitable arena than inquiry into Nature in the wider sense, the mathematics included. And it is not only the pleasure at the successful activity of one of our most essential mental powers; and the victorious subjections to the power of our thought and will of an external world, partly unfamiliar, and partly hostile, which is the reward of this labour; but there is a kind, I might almost say, of artistic satisfaction, when we are able to survey the enormous wealth of Nature as a regularly-ordered whole—a kosmos, an image of the logical thought of our own mind.

The last decades of scientific development have led us to the recognition of a new universal law of all natural phenomena, which, from its extraordinarily extended range, and from the connection which it constitutes between natural phenomena of all kinds, even of the remotest times and the most distant places, is especially fitted to give us an idea of what I have described as the character of the natural sciences, which I have chosen as the subject of this lecture.

This law is *the Law of the Conservation of Force,* a term the meaning of which I must first explain. It is not absolutely new; for individual domains of natural phenomena it was enunciated by Newton and Daniel Bernoulli; and Rumford and Humphry Davy have recognised distinct features of its presence in the laws of heat.

The possibility that it was of universal application was first stated by Dr. Julius Robert Mayer, a Schwabian physician (now living in Heilbronn), in the year 1842, while almost simultaneously with, and independently of him, James Prescot Joule, an English manufacturer, made a series of important and difficult experiments on the relation of heat to mechanical force, which supplied the chief points in which the comparison of the new theory with experience was still wanting.

The law in question asserts, that the *quantity of force which can be brought into action in the whole of Nature is unchangeable,* and can neither be increased nor diminished. My first object will be to explain to you what is understood by *quantity of force;* or, as the same idea is more popularly expressed with reference to its technical

application, what we call *amount of work* in the mechanical sense of the word.

The idea of work for machines, or natural processes, is taken from comparison with the working power of man; and we can therefore best illustrate from human labour the most important features of the question with which we are concerned. In speaking of the work of machines and of natural forces we must, of course, in this comparison eliminate anything in which activity of intelligence comes into play. The latter is also capable of the hard and intense work of thinking, which tries a man just as muscular exertion does. But whatever of the actions of intelligence is met with in the work of machines, of course is due to the mind of the constructor and cannot be assigned to the instrument at work.

Now, the external work of man is of the most varied kind as regards the force or ease, the form and rapidity, of the motions used on it, and the kind of work produced. But both the arm of the blacksmith who delivers his powerful blows with the heavy hammer, and that of the violinist who produces the most delicate variations in sound, and the hand of the lace-maker who works with threads so fine that they are on the verge of the invisible, all these acquire the force which moves them in the same manner and by the same organs, namely, the muscles of the arms. An arm the muscles of which are lamed is incapable of doing any work; the moving force of the muscle must be at work in it, and these must obey the nerves, which bring to them orders from the brain. That member is then capable of the greatest variety of motions; it can compel the most varied instruments to execute the most diverse tasks.

Just so it is with machines: they are used for the most diversified arrangements. We produce by their agency an infinite variety of movements, with the most various degrees of force and rapidity, from powerful steam hammers and rolling mills, where gigantic masses of iron are cut and shaped like butter, to spinning and weaving frames, the work of which rivals that of the spider. Modern mechanism has the richest choice of means of transferring the motion of one set of rolling wheels to another with greater or less velocity; of changing the rotating motion of wheels into the up-and-down motion of the piston rod, of the shuttle, of falling hammers and

stamps; or, conversely, of changing the latter into the former; or it can, on the other hand, change movements of uniform into those of varying velocity, and so forth. Hence this extraordinarily rich utility of machines for so extremely varied branches of industry. But one thing is common to all these differences; they all need a *moving force,* which sets and keeps them in motion, just as the works of the human hand all need the moving force of the muscles.

Now, the work of the smith requires a far greater and more intense exertion of the muscles than that of the violin player; and there are in machines corresponding differences in the power and duration of the moving force required. These differences, which correspond to the different degree of exertion of the muscles in human labour, are alone what we have to think of when we speak of the *amount of work* of a machine. We have nothing to do here with the manifold character of the actions and arrangements which the machines produce; we are only concerned with an expenditure of force.

This very expression which we use so fluently, 'expenditure of force,' which indicates that the force applied has been expended and lost, leads us to a further characteristic analogy between the effects of the human arm and those of machines. The greater the exertion, and the longer it lasts, the more is the arm *tired,* and the more *is the store of its moving force for the time exhausted.* We shall see that this peculiarity of becoming exhausted by work is also met with in the moving forces of inorganic nature; indeed, that this capacity of the human arm of being tired is only one of the consequences of the law with which we are now concerned. When fatigue sets in, recovery is needed, and this can only be effected by rest and nourishment. We shall find that also in the inorganic moving forces, when their capacity for work is spent, there is a possibility of reproduction, although in general other means must be used to this end than in the case of the human arm.

From the feeling of exertion and fatigue in our muscles, we can form a general idea of what we understand by amount of work; but we must endeavour, instead of the indefinite estimate afforded by this comparison, to form a clear and precise idea of the standard by which we have to measure the amount of work. This we can do

better by the simplest inorganic moving forces than by the actions of our muscles, which are a very complicated apparatus, acting in an extremely intricate manner.

Let us now consider that moving force which we know best, and which is simplest—gravity. It acts, for example, as such in those clocks which are driven by a weight. This weight, fastened to a string, which is wound round a pulley connected with the first toothed wheel of the clock, cannot obey the pull of gravity without setting the whole clockwork in motion. Now I must beg you to pay special attention to the following points: the weight cannot put the clock in motion without itself sinking; did the weight not move, it could not move the clock, and its motion can only be such a one as obeys the action of gravity. Hence, if the clock is to go, the weight must continually sink lower and lower, and must at length sink so far that the string which supports it is run out. The clock then stops. The usual effect of its weight is for the present exhausted. Its gravity is not lost or diminished; it is attracted by the earth as before, but the capacity of this gravity to produce the motion of the clockwork is lost. It can only keep the weight at rest in the lowest point of its path, it cannot farther put it in motion.

But we can wind up the clock by the power of the arm, by which the weight is again raised. When this has been done, it has regained its former capacity, and can again set the clock in motion.

We learn from this that a raised weight possesses a *moving force,* but that it must necessarily sink if this force is to act; that by sinking, this moving force is exhausted, but by using another extraneous moving force—that of the arm—its activity can be restored.

The work which the weight has to perform in driving the clock is not indeed great. It has continually to overcome the small resistances which the friction of the axles and teeth, as well as the resistance of the air, oppose to the motion of the wheels, and it has to furnish the force for the small impulses and sounds which the pendulum produces at each oscillation. If the weight is detached from the clock, the pendulum swings for a while before coming to a rest, but its motion becomes each moment feebler, and ultimately ceases entirely, being gradually used up by the small hindrances I have mentioned. Hence, to keep the clock going, there must be a

moving force, which, though small, must be continually at work. Such a one is the weight.

We get, moreover, from this example, a measure for the amount of work. Let us assume that a clock is driven by a weight of a pound, which falls five feet in twenty-four hours. If we fix ten such clocks, each with a weight of one pound, then ten clocks will be driven twenty-four hours; hence, as each has to overcome the same resistances in the same time as the others, ten times as much work is performed for ten pounds fall through five feet. Hence, we conclude that the height of the fall being the same, the work increases directly as the weight.

Now, if we increase the length of the string so that the weight runs down ten feet, the clock will go two days instead of one; and, with double the height of fall, the weight will overcome on the second day the same resistances as on the first, and will therefore do twice as much work as when it can only run down five feet. The weight being the same, the work increases as the height of fall. Hence, we may take the product of the weight into the height of fall as a measure of work, at any rate, in the present case. The application of this measure is, in fact, not limited to the individual case, but the universal standard adopted in manufactures for measuring magnitude of work is a *foot pound*—that is, the amount of work which a pound raised through a foot can produce.[1]

We may apply this measure of work to all kinds of machines, for we should be able to set them all in motion by means of a weight sufficient to turn a pulley. We could thus always express the magnitude of any driving force, for any given machine, by the magnitude and height of fall of such a weight as would be necessary to keep the machine going with its arrangements until it had performed a certain work. Hence it is that the measurement of work by foot pounds is universally applicable. The use of such a weight as a driving force would not indeed be practically advantageous in those cases in which we were compelled to raise it by the power of our own arm; it would in that case be simpler to work the machine by the direct action of the arm. In the clock we use a weight so that

[1] This is the *technical* measure of work; to convert it into scientific measure it must be multiplied by the intensity of gravity.

we need not stand the whole day at the clockwork, as we should have to do to move it directly. By winding up the clock we accumulate a store of working capacity in it, which is sufficient for the expenditure of the next twenty-four hours.

The case is somewhat different when Nature herself raises the weight, which then works for us. She does not do this with solid

FIG. 90

bodies, at least not with such regularity as to be utilised; but she does it abundantly with water, which, being raised to the tops of mountains by meteorological processes, returns in streams from them. The gravity of water we use as moving force, the most direct application being in what are called *overshot* wheels, one of which is represented in FIG. 90. Along the circumference of such a wheel are a series of buckets, which act as receptacles for the water, and, on the side turned to the observer, have the tops uppermost; on the

opposite side the tops of the buckets are upside-down. The water flows at M into the buckets of the front of the wheel, and at F, where the mouth begins to incline downwards, it flows out. The buckets on the circumference are filled on the side turned to the observer, and empty on the other side. Thus the former are weighted by the water contained in them, the latter not; the weight of the water acts continuously on only one side of the wheel, draws this down, and thereby turns the wheel; the other side of the wheel offers no resistance, for it contains no water. It is thus the weight of the falling water which turns the wheel, and furnishes the motive power. But you will at once see that the mass of water which turns the wheel must necessarily fall in order to do so, and that though, when it has reached the bottom, it has lost none of its gravity, it is no longer in a position to drive the wheel, if it is not restored to its original position, either by the power of the human arm or by means of some other natural force. If it can flow from the mill-stream to still lower levels, it may be used to work other wheels. But when it has reached its lowest level, the sea, the last remainder of the moving force is used up, which is due to gravity—that is, to the attraction of the earth, and it cannot act by its weight until it has been again raised to a high level. As this is actually effected by meteorological processes, you will at once observe that these are to be considered as sources of moving force.

Water power was the first inorganic force which man learnt to use instead of his own labour or of that of domestic animals. According to Strabo, it was known to King Mithridates of Pontus, who was also otherwise celebrated for his knowledge of Nature; near his palace there was a water wheel. Its use was first introduced among the Romans in the time of the first Emperors. Even now we find water mills in all mountains, valleys, or wherever there are rapidly-flowing regularly-filled brooks and streams. We find water power used for all purposes which can possibly be effected by machines. It drives mills which grind corn, sawmills, hammers and oil presses, spinning frames and looms, and so forth. It is the cheapest of all motive powers, it flows spontaneously from the inexhaustible stores of Nature; but it is restricted to a particular place, and only in mountainous countries is it present in any quantity; in level

countries extensive reservoirs are necessary for damming the rivers
to produce any amount of water power.

Before passing to the discussion of other motive forces I must
answer an objection which may readily suggest itself. We all know
that there are numerous machines, systems of pulleys, levers and
cranes, by the aid of which heavy burdens may be
lifted by a comparatively small expenditure of
force. We have all of us often seen one or two
workmen hoist heavy masses of stones to great
heights, which they would be quite unable to do
directly; in like manner, one or two men, by
means of a crane, can transfer the largest and
heaviest chests from a ship to the quay.
Now, it may be asked, If a large, heavy
weight had been used for driving a machine,
would it not be very easy, by means of a
crane or a system of pulleys, to raise it anew,
so that it could again be used as a motor, and thus
acquire motive power, without being compelled to use
a corresponding exertion in raising the weight?

The answer to this is, that all these machines, in that
degree in which for the moment they facilitate the exer-
tion, also prolong it, so that by their help no motive
power is ultimately gained. Let us assume that four
labourers have to raise a load of four hundredweight
by means of a rope passing over a single pulley. Every
time the rope is pulled down through four feet, the
load is also raised through four feet. But now, for the
sake of comparison, let us suppose the same load hung
to a block of four pulleys, as represented in Fig. 91. A
single labourer would now be able to raise the load by
the same exertion of force as each one of the four put
forth. But when he pulls the rope through four feet, the
load only rises one foot, for the length through which
he pulls the rope, at *a*, is uniformly distributed in the
block over four ropes, so that each of these is only shortened by a
foot. To raise the load, therefore, to the same height, the one man

FIG. 91

must necessarily work four times as long as the four together did. But the total expenditure of work is the same, whether four labourers work for a quarter of an hour or one works for an hour.

If, instead of human labour, we introduce the work of a weight, and hang to the block a load of 400, and at *a*, where otherwise the labourer works, a weight of 100 pounds, the block is then in equilibrium, and, without any appreciable exertion of the arm, may be set in motion. The weight of 100 pounds sinks, that of 400 rises.

FIG. 92

Without any measurable expenditure of force, the heavy weight has been raised by the sinking of the smaller one. But observe that the smaller weight will have sunk through four times the distance that the greater one has risen. But a fall of 100 pounds through four feet is just as much 400 foot-pounds as a fall of 400 pounds through one foot.

The action of levers in all their various modifications is precisely similar. Let *a b*, FIG. 92, be a simple lever, supported at *c*, the arm *c b* being four times as long as the other arm *a c*. Let a weight of one pound be hung at *b*, and a weight of four pounds at *a*, the lever is then in equilibrium, and the least pressure of the finger is sufficient, without any appreciable exertion of force, to place it in the position $a^1 b^1$, in which the heavy weight of four pounds has been raised, while the one-pound weight has sunk. But here, also, you will observe no work has been gained, for while the heavy weight has been

raised through one inch, the lighter one has fallen through four inches; and four pounds through one inch is, as work, equivalent to the product of one pound through four inches.

Most other fixed parts of machines may be regarded as modified and compound levers; a toothed-wheel, for instance as a series of levers, the ends of which are represented by the individual teeth, and one after the other of which is put in activity in the degree in

FIG. 93

which the tooth in question seizes or is seized by the adjacent pinion. Take, for instance, the crabwinch, represented in FIG. 93. Suppose the pinion on the axis of the barrel of the winch has twelve teeth, and the toothed-wheel, H H, seventy-two teeth, that is, six times as many as the former. The winch must now be turned round six times before the toothed-wheel, H, and the barrel, D, have made one turn, and before the rope which raises the load has been lifted by a length equal to the circumference of the barrel. The workman thus requires six times the time, though to be sure only one-sixth of the exertion, which he would have to use if the handle were directly applied to the barrel, D. In all these machines, and parts of ma-

chines, we find it confirmed that in proportion as the velocity of the motion increases its power diminishes, and that when the power increases the velocity diminishes, but that the amount of work is never thereby increased.

In the overshot mill wheel, described above, water acts by its weight. But there is another form of mill wheels, what is called the

Fig. 94

undershot wheel, in which it only acts by its impact, as represented in Fig. 94. These are used where the height from which the water comes is not great enough to flow on the upper part of the wheel. The lower part of undershot wheels dips in the flowing water which strikes against their float-boards and carries them along. Such wheels are used in swift-flowing streams which have a scarcely perceptible fall, as, for instance, on the Rhine. In the immediate neighborhood of such a wheel, the water need not necessarily have a great fall if it only strikes with considerable velocity. It is the velocity of the water, exerting an impact against the float-boards, which acts in this case, and which produces the motive power.

Windmills, which are used in the great plains of Holland and North Germany to supply the want of falling water, afford another

instance of the action of velocity. The sails are driven by air in motion—by wind. Air at rest could just as little drive a windmill as water at rest a water wheel. The driving force depends here on the velocity of moving masses.

A bullet resting in the hand is the most harmless thing in the world; by its gravity it can exert no great effect; but when fired and endowed with great velocity it drives through all obstacles with the most tremendous force.

If I lay the head of a hammer gently on a nail, neither its small weight nor the pressure of my arm is quite sufficient to drive the nail into the wood; but if I swing the hammer and allow it to fall with great velocity, it acquires a new force, which can overcome far greater hindrances.

These examples teach us that the velocity of a moving mass can act as motive force. In mechanics, velocity in so far as it is motive force, and can produce work, is called *vis viva*. The name is not well chosen; it is too apt to suggest to us the force of living beings. Also in this case you will see, from the instances of the hammer and of the bullet, that velocity is lost, as such, when it produces working power. In the case of the water mill, or of the windmill, a more careful investigation of the moving masses of water and air is necessary to prove that part of their velocity has been lost by the work which they have performed.

The relation of velocity to working power is most simply and clearly seen in a simple pendulum, such as can be constructed by any weight which we suspend to a cord. Let M, Fig. 95, be such a weight, of a spherical form; A B, a horizontal line drawn through the centre of the sphere; P the point at which the cord is fastened. If now I draw the weight M on one side towards A, it moves in the arc M *a*, the end of which, *a*, is somewhat higher than the point A in the horizontal line. The weight is thereby raised to the height A *a*. Hence my arm must exert a certain force to bring the weight to *a*. Gravity resists this motion, and endeavours to bring back the weight to M, the lowest point which it can reach.

Now, if after I have brought the weight to *a* I let it go, it obeys this force of gravity and returns to M, arrives there with a certain velocity, and no longer remains quietly hanging at M as it did

before, but swings beyond M towards *b*, where its motion stops as
soon as it has traversed on the side of B an arc equal in length to
that on the side of A, and after it has risen to a distance B *b* above
the horizontal line, which is equal to the height A *a*, to which my
arm had previously raised it. In *b* the pendulum returns, swings the
same way back through M towards *a*, and so on, until its oscillations

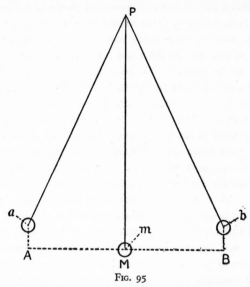

FIG. 95

are gradually diminished, and ultimately annulled by the resistance
of the air and by friction.

You see here that the reason why the weight, when it comes from
a to M, and does not stop there, but ascends to *b*, in opposition to
the action of gravity, is only to be sought in its velocity. The velocity
which it has acquired in moving from the height A *a* is capable of
again raising it to an equal height, B *b*. The velocity of the moving
mass, M, is thus capable of raising this mass; that is to say, in the
language of mechanics, of performing work. This would also be
the case if we had imparted such a velocity to the suspended weight
by a blow.

From this we learn further how to measure the working power of
velocity—or, what is the same thing, the *vis viva* of the *moving*

mass. It is equal to the work, expressed in foot-pounds, which the same mass can exert after its velocity has been used to raise it, under the most favourable circumstances, to as great a height as possible.[2] This does not depend on the direction of the velocity; for if we swing a weight attached to a thread in a circle, we can even change a downward motion into an upward one.

The motion of the pendulum shows us very distinctly how the forms of working power hitherto considered—that of a raised weight and that of a moving mass—may merge into one another. In the points *a* and *b,* Fig. 95, the mass has no velocity; at the point M it has fallen as far as possible, but possesses velocity. As the weight goes from *a* to *m* the work of the raised weight is changed into *vis viva;* as the weight goes further from *m* to *b* the *vis viva* is changed into the work of a raised weight. Thus the work which the arm originally imparted to the pendulum is not lost in these oscillations provided we may leave out of consideration the influence of the resistance of the air and of friction. Neither does it increase, but it continually changes the form of its manifestation.

Let us now pass to other mechanical forces, those of elastic bodies. Instead of the weights which drive our clocks, we find in timepieces and in watches, steel springs which are coiled in winding up the clock, and are uncoiled by the working of the clock. To coil up the spring we consume the force of the arm; this has to overcome the resisting elastic force of the spring as we wind it up, just as in the clock we have to overcome the force of gravity which the weight exerts. The coiled spring can, however, perform work; it gradually expends this acquired capability in driving the clockwork.

If I stretch a crossbow and afterwards let it go, the stretched string moves the arrow; it imparts to it force in the form of velocity. To stretch the cord my arm must work for a few seconds; this work is imparted to the arrow at the moment it is shot off. Thus the crossbow concentrates into an extremely short time the entire work which the arm had communicated in the operation of stretching; the

[2] The measure of *vis viva* in theoretical mechanics is half the product of the weight into the square of the velocity. To reduce it to the technical measure of the work we must divide it by the intensity of gravity; that is, by the velocity at the end of the first second of a freely falling body.

clock, on the contrary, spreads it over one or several days. In both cases no work is produced which my arm did not originally impart to the instrument; it is only expended more conveniently.

The case is somewhat different if by any other natural process I can place an elastic body in a state of tension without having to exert my arm. This is possible and is most easily observed in the case of gases.

If, for instance, I discharge a firearm loaded with gunpowder, the greater part of the mass of the powder is converted into gases at a very high temperature, which have a powerful tendency to expand, and can only be retained in the narrow space in which they are formed, by the exercise of the most powerful pressure. In expanding with enormous force they propel the bullet, and impart to it a great velocity, which we have already seen is a form of work.

In this case, then, I have gained work which my arm has not performed. Something, however, has been lost—the gunpowder, that is to say, whose constituents have changed into other chemical compounds, from which they cannot, without further ado, be restored to their original condition. Here, then, a chemical change has taken place, under the influence of which work has been gained.

Elastic forces are produced in gases by the aid of heat, on a far greater scale.

Let us take, as the most simple instance, atmospheric air. In Fig. 96 an apparatus is represented such as Regnault used for measuring the expansive force of heated gases. If no great accuracy is required in the measurement, the apparatus may be arranged more simply. At C is a glass globe filled with dry air, which is placed in a metal vessel, in which it can be heated by steam. It is connected with the U-shaped tube, S s, which contains a liquid, and the limbs of which communicate with each other when the stopcock R is closed. If the liquid is in equilibrium in the tube S s when the globe is cold, it rises in the leg s, and ultimately overflows when the globe is heated. If, on the contrary, when the globe is heated, equilibrium be restored by allowing some of the liquid to flow out at R, as the globe cools it will be drawn up towards n. In both cases liquid is raised, and work thereby produced.

The same experiment is continuously repeated on the largest scale in steam engines, though, in order to keep up a continual disengagement of compressed gases from the boiler, the air in the globe in Fig. 96, which would soon reach the maximum of its expansion, is replaced by water, which is gradually changed into steam by the application of heat. But steam, so long as it remains as such, is an

FIG. 96

elastic gas which endeavours to expand exactly like atmospheric air. And instead of the column of liquid which was raised in our last experiment, the machine is caused to drive a solid piston which imparts its motion to other parts of the machine. FIG. 97 represents a front view of the working parts of a high-pressure engine, and FIG. 98 a section. The boiler in which steam is generated is not represented; the steam passes through the tube z z, FIG. 98, to the cylinder A A, in which moves a tightly fitting piston C. The parts between the tube z z and the cylinder A A, that is the slide valve in the valve-chest K K, and the two tubes d and e allow the steam to

Fig. 97

pass first below and then above the piston, while at the same time the steam has free exit from the other half of the cylinder. When the steam passes under the piston, it forces it upward; when the piston has reached the top of its course the position of the valve in K K changes, and the steam passes above the piston and forces it down again. The piston rod acts by means of the connecting rod P, on the crank Q of the flywheel X and sets this in motion. By means of the rod *s,* the motion of the rod regulates the opening and closing of the valve. But we need not here enter into those mechanical arrangements, however ingeniously they have been devised. We are only interested in the manner in which heat produces elastic vapour, and how this vapour, in its endeavour to expand, is compelled to move the solid parts of the machine, and furnish work.

You all know how powerful and varied are the effects of which steam engines are capable; with them has really begun the great development of industry which has characterised our century before all others. Its most essential superiority over motive powers formerly known is that it is not restricted to a particular place. The store of coal and the small quantity of water which are the sources of its power can be brought everywhere, and steam engines can even be made movable, as is the case with steam ships and locomotives. By means of these machines we can develop motive power to almost an indefinite extent at any place on the earth's surface, in deep mines and even on the middle of the ocean; while water and windmills are bound to special parts of the surface of the land. The locomotive transports travellers and goods over the land in numbers and with a speed which must have seemed an incredible fable to our forefathers, who looked upon the mailcoach with its six passengers in the inside, and its ten miles an hour, as an enormous progress. Steam engines traverse the ocean independently of the direction of the wind, and, successfully resisting storms which would drive sailing vessels far away, reach their goal at the appointed time. The advantages which the concourse of numerous and variously skilled workmen in all branches offers in large towns where wind and water power are wanting, can be utilised, for steam engines find place everywhere, and supply the necessary crude force; thus the more

FIG. 98

intelligent human force may be spared for better purposes; and, indeed, wherever the nature of the ground or the neighbourhood of suitable lines of communication present a favourable opportunity for the development of industry, the motive power is also present in the form of steam engines.

We see, then, that heat can produce mechanical power; but in the cases which we have discussed we have seen that the quantity of force which can be produced by a given measure of a physical process is always accurately defined, and that the further capacity for work of the natural forces is either diminished or exhausted by the work which has been performed. How is it now with *Heat* in this respect?

This question was of decisive importance in the endeavour to extend the law of the Conservation of Force to all natural processes. In the answer lay the chief difference between the older and newer views in these respects. Hence it is that many physicists designate that view of Nature corresponding to the law of the conservation of force with the name of *Mechanical Theory of Heat*.

The older view of the nature of heat was that it is a substance, very fine and imponderable indeed, but indestructible, and unchangeable in quantity, which is an essential fundamental property of all matter. And, in fact, in a large number of natural processes, the quantity of heat which can be demonstrated by the thermometer is unchangeable.

By conduction and radiation, it can indeed pass from hotter to colder bodies; but the quantity of heat which the former lose can be shown by the thermometer to have reappeared in the latter. Many processes, too, were known, especially in the passage of bodies from the solid to the liquid and gaseous states, in which heat disappeared —at any rate, as regards the thermometer. But when the gaseous body was restored to the liquid, and the liquid to the solid state, exactly the same quantity of heat reappeared which formerly seemed to have been lost. Heat was said *to have become latent*. On this view, liquid water differed from solid ice in containing a certain quantity of heat bound, which, just because it was bound, could not pass to the thermometer, and therefore was not indicated by it. Aqueous vapour contains a far greater quantity of heat thus bound.

But if the vapour be precipitated, and the liquid water restored to the state of ice, exactly the same amount of heat is liberated as had become latent in the melting of the ice and in the vaporisation of the water.

Finally, heat is sometimes produced and sometimes disappears in chemical processes. But even here it might be assumed that the various chemical elements and chemical compounds contain certain constant quantities of latent heat, which, when they change their composition, are sometimes liberated and sometimes must be supplied from external sources. Accurate experiments have shown that the quantity of heat which is developed by a chemical process—for instance, in burning a pound of pure carbon into carbonic acid—is perfectly constant, whether the combustion is slow or rapid, whether it takes place all at once or by intermediate stages. This also agreed very well with the assumption, which was the basis of the theory of heat, that heat is a substance entirely unchangeable in quantity. The natural processes which have here been briefly mentioned, were the subject of extensive experimental and mathematical investigations, especially of the great French physicists in the last decade of the former, and the first decade of the present, century; and a rich and accurately-worked chapter of physics had been developed, in which everything agreed excellently with the hypothesis—that heat is a substance. On the other hand, the invariability in the quantity of heat in all these processes could at that time be explained in no other manner than that heat is a substance.

But one relation of heat—namely, that to mechanical work—had not been accurately investigated. A French engineer, Sadi Carnot, son of the celebrated War Minister of the Revolution, had indeed endeavoured to deduce the work which heat performs, by assuming that the hypothetical caloric endeavoured to expand like a gas; and from this assumption he deduced in fact a remarkable law as to the capacity of heat for work, which even now, though with an essential alteration introduced by Clausius, is among the bases of the modern mechanical theory of heat, and the practical conclusions from which, so far as they could at that time be compared with experiments, have held good.

But it was already known that whenever two bodies in motion

rubbed against each other, heat was developed anew, and it could not be said whence it came.

The fact is universally recognised; the axle of a carriage which is badly greased and where the friction is great, becomes hot—so hot, indeed, that it may take fire; machine wheels with iron axles going at a great rate may become so hot that they weld to their sockets.

Fig. 99

A powerful degree of friction is not, indeed, necessary to disengage an appreciable degree of heat; thus, a lucifer match, which by rubbing is so heated that the phosphoric mass ignites, teaches this fact. Nay, it is enough to rub the dry hands together to feel the heat produced by friction, and which is far greater than the heating which takes place when the hands lie gently on each other. Uncivilised people use the friction of two pieces of wood to kindle a fire. With this view, a sharp spindle of hard wood is made to revolve rapidly on a base of soft wood in the manner represented in Fig. 99.

So long as it was only a question of the friction of solids, in which particles from the surface become detached and compressed, it might

be supposed that some changes in structure of the bodies rubbed might here liberate latent heat, which would thus appear as heat of friction.

But heat can also be produced by the friction of liquids, in which there could be no question of changes in structure, or of the liberation of latent heat. The first decisive experiment of this kind was made by Sir Humphry Davy in the commencement of the present century. In a cooled space he made two pieces of ice rub against each other, and thereby caused them to melt. The latent heat which the newly formed water must have here assimilated could not have been conducted to it by the cold ice, or have been produced by a change of structure; it could have come from no other cause than from friction, and must have been created by friction.

Heat can also be produced by the impact of imperfectly elastic bodies as well as by friction. This is the case, for instance, when we produce fire by striking flint against steel, or when an iron bar is worked for some time by powerful blows of the hammer.

If we inquire into the mechanical effects of friction and of inelastic impact, we find at once that these are the processes by which all terrestrial movements are brought to rest. A moving body whose motion was not retarded by any resisting force would continue to move to all eternity. The motions of the planets are an instance of this. This is apparently never the case with the motion of the terrestrial bodies, for they are always in contact with other bodies which are at rest, and rub against them. We can, indeed, very much diminish their friction, but never completely annul it. A wheel which turns about a well-worked axle, once set in motion, continues it for a long time; and the longer, the more truly and smoother the axle is made to turn, the better it is greased, and the less the pressure it has to support. Yet the *vis viva* of the motion which we have imparted to such a wheel when we started it, is gradually lost in consequence of friction. It disappears, and if we do not carefully consider the matter, it seems as if the *vis viva* which the wheel had possessed had been simply destroyed without any substitute.

A bullet which is rolled on a smooth horizontal surface continues to roll until its velocity is destroyed by friction on the path, caused by the very minute impacts on its little roughnesses.

A pendulum which has been put in vibration can continue to oscillate for hours if the suspension is good, without being driven by a weight; but by the friction against the surrounding air, and by that at its place of suspension, it ultimately comes to rest.

A stone which has fallen from a height has acquired a certain velocity on reaching the earth; this we know is the equivalent of a mechanical work; so long as this velocity continues as such, we can direct it upwards by means of suitable arrangements, and thus utilise it to raise the stone again. Ultimately the stone strikes against the earth and comes to rest; the impact has destroyed its velocity, and therewith apparently also the mechanical work which this velocity could have affected.

If we review the results of all these instances, which each of you could easily add to from your own daily experience, we shall see that friction and inelastic impact are processes in which mechanical work is destroyed, and heat produced in its place.

The experiments of Joule, which have been already mentioned, lead us a step further. He has measured in foot pounds the amount of work which is destroyed by the friction of solids and by the friction of liquids; and, on the other hand, he has determined the quantity of heat which is thereby produced, and has established a definite relation between the two. His experiments show that when heat is produced by the consumption of work, a definite quantity of work is required to produce that amount of heat which is known to physicists as the *unit of heat;* the heat, that is to say, which is necessary to raise one gramme of water through one degree centigrade. The quantity of work necessary for this is, according to Joule's best experiments, equal to the work which a gramme would perform in falling through a height of 425 metres.

In order to show how closely concordant are his numbers, I will adduce the results of a few series of experiments which he obtained after introducing the latest improvements in his methods.

1. A series of experiments in which water was heated by friction in a brass vessel. In the interior of this vessel a vertical axle provided with sixteen paddles was rotated, the eddies thus produced being broken by a series of projecting barriers, in which parts were cut out, large enough for the paddles to pass through. The value of the equivalent was 424.9 metres.

2. Two similar experiments, in which mercury in an iron vessel was substituted for water in a brass one, gave 425 and 426.3 metres.

3. Two series of experiments, in which a conical ring rubbed against another, both surrounded by mercury, gave 426.7 and 425.6 metres.

Exactly the same relations between heat and work were also found in the reverse process—that is, when work was produced by heat. In order to execute this process under physical conditions that could be controlled as perfectly as possible, permanent gases and not vapours were used, although the latter are, in practice, more convenient for producing large quantities of work, as in the case of the steam engine. A gas which is allowed to expand with moderate velocity becomes cooled. Joule was the first to show the reason of this cooling. For the gas has, in expanding, to overcome the resistance which the pressure of the atmosphere and the slowly yielding side of the vessel oppose to it: or, if it cannot of itself overcome this resistance, it supports the arm of the observer which does it. Gas thus performs work, and this work is produced at the cost of its heat. Hence the cooling. If, on the contrary, the gas is suddenly allowed to issue into a perfectly exhausted space where it finds no resistance, it does not become cool, as Joule has shown; or if individual parts of it become cool, others become warm; and, after the temperature has become equalised, this is exactly as much as before the sudden expansion of the gaseous mass.

How much heat the various gases disengage when they are compressed, and how much work is necessary for their compression; or, conversely, how much heat disappears when they expand under a pressure equal to their own counterpressure, was partly known from the older physical experiments, and has partly been determined by the recent experiments of Regnault by extremely perfect methods. Calculations with the best data of this kind give us the value of the thermal equivalent from experiments:—

With atmospheric air 426.0 metres
 " oxygen 425.7 "
 " nitrogen 431.3 "
 " hydrogen 425.3 "

Comparing these numbers with those which determine the equivalence of heat and mechanical work in friction, as close an agree-

ment is seen as can at all be expected from numbers which have been obtained by such varied investigations of different observers.

Thus then: a certain quantity of heat may be changed into a definite quantity of work; this quantity of work can also be retransformed into heat, and, indeed, into exactly the same quantity of heat as that from which it originated; in a mechanical point of view, they are exactly equivalent. Heat is a new form in which a quantity of work may appear.

These facts no longer permit us to regard heat as a substance, for its quantity is not unchangeable. It can be produced anew from the *vis viva* of motion destroyed; it can be destroyed, and then produces motion. We must rather conclude from this that heat itself is a motion, an internal invisible motion of the smallest elementary particles of bodies. If, therefore, motion seems lost in friction and impact, it is not actually lost, but only passes from the great visible masses to their smallest particles; while in steam engines the internal motion of the heated gaseous particles is transferred to the piston of the machine, accumulated in it, and combined in a resultant whole.

But what is the nature of this internal motion can only be asserted with any degree of probability in the case of gases. Their particles probably cross one another in rectilinear paths in all directions, until, striking another particle, or against the side of the vessel, they are reflected in another direction. A gas would thus be analogous to a swarm of gnats, consisting, however, of particles infinitely small and infinitely more closely packed. This hypothesis, which has been developed by Krönig, Clausius, and Maxwell, very well accounts for all the phenomena of gases.

What appeared to the earlier physicists to be the constant quantity of heat is nothing more than the whole motive power of the motion of heat, which remains constant so long as it is not transformed into other forms of work, or results afresh from them.

We turn now to another kind of natural forces which can produce work—I mean the chemical. We have to-day already come across them. They are the ultimate cause of the work which gunpowder and the steam engine produce; for the heat which is consumed in the latter, for example, originates in the combustion of carbon—that

is to say, in a chemical process. The burning of coal is the chemical union of carbon with the oxygen of the air, taking place under the influence of the chemical affinity of the two substances.

We may regard this force as an attractive force between the two, which, however, only acts through them with extraordinary power, if the smallest particles of the two substances are in closest proximity to each other. In combustion this force acts; the carbon and oxygen atoms strike against each other and adhere firmly, inasmuch as they form a new compound—carbonic acid—a gas known to all of you as that which ascends from all fermenting and fermented liquids— from beer and champagne. Now this attraction between the atoms of carbon and of oxygen performs work just as much as that which the earth in the form of gravity exerts upon a raised weight. When the weight falls to the ground, it produces an agitation, which is partly transmitted to the vicinity as sound waves, and partly remains as the motion of heat. The same result we must expect from chemical action. When carbon and oxygen atoms have rushed against each other, the newly-formed particles of carbonic acid must be in the most violent molecular motion—that is, in the motion of heat. And this is so. A pound of carbon burned with oxygen to form carbonic acid, gives as much heat as is necessary to raise 80.9 pounds of water from the freezing to the boiling point; and just as the same amount of work is produced when a weight falls, whether it falls slowly or fast, so also the same quantity of heat is produced by the combustion of carbon, whether this is slow or rapid, whether it takes place all at once, or by successive stages.

When the carbon is burned, we obtain in its stead, and in that of the oxygen, the gaseous product of combustion—carbonic acid. Immediately after combustion it is incandescent. When it has afterwards imparted heat to the vicinity, we have in the carbonic acid the entire quantity of carbon and the entire quantity of oxygen, and also the force of affinity quite as strong as before. But the action of the latter is now limited to holding the atoms of carbon and oxygen firmly united; they can no longer produce either heat or work any more than a fallen weight can do work if it has not been again raised by some extraneous force. When the carbon has been burnt we take no further trouble to retain the carbonic acid; it can do no more

service, we endeavour to get it out of the chimneys of our houses as fast as we can.

Is it possible, then, to tear asunder the particles of carbonic acid, and give to them once more the capacity of work which they had before they were combined, just as we can restore the potentiality of a weight by raising it from the ground? It is indeed possible. We shall afterwards see how it occurs in the life of plants; it can also be effected by inorganic processes, though in roundabout ways, the explanation of which would lead us too far from our present course.

This can, however, be easily and directly shown for another element, hydrogen, which can be burnt just like carbon. Hydrogen with carbon is a constituent of all combustible vegetable substances, among others, it is also an essential constituent of the gas which is used for lighting our streets and rooms; in the free state it is also a gas, the lightest of all, and burns when ignited with a feebly luminous blue flame. In this combustion—that is, in the chemical combination of hydrogen with oxygen, a very considerable quantity of heat is produced; for a given weight of hydrogen, four times as much heat as in the combustion of the same weight of carbon. The product of combustion is water, which, therefore, is not of itself further combustible, for the hydrogen in it is completely saturated with oxygen. The force of affinity, therefore, of hydrogen for oxygen, like that of carbon for oxygen, performs work in combustion, which appears in the form of heat. In the water which has been formed during combustion, the force of affinity is exerted between the elements as before, but its capacity for work is lost. Hence the two elements must be again separated, their atoms torn apart, if new effects are to be produced from them.

This we can do by the aid of currents of electricity. In the apparatus depicted in Fig. 100, we have two glass vessels filled with acidulated water a and a_1, which are separated in the middle by a porous plate moistened with water. In both sides are fitted platinum wires, k, which are attached to platinum plates, i and i_1. As soon as a galvanic current is transmitted through the water by the platinum wires, k, you see bubbles of gas ascend from the plates i and i_1. These bubbles are the two elements of water, hydrogen on the one hand, and oxygen on the other. The gases emerge through the tubes g and

g_1. If we wait until the upper part of the vessels and the tubes have been filled with it, we can inflame hydrogen at one side; it burns with a blue flame. If I bring a glimmering spill near the mouth of the other tube, it bursts into flame, just as happens with oxygen gas, in which the processes of combustion are far more intense than

FIG. 100

in atmospheric air, where the oxygen mixed with nitrogen is only one-fifth of the whole volume.

If I hold a glass flask filled with water over the hydrogen flame, the water, newly formed in combustion, condenses upon it.

If a platinum wire be held in the almost non-luminous flame, you see how intensely it is ignited; in a plentiful current of a mixture of the gases, hydrogen and oxygen, which have been liberated in the above experiment, the almost infusible platinum might even be melted. The hydrogen which has here been liberated from the water by the electrical current has regained the capacity of producing large quantities of heat by a fresh combination with oxygen; its affinity for oxygen has regained for it its capacity for work.

We here become acquainted with a new source of work, the electric current which decomposes water. This current is itself produced by a galvanic battery, FIG. 101. Each of the four vessels contains nitric acid, in which there is a hollow cylinder of very compact carbon. In the middle of the carbon cylinder is a cylindrical porous vessel of white clay, which contains dilute sulphuric acid; in this

dips a zinc cylinder. Each zinc cylinder is connected by a metal ring
with the carbon cylinder of the next vessel, the last zinc cylinder, *n,*
is connected with one platinum plate, and the first carbon cylinder, *p,*
with the other platinum plate of the apparatus for the decomposition
of water.

If now the conducting circuit of this galvanic apparatus is com-
pleted, and the decomposition of water begins, a chemical process

FIG. 101

takes place simultaneously in the cells of the voltaic battery. Zinc
takes oxygen from the surrounding water and undergoes a slow
combustion. The product of combustion thereby produced, oxide
of zinc, unites further with sulphuric acid, for which it has a power-
ful affinity, and sulphate of zinc, a saline kind of substance, dissolves
in the liquid. The oxygen, moreover, which is withdrawn from it
is taken by the water from the nitric acid surrounding the cylinder
of carbon, which is very rich in it, and readily gives it up. Thus, in
the galvanic battery, zinc burns to sulphate of zinc at the cost of the
oxygen of nitric acid.

Thus, while one product of combustion, water, is again separated,
a new combustion is taking place—that of zinc. While we there
reproduce chemical affinity which is capable of work, it is here lost.
The electrical current is, as it were, only the carrier which transfers

the chemical force of the zinc uniting with oxygen and acid to water in the decomposing cell, and uses it for overcoming the chemical force of hydrogen and oxygen.

FIG. 102

In this case, we can restore work which has been lost, but only by using another force, that of oxidising zinc.

Here we have overcome chemical forces by chemical forces, through the instrumentality of the electrical current. But we can

attain the same object by mechanical forces, if we produce the electrical current by a magneto-electrical machine, FIG. 102. If we turn the handle, the anker R R^1, on which is coiled copper-wire, rotates in front of the poles of the horseshoe magnet, and in these coils electrical currents are produced, which can be led from the points a and b. If the ends of these wires are connected with the apparatus for decomposing water, we obtain hydrogen and oxygen, though in far smaller quantity than by the aid of the battery which we used before. But this process is interesting, for the mechanical force of the arm which turns the wheel produces the work which is required for separating the combined chemical elements. Just as the steam engine changes chemical into mechanical force the magneto-electrical machine transforms mechanical force into chemical.

The application of electrical currents opens out a large number of relations between the various natural forces. We have decomposed water into its elements by such currents, and should be able to decompose a large number of other chemical compounds. On the other hand, in ordinary galvanic batteries electrical currents are produced by chemical forces.

In all conductors through which electrical currents pass they produce heat; I stretch a thin platinum wire between the ends n and p of the galvanic battery, FIG. 101; it becomes ignited and melts. On the other hand, electrical currents are produced by heat in what are called thermo-electric elements.

Iron which is brought near a spiral of copper wire, traversed by an electrical current, becomes magnetic, and then attracts other pieces of iron, or a suitably placed steel magnet. We thus obtain mechanical actions which meet with extended applications in the electrical telegraph, for instance. FIG. 103 represents a Morse's telegraph in one-third of the natural size. The essential part is a horseshoe shaped iron core, which stands in the copper spirals $b\ b$. Just over the top of this is a small steel magnet $c\ c$, which is attracted the moment an electrical current, arriving by the telegraph wire, traverses the spirals $b\ b$. The magnet $c\ c$ is rigidly fixed in the lever $d\ d$, at the other end of which is a style; this makes a mark on a paper band, drawn by a clock-work, as often and as long as $c\ c$ is attracted by the magnetic action of the electrical current. Conversely, by reversing the mag-

netism in the iron core of the spirals $b\ b,$ we should obtain in them an electrical current just as we have obtained such currents in the magneto-electrical machine, Fig. 102; in the spirals of that machine there is an iron core which, by being approached to the poles of the large horseshoe magnet, is sometimes magnetised in one and sometimes in the other direction.

I will not accumulate examples of such relations; in subsequent lectures we shall come across them. Let us review these examples

FIG. 103

once more, and recognise in them the law which is common to all.

A raised weight can produce work, but in doing so it must necessarily sink from its height, and, when it has fallen as deep as it can fall, its gravity remains as before, but it can no longer do work.

A stretched spring can do work, but in so doing it becomes loose. The velocity of a moving mass can do work, but in doing so it comes to rest. Heat can perform work; it is destroyed in the operation. Chemical forces can perform work, but they exhaust themselves in the effort.

Electrical currents can perform work, but to keep them up we must consume either chemical or mechanical forces, or heat.

We may express this generally. *It is a universal character of all known natural forces that their capacity for work is exhausted in the degree in which they actually perform work.*

We have seen, further, that when a weight fell without performing any work, it *either* acquired velocity or produced heat. We might also drive a magneto-electrical machine by a falling weight; it would then furnish electrical currents.

We have seen that chemical forces, when they come into play, produce either heat or electrical currents or mechanical work.

We have seen that heat may be changed into work; there are apparatus (thermo-electric batteries) in which electrical currents are produced by it. Heat can directly separate chemical compounds; thus, when we burn limestone, it separates carbonic acid from lime.

Thus, whenever the capacity for work of one natural force is destroyed, it is transformed into another kind of activity. Even within the circuit of inorganic natural forces, we can transform each of them into an active condition by the aid of any other natural force which is capable of work. The connections between the various natural forces which modern physics has revealed, are so extraordinarily numerous that several entirely different methods may be discovered for each of these problems.

I have stated how we are accustomed to measure mechanical work, and how the equivalent in work of heat may be found. The equivalent in work of chemical processes is again measured by the heat which they produce. By similar relations, the equivalent in work of the other natural forces may be expressed in terms of mechanical work.

If, now, a certain quantity of mechanical work is lost, there is obtained, as experiments made with the object of determining this point show, an equivalent quantity of heat, or, instead of this, of chemical force; and, conversely, when heat is lost, we gain an equivalent quantity of chemical or mechanical force; and, again, when chemical force disappears, an equivalent of heat or work; so that in all these interchanges between various inorganic natural forces working force may indeed disappear in one form, but then it reappears in exactly equivalent quantity in some other form; it is thus neither increased nor diminished, but always remains in exactly the same

quantity. We shall subsequently see that the same law holds good also for processes in organic nature, so far as the facts have been tested.

It follows thence *that the total quantity of all the forces* capable of work *in the whole universe remains eternal and unchanged throughout all their changes.* All change in nature amounts to this, that force can change its form and locality without its quantity being changed. The universe possesses, once for all, a store of force which is not altered by any change of phenomena, can neither be increased nor diminished, and which maintains any change which takes place on it.

You see how, starting from considerations based on the immediate practical interests of technical work, we have been led up to a universal natural law, which, as far as all previous experience extends, rules and embraces all natural processes; which is no longer restricted to the practical objects of human utility, but expresses a perfectly general and particularly characteristic property of all natural forces, and which, as regards generality, is to be placed by the side of the laws of the unalterability of mass, and the unalterability of the chemical elements.

At the same time, it also decides a great practical question which has been much discussed in the last two centuries, to the decision of which an infinity of experiments has been made and an infinity of apparatus constructed—that is, the question of the possibility of a perpetual motion. By this was understood a machine which was to work continuously without the aid of any external driving force. The solution of this problem promised enormous gains. Such a machine would have had all the advantages of steam without requiring the expenditure of fuel. Work is wealth. A machine which could produce work from nothing was as good as one which made gold. This problem had thus for a long time occupied the place of gold making, and had confused many a pondering brain. That a perpetual motion could not be produced by the aid of the then known mechanical forces could be demonstrated in the last century by the aid of the mathematical mechanics which had at that time been developed. But to show also that it is not possible even if heat, chemical forces, electricity, and magnetism were made to co-operate,

could not be done without a knowledge of our law in all its generality. The possibility of a perpetual motion was first finally negatived by the law of the conservation of force, and this law might also be expressed in the practical form that no perpetual motion is possible, that force cannot be produced from nothing; something must be consumed.

You will only be ultimately able to estimate the importance and the scope of our law when you have before your eyes a series of its applications to individual processes in nature.

What I have to-day mentioned as to the origin of the moving forces which are at our disposal, directs us to something beyond the narrow confines of our laboratories and our manufactories, to the great operations at work in the life of the earth and of the universe. The force of falling water can only flow down from the hills when rain and snow bring it to them. To furnish these, we must have aqueous vapour in the atmosphere, which can only be effected by the aid of heat, and this heat comes from the sun. The steam engine needs the fuel which the vegetable life yields, whether it be the still active life of the surrounding vegetation, or the extinct life which has produced the immense coal deposits in the depths of the earth. The forces of man and animals must be restored by nourishment; all nourishment comes ultimately from the vegetable kingdom, and leads us back to the same source.

You see then that when we inquire into the origin of the moving forces which we take into our service, we are thrown back upon the meteorological processes in the earth's atmosphere, on the life of plants in general, and on the sun.

ICE AND GLACIERS

A LECTURE DELIVERED AT FRANKFORT-ON-MAIN, AND AT HEIDELBERG, IN FEBRUARY, 1865

THE world of ice and of eternal snow, as unfolded to us on the summits of the neighbouring Alpine chain, so stern, so solitary, so dangerous, it may be, has yet its own peculiar charm. Not only does it enchain the attention of the natural philosopher, who finds in it the most wonderful disclosures as to the present and past history of the globe, but every summer it entices thousands of travellers of all conditions, who find there mental and bodily recreation. While some content themselves with admiring from afar the dazzling adornment which the pure, luminous masses of snowy peaks, interposed between the deeper blue of the sky and the succulent green of the meadows, lend to the landscape, others more boldly penetrate into the strange world, willingly subjecting themselves to the most extreme degrees of exertion and danger, if only they may fill themselves with the aspect of its sublimity.

I will not attempt what has so often been attempted in vain—to depict in words the beauty and magnificence of nature, whose aspect delights the Alpine traveller. I may well presume that it is known to most of you from your own observation; or, it is to be hoped, will be so. But I imagine that the delight and interest in the magnificence of those scenes will make you the more inclined to lend a willing ear to the remarkable results of modern investigations on the more prominent phenomena of the glacial world. There we see that minute peculiarities of ice, the mere mention of which might at other times be regarded as a scientific subtlety, are the causes of the most important changes in glaciers; shapeless masses of rock begin to relate their histories to the attentive observer, histories which often

stretch far beyond the past of the human race into the obscurity of the primeval world; a peaceful, uniform, and beneficent sway of enormous natural forces, where at first sight only desert wastes are seen, either extended indefinitely in cheerless, desolate solitudes, or full of wild, threatening confusion—an arena of destructive forces. And thus I think I may promise that the study of the connection of those phenomena of which I can now only give you a very short outline, will not only afford you some prosaic instruction, but will make your pleasure in the magnificent scenes of the high mountains more vivid, your interest deeper, and your admiration more exalted.

Let me first of all recall to your remembrance the chief features of the external appearance of the snow fields and of the glaciers; and let me mention the accurate measurements which have contributed to supplement observation, before I pass to discuss the casual connection of those processes.

The higher we ascend the mountains the colder it becomes. Our atmosphere is like a warm covering spread over the earth; it is well-nigh entirely transparent for the luminous darting rays of the sun, and allows them to pass almost without appreciable change. But it is not equally penetrable by obscure heat rays, which, proceeding from heated terrestrial bodies, struggle to diffuse themselves into space. These are absorbed by atmospheric air, especially when it is moist; the mass of air is itself heated thereby, and only radiates slowly into space the heat which has been gained. The expenditure of heat is thus retarded as compared with the supply, and a certain store of heat is retained along the whole surface of the earth. But on high mountains the protective coating of the atmosphere is far thinner—the radiated heat of the ground can escape thence more freely into space; there, accordingly, the accumulated store of heat and the temperature are far smaller than at lower levels.

To this must be added another property of air which acts in the same direction. In a mass of air which expands, part of its store of heat disappears; it becomes cooler, if it cannot acquire fresh heat from without. Conversely, by renewed compression of the air, the same quantity of heat is reproduced which had disappeared during expansion. Thus if, for instance, south winds drive the warm air of the Mediterranean towards the north, and compel it to ascend along

the great mountain wall of the Alps, where the air, in consequence of the diminished pressure, expands by about half its volume, it thereby becomes very greatly cooled—for a mean height of 11,000 feet, by from 18° to 30° C., according as it is moist or dry—and it thereby deposits the greater part of its moisture as rain or snow. If the same wind, passing over to the north side of the mountains as Föhn-wind, reaches the valleys and plains, it again becomes condensed, and is again heated. Thus the same current of air which is warm in the plains, both on this side of the chain and on the other, is bitterly cold on the heights, and can there deposit snow, while in the plain we find it insupportably hot.

The lower temperature at greater heights, which is due to both these causes, is, as we know, very marked on the lower mountain chains of our neighbourhood. In central Europe it amounts to about 1° C. for an ascent of 480 feet; in winter it is less—1° for about 720 feet of ascent. In the Alps the differences of temperature at great heights are accordingly far more considerable, so that upon the higher parts of their peaks and slopes the snow which has fallen in winter no longer melts in summer. This line, above which snow covers the ground throughout the entire year, is well known as the *snow line;* on the northern side of the Alps it is about 8,000 feet high, on the southern side about 8,800 feet. Above the snow line it may on sunny days be very warm; the unrestrained radiation of the sun, increased by the light reflected from the snow, often becomes utterly unbearable, so that the tourist of sedentary habits, apart from the dazzling of his eyes, which he must protect by dark spectacles or by a veil, usually gets severely sunburnt in the face and hands, the result of which is an inflammatory swelling of the skin and great blisters on the surface. More pleasant testimonies to the power of the sunshine are the vivid colours and the powerful odour of the small Alpine flowers which bloom in the sheltered rocky clefts among the snow fields. Notwithstanding the powerful radiation of the sun the temperature of the air above the snow fields only rises to 5°, or at most 8°; this, however, is sufficient to melt a tolerable amount of the superficial layers of snow. But the warm hours and days are too short to overpower the great masses of snow which have fallen during colder times. Hence the height of the snow line does

not depend merely on the temperature of the mountain slope, but also essentially on the amount of the yearly snowfall. It is lower, for instance, on the moist and warm south slope of the Himalayas than on the far colder but also far drier north slope of the same mountain. Corresponding to the moist climate of western Europe, the snowfall upon the Alps is very great, and hence the number and extent of their glaciers are comparatively considerable, so that few mountains of the earth can be compared with them in this respect. Such a development of the glacial world is, as far as we know, met with only on the Himalayas, favoured by the greater height; in Greenland and in Northern Norway, owing to the colder climate; in a few islands in Iceland; and in New Zealand, from the more abundant moisture.

Places above the snow line are thus characterised by the fact that the snow which in the course of the year falls on its surface does not quite melt away in summer, but remains to some extent. This snow, which one summer has left, is protected from the further action of the sun's heat by the fresh quantities that fall upon it during the next autumn, winter, and spring. Of this new snow also next summer leaves some remains, and thus year by year fresh layers of snow are accumulated one above the other. In those places where such an accumulation of snow ends in a steep precipice, and its inner structure is thereby exposed, the regularly stratified yearly layers are easily recognised.

But it is clear that this accumulation of layer upon layer cannot go on indefinitely, for otherwise the height of the snow peak would continually increase year by year. But the more the snow is accumulated the steeper are the slopes, and the greater the weight which presses upon the lower and older layers and tries to displace them. Ultimately a state must be reached in which the snow slopes are too steep to allow fresh snow to rest upon them, and in which the burden which presses the lower layers downwards is so great that these can no longer retain their position on the sides of the mountain. Thus, part of the snow which had originally fallen on the higher regions of the mountain above the snow line, and had there been protected from melting, is compelled to leave its original position and seek a new one, which it of course finds only below the

snow line on the lower slopes of the mountain, and especially in the valleys, where, however, being exposed to the influence of a warmer air, it ultimately melts and flows away as water. The descent of masses of snow from their original positions sometimes happens suddenly in *avalanches,* but it is usually very gradual in the form of *glaciers.*

Thus we must discriminate between two distinct parts of the ice fields; that is, first, the snow which originally fell—called *firn* in Switzerland—above the snow line, covering the slopes of the peaks as far as it can hang on to them, and filling up the upper wide kettle-shaped ends of the valleys forming widely extending fields of snow or *firnmeere.* Secondly, the glaciers, called in the Tyrol *firner,* which as prolongations of the snow fields often extend to a distance of from 4,000 to 5,000 feet below the snow line, and in which the loose snow of the snow fields is again found changed into transparent solid ice. Hence the name *glacier,* which is derived from the Latin, *glacies;* French, *glace, glacier.*

The outward appearance of glaciers is very characteristically described by comparing them, with Goethe, to currents of ice. They generally stretch from the snow fields along the depth of the valleys, filling them throughout their entire breadth, and often to a considerable height. They thus follow all the curvatures, windings, contractions, and enlargements of the valley. Two glaciers frequently meet the valleys of which unite. The two glacial currents then join in one common principal current, filling up the valley common to them both. In some places these ice currents present a tolerably level and coherent surface, but they are usually traversed by *crevasses,* and both over the surface and through the crevasses countless small and large water rills ripple, which carry off the water formed by the melting of the ice. United, and forming a stream, they burst, through a vaulted and clear blue gateway of ice, out at the lower end of the larger glacier.

On the surface of the ice there is a large quantity of blocks of stone, and of rocky *débris,* which at the lower end of the glacier are heaped up and form immense walls; these are called the *lateral* and *terminal moraine* of the glacier. Other heaps of rock, the *central moraine,* stretch along the surface of the glacier in the direction of its

length, forming long regular dark lines. These always start from the places where two glacier streams coincide and unite. The central moraines are in such places to be regarded as the continuations of the united lateral moraines of the two glaciers.

The formation of the central moraine is well represented in the view below given of the Unteraar Glacier (FIG. 104). In the background are seen the two glacier currents emerging from different

FIG. 104

valleys; on the right from the Shreckhorn, and on the left from the Finsteraarhorn. From the place where they unite the rocky wall occupying the middle of the picture descends, constituting the central moraine. On the left are seen individual large masses of rock resting on pillars of ice, which are known as glacier tables.

To exemplify these circumstances still further, I lay before you in FIG. 105 a map of the *Mer de Glace* of Chamouni, copied from that of Forbes.

The *Mer de Glace* in size is well known as the largest glacier in Switzerland, although in length it is exceeded by the Aletsch Glacier.

It is formed from the snow fields that cover the heights directly north of Mont Blanc, several of which, as the Grande Jorasse, the Aiguille Verte (a, Figs. 105 and 106), the Aiguille du Géant (b), Aiguille du Midi (c), and the Aiguille du Dru (d), are only 2,000 to 3,000 feet below that king of the European mountains. The snow fields which lie on the slopes and in the basins between these mountains collect in three principal currents, the Glacier du Géant, Glacier de Léchaud, and Glacier du Talèfre, which, ultimately united as represented in the map, form the Mer de Glace; this stretches as an ice current 2,600 to 3,000 feet in breadth down into the valley of Chamouni, where a powerful stream, the Arveyron, bursts from its lower end at k, and plunges into the Arve. The lowest precipice of the Mer de Glace, which is visible from the valley of Chamouni, and forms a large cascade of ice, is commonly called Glacier des Bois, from a small village which lies below.

Most of the visitors at Chamouni only set foot on the lowest part of the Mer de Glace from the inn at the Montanvert, and when they are free from giddiness cross the glacier at this place to the little house on the opposite side, the Chapeau (n). Although, as the map shows, only a comparatively very small portion of the glacier is thus seen and crossed, this way shows sufficiently the magnificent scenes, and also the difficulties of a glacier excursion. Bolder wanderers march upwards along the glacier to the Jardin, a rocky cliff clothed with some vegetation, which divides the glacial current of the Glacier du Talèfre into two branches; and bolder still they ascend yet higher, to the Col du Géant (11,000 feet above the sea), and down the Italian side to the valley of Aosta.

The surface of the Mer de Glace shows four of the rocky walls which we have designated as medial moraines. The first, nearest the side of the glacier, is formed where the two arms of the Glacier du Talèfre unite at the lower end of the Jardin; the second proceeds from the union of the glacier in question with the Glacier de Léchaud; the third, from the union of the last with the Glacier du Géant; and the fourth, finally, from the top of the rock ledge which stretches from the Aiguille du Géant towards the cascade (g) of the Glacier du Géant.

To give you an idea of the slope and the fall of the glacier, I have

given in Fig. 106 a longitudinal section of it according to the levels
and measurements taken by Forbes, with the view of the right bank
of the glacier. The letters stand for the same objects as in Fig. 105;
p is the Aiguille de Léchaud, q the Aiguille Noire, r the Mont Tacul,
f is the Col du Géant, the lowest point in the high wall of rock that
surrounds the upper end of the snow fields which feed the Mer de
Glace. The base line corresponds to a length of a little more than

Fig. 105

nine miles: on the right the heights above the sea are given in feet.
The drawing shows very distinctly how small in most places is the
fall of the glacier. Only an approximate estimate could be made of
the depth, for hitherto nothing certain has been made out in refer-
ence to it. But that it is very deep is obvious from the following
individual and accidental observations.

At the end of a vertical rock wall of the Tacul, the edge of the
Glacier du Géant is pushed forth, forming an ice wall 140 feet in
height. This would give the depth of one of the upper arms of the
glacier at the edge. In the middle and after the union of the three

glaciers the depth must be far greater. Somewhat below the junction Tyndall and Hirst sounded a moulin, that is, a cavity through which the surface glacier waters escape, to a depth of 160 feet; the guides alleged that they had sounded a similar aperture to a depth of 350 feet, and had found no bottom. From the usually deep trough-shaped or gorge-like form of the bottom of the valleys, which is constructed solely of rock walls, it seems improbable that for a breadth of 3,000 feet the mean depth should only be 350 feet; moreover, from the manner in which ice moves, there must necessarily be a very thick coherent mass beneath the crevassed part.

To render these magnitudes more intelligible by reference to more familiar objects, imagine the valley of Heidelberg filled with ice up

FIG. 106

to the Molkencur, or higher, so that the whole town, with all its steeples and the castle, is buried deeply beneath it; if, further, you imagine this mass of ice, gradually extending in height, continued from the mouth of the valley up to Neckargemünd, that would about correspond to the lower united ice current of the Mer de Glace. Or, instead of the Rhine and the Nahe at Bingen, suppose two ice currents united which fill the Rhine valley to its upper border as far as we can see from the river, and then the united currents stretching downwards to beyond Asmannshausen and Burg Rheinstein; such a current would also about correspond to the size of the Mer de Glace.

FIG. 107, which is a view of the magnificent Gorner Glacier seen from below, also gives an idea of the size of the masses of ice of the larger glaciers.

The surface of most glaciers is dirty, from the numerous pebbles and sand which lie upon it, and which are heaped together the more the ice under them and among them melts away. The ice of the

surface has been partially destroyed and rendered crumbly. In the depths of the crevasses ice is seen of a purity and clearness with which nothing that we are acquainted with on the plains can be compared. From its purity it shows a splendid blue, like that of the sky, only with a greenish hue. Crevasses in which pure ice is visible in the interior occur of all sizes; in the beginning they form slight cracks in which a knife can scarcely be inserted; becoming gradually enlarged to chasms, hundreds or even thousands, of feet

FIG. 107

in length, and twenty, fifty, and as much as a hundred feet in breadth, while some of them are immeasurably deep. Their vertical dark blue walls of crystal ice, glistening with moisture from the trickling water, form one of the most splendid spectacles which nature can present to us; but, at the same time, a spectacle strongly impregnated with the excitement of danger, and only enjoyable by the traveller who feels perfectly free from the slightest tendency to giddiness. The tourist must know how, with the aid of well-nailed shoes and a pointed Alpenstock, to stand even on slippery ice, and at the edge of a vertical precipice the foot of which is lost in the darkness of night, and at an unknown depth. Such crevasses cannot always be evaded in crossing the glacier; at the lower part of the Mer de Glace, for instance, where it is usually crossed by travellers, we are compelled to travel along some extent of precipitous banks of ice which

are occasionally only four to six feet in breadth, and on each side of which is such a blue abyss. Many a traveller, who has crept along the steep rocky slopes without fear, there feels his heart sink, and cannot turn his eyes from the yawning chasm, for he must first carefully select every step for his feet. And yet these blue chasms, which lie open and exposed in the daylight, are by no means the worst dangers of the glacier; though, indeed, we are so organised that a danger which we perceive, and which therefore we can safely avoid, frightens us far more than one which we know to exist, but which is veiled from our eyes. So also it is with glacier chasms. In the lower part of the glacier they yawn before us, threatening death and destruction, and lead us, timidly collecting all our presence of mind, to shrink from them; thus accidents seldom occur. On the upper part of the glacier, on the contrary, the surface is covered with snow; this, when it falls thickly, soon arches over the narrower crevasses of a breadth of from four to eight feet, and forms bridges which quite conceal the crevasse, so that the traveller only sees a beautiful plane snow surface before him. If the snow bridges are thick enough, they will support a man; but they are not always so, and these are the places where men, and even chamois, are so often lost. These dangers may readily be guarded against if two or three men are roped together at intervals of ten or twelve feet. If then one of them falls into a crevasse, the two others can hold him, and draw him out again.

In some places the crevasses may be entered, especially at the lower end of a glacier. In the well-known glaciers of Grindelwald, Rosenlaui, and other places, this is facilitated by cutting steps and arranging wooden planks. Then any one who does not fear the perpetually trickling water may explore these crevasses, and admire the wonderfully transparent and pure crystal walls of these caverns. The beautiful blue colour which they exhibit is the natural colour of perfectly pure water; liquid water as well as ice is blue, though to an extremely small extent, so that the colour is only visible in layers of from ten to twelve feet in thickness. The water of the Lake of Geneva and of the Lago di Garda exhibits the same splendid colour as ice.

The glaciers are not everywhere crevassed; in places where the ice

meets with an obstacle, and in the middle of great glacier currents
the motion of which is uniform, the surface is perfectly coherent.

FIG. 108 represents one of the more level parts of the Mer de Glace
at the Montanvert, the little house of which is seen in the back-

FIG. 108

ground. The Gries Glacier, where it forms the height of the pass
from the Upper Rhone valley to the Tosa valley, may even be crossed
on horseback. We find the greatest disturbance of the surface of the
glacier in those places where it passes from a slightly inclined part
of its bed to one where the slope is steeper. The ice is there torn in
all directions into a quantity of detached blocks, which by melting

are usually changed into wonderfully shaped sharp ridges and pyramids, and from time to time fall into the interjacent crevasses with a loud rumbling noise. Seen from a distance such a place appears like a wild frozen waterfall, and is therefore called a cascade; such a cascade is seen in the Glacier du Talèfre at l, another is seen in the

FIG. 109

Glacier du Géant at g, FIG. 110, while a third forms the lower end of the Mer de Glace. The latter, already mentioned as the Glacier des Bois, which rises directly from the trough of the valley at Chamouni to a height of 1,700 feet, the height of the Königstuhl at Heidelberg, affords at all times a chief object of admiration to the Chamouni tourist. FIG. 109 represents a view of its fantastically rent blocks of ice.

We have hitherto compared the glacier with a current as regards its outer form and appearance. This similarity, however, is not merely an external one: the ice of the glacier does, indeed, move forwards like the water of a stream, only more slowly. That this must be the case follows from the considerations by which I have endeavoured to explain the origin of a glacier. For as the ice is being constantly diminished at the lower end by melting, it would entirely disappear if fresh ice did not continually press forward from above, which, again, is made up by the snowfalls on the mountain tops.

But by careful ocular observation we may convince ourselves that the glacier does actually move. For the inhabitants of the valleys, who have the glaciers constantly before their eyes, often cross them, and in so doing make use of the larger blocks of stone as sign posts—detect this motion by the fact that their guide posts gradually descend in the course of each year. And as the yearly displacement of the lower half of the Mer de Glace at Chamouni amounts to no less than from 400 to 600 feet, you can readily conceive that such displacements must ultimately be observed, notwithstanding the slow rate at which they take place, and in spite of the chaotic confusion of crevasses and rocks which the glacier exhibits.

Besides rocks and stones, other objects which have accidentally alighted upon the glacier are dragged along. In 1788 the celebrated Genevese Saussure, together with his son and a company of guides and porters, spent sixteen days on the Col du Géant. On descending the rocks at the side of the cascade of the Glacier du Géant, they left behind them a wooden ladder. This was at the foot of the Aiguille Noire, where the fourth band of the Mer de Glace begins; this line thus marks at the same time the direction in which ice travels from this point. In the year 1832, that is, forty-four years after, fragments of this ladder were found by Forbes and other travellers not far below the junction of the three glaciers of the Mer de Glace, in the same line (at s, Fig. 110), from which it results that these parts of the glacier must on the average have each year descended 375 feet.

In the year 1827 Hugi had built a hut on the central moraine of the Unteraar Glacier for the purpose of making observations; the exact position of this hut was determined by himself and afterwards

by Agassiz, and they found that each year it had moved downwards. Fourteen years later, in the year 1841, it was 4,884 feet lower, so that every year it had on the average moved through 349 feet. Agassiz afterwards found that his own hut, which he had erected on the same glacier, had moved to a somewhat smaller extent. For these observations a long time was necessary. But if the motion of the glacier be observed by means of accurate measuring instruments,

FIG. 110

such as theodolites, it is not necessary to wait for years to observe that ice moves—a single day is sufficient.

Such observations have in recent times been made by several observers, especially by Forbes and by Tyndall. They show that in summer the middle of the Mer de Glace moves through twenty inches a day, while towards the lower terminal cascade the motion amounts to as much as thirty-five inches in a day. In winter the velocity is only about half as great. At the edges and in the lower layers of the glacier, as in a flow of water, it is considerably smaller than in the centre of the surface.

The upper sources of the Mer de Glace also have a slower motion, the Glacier du Géant thirteen inches a day, and the Glacier du Léchaud nine inches and a half. In different glaciers the velocity is in general very various, according to the size, the inclination, the amount of snowfall, and other circumstances.

Such an enormous mass of ice thus gradually and gently moves on, imperceptibly to the casual observer, about an inch an hour—the ice of the Col du Géant will take 120 years before it reaches the lower end of the Mer de Glace—but it moves forward with uncontrollable force, before which any obstacles that man could oppose to it yield like straws, and the traces of which are distinctly seen even on the granite walls of the valley. If, after a series of wet seasons, and an abundant fall of snow on the heights, the base of a glacier advances, not merely does it crush dwelling houses, and break the trunks of powerful trees, but the glacier pushes before it the boulder walls which form its terminal moraine without seeming to experience any resistance. A truly magnificent spectacle is this motion, so gentle and so continuous, and yet so powerful and so irresistible.

I will mention here that from the way in which the glacier moves we can easily infer in what places and in what directions crevasses will be formed. For as all layers of the glacier do not advance with equal velocity, some points remain behind others; for instance, the edges as compared with the middle. Thus if we observe the distance from a given point at the edge to a given point of the middle, both of which were originally in the same line, but the latter of which afterwards descended more rapidly, we shall find that this distance continually increases; and since the ice cannot expand to an extent corresponding to the increasing distance, it breaks up and forms crevasses, as seen along the edge of the glacier in Fig. 111, which represents the Gorner Glacier at Zermatt. It would lead me too far if I were here to attempt to give a detailed explanation of the formation of the more regular system of crevasses, as they occur in certain parts of all glaciers; it may be sufficient to mention that the conclusions deducible from the considerations above stated are fully borne out by observation.

I will only draw attention to one point—what extremely small displacements are sufficient to cause ice to form hundreds of crevasses.

The section of the Mer de Glace (FIG. 112, at g, c, h) shows places where a scarcely perceptible change in the inclination of the surface of the ice occurs of from two to four degrees. This is sufficient to produce a system of cross crevasses on the surface. Tyndall more especially has urged and confirmed by observation and measurements, that the mass of ice of the glacier does not give way in the

FIG. 111

smallest degree to extension, but when subjected to a pull is invariably torn asunder.

The distribution of the boulders, too, on the surface of the glacier is readily explained when we take their motion into account. These boulders are fragments of the mountains between which the glacier flows. Detached partly by the weathering of the stone, and partly by the freezing of water in its crevices, they fall, and for the most part on the edge of the mass of ice. There they either remain lying on the surface, or if they have originally burrowed in the snow, they ultimately reappear in consequence of the melting of the superficial layers of ice and snow, and they accumulate especially at the lower end of the glacier, where more of the ice between them has

been melted. The blocks which are gradually borne down to the lower end of the glacier are sometimes quite colossal in size. Solid rocky masses of this kind are met with in the lateral and terminal moraines, which are as large as a two-storied house.

The masses of stone move in lines which are always nearly parallel to each other and to the longitudinal direction of the glacier. Those, therefore, that are already in the middle remain in the middle, and those that lie on the edge remain at the edge. These latter are the more numerous, for during the entire course of the glacier fresh boulders are constantly falling on the edge, but cannot fall on the middle. Thus are formed on the edge of the mass of ice the lateral moraines, the boulders of which partly move along with the ice, partly glide over its surface, and partly rest on the solid rocky base

Fig. 112

near the ice. But when two glacier streams unite, their coinciding lateral moraines come to lie upon the centre of the united ice-stream, and then move forward as central moraines parallel to each other and to the banks of the stream, and they show, as far as the lower end, the boundary line of the ice which originally belonged to one or the other of the arms of the glacier. They are very remarkable as displaying in what regular parallel bands the adjacent parts of the ice-stream glide downwards. A glance at the map of the Mer de Glace, and its four central moraines, exhibits this very distinctly.

On the Glacier du Géant and its continuation in the Mer de Glace, the stones on the surface of the ice delineate, in alternately greyer and whiter bands, a kind of yearly rings which were first observed by Forbes. For since in the cascade at g, Fig. 112, more ice slides down in summer than in winter, the surface of the ice below the cascade forms a series of terraces as seen in the drawing, and as those slopes of the terraces which have a northern aspect melt less than

their upper plane surfaces, the former exhibit purer ice than the lat-
ter. This, according to Tyndall, is the probable origin of these dirt
bands. At first they run pretty much across the glacier, but as after-
wards their centre moves somewhat more rapidly than the ends, they
acquire farther down a curved shape, as represented in the map,
FIG. 110. By their curvature they thus show to the observer with
what varying velocity ice advances in the different parts of its course.

A very peculiar part is played by certain stones which are imbedded
in the lower surface of the mass of ice, and which have partly fallen
there through crevasses, and may partly have been detached from
the bottom of the valley. For these stones are gradually pushed with
the ice along the base of the valley, and at the same time are pressed
against this base by the enormous weight of the superincumbent ice.
Both the stones imbedded in the ice as well as the rocky base are
equally hard, but by their friction against each other they are ground
to powder with a power compared to which any human exertion of
force is infinitely small. The product of this friction is an extremely
fine powder, which, swept away by water, appears lower down in
the glacier brook, imparting to it a whitish or yellowish muddy
appearance.

The rocks of the trough of the valley, on the contrary, on which
the glacier exerts year by year its grinding power, are polished as if
in an enormous polishing machine. They remain as rounded,
smoothly polished masses, in which are occasional scratches pro-
duced by individual harder stones. Thus we see them appear at the
edge of existing glaciers, when after a series of dry and hot seasons
the glaciers have somewhat receded. But we find such polished rocks
as remains of gigantic ancient glaciers to a far greater extent in the
lower parts of many Alpine valleys. In the valley of the Aar more
especially, as far down as Meyringen, the rock-walls polished to a
considerable height are very characteristic. There also we find the
celebrated polished plates, over which the way passes, and which are
so smooth that furrows have had to be hewn into them and rails
erected to enable men and animals to traverse them in safety.

The former enormous extent of glaciers is recognised by ancient
moraine-dykes and by transported blocks of stone, as well as by these
polished rocks. The blocks of stone which have been carried away

by the glacier are distinguished from those which water has rolled
down, by their enormous magnitude, by the perfect retention of all
their edges which are not at all rounded off, and finally by their
being deposited on the glacier in exactly the same order in which the
rocks of which they formed part stand in the mountain ridge; while
the stones which currents of water carry along are completely mixed
together.

From these indications, geologists have been able to prove that
the glaciers of Chamouni, of Monte Rosa, of the St. Gotthard, and
the Bernese Alps, formerly penetrated through the valley of the
Arve, the Rhone, the Aar, and the Rhine to the more level part of
Switzerland and the Jura, where they have deposited their boulders
at a height of more than a thousand feet above the present level of
the lake of Neufchatel. Similar traces of ancient glaciers are found
upon the mountains of the British Islands, and upon the Scandi-
navian Peninsula.

The drift ice too of the Arctic Sea is glacier ice; it is pushed down
into the sea by the glaciers of Greenland, becomes detached from the
rest of the glacier, and floats away. In Switzerland we find a similar
formation of drift ice, though on a far smaller scale, in the little
Marjelen See, into which part of the ice of the great Aletsch Glacier
pushes down. Blocks of stone which lie in drift ice may make long
voyages over the sea. The vast number of blocks of granite which
are scattered on the North German plains, and whose granite belongs
to the Scandinavian mountains, has been transported by drift ice at
the time when the European glaciers had such an enormous extent.

I must unfortunately content myself with these few references to
the ancient history of glaciers, and revert now to the processes at
present at work in them.

From the facts which I have brought before you it results that the
ice of a glacier flows slowly like the current of a very viscous sub-
stance, such for instance as honey, tar, or thick magma of clay. The
mass of ice does not merely flow along the ground like a solid which
glides over a precipice, but it bends and twists in itself; and although
even while doing this it moves along the base of the valley, yet the
parts which are in contact with the bottom and the sides of the valley
are perceptibly retarded by the powerful friction; the middle of the

surface of the glacier, which is most distant both from the bottom and the sides, moving most rapidly. Rendu, a Savoyard priest, and the celebrated natural philosopher Forbes, were the first to suggest the similarity of a glacier with a current of a viscous substance.

Now you will perhaps inquire with astonishment how it is possible that ice, which is the most brittle and fragile of substances, can flow in the glacier like a viscous mass; and you may perhaps be disposed to regard this as one of the wildest and most improbable statements that have ever been made by philosophers. I will at once admit that philosophers themselves were not a little perplexed by these results of their investigations. But the facts were there, and could not be got rid of. How this mode of motion originated was for a long time quite enigmatical, the more so since the numerous crevasses in glaciers were a sufficient indication of the well-known brittleness of ice; and as Tyndall correctly remarked, this constituted an essential difference between a stream of ice and the flow of lava, of tar, of honey, or of a current of mud.

The solution of this strange problem was found, as is so often the case in the natural sciences, in apparently recondite investigations into the nature of heat, which form one of the most important conquests of modern physics, and which constitute what is known as the *mechanical theory of heat*. Among a great number of deductions as to the relations of the diverse natural forces to each other, the principles of the mechanical theory of heat lead to certain conclusions as to the dependence of the freezing point of water on the pressure to which ice and water are exposed.

Every one knows that we determine that one fixed point of our thermometer scale which we call the *freezing point* or *zero* by placing the thermometer in a mixture of pure water and ice. Water, at any rate when in contact with ice, cannot be cooled below zero without itself being converted into ice; ice cannot be heated above the freezing point without melting. Ice and water can exist in each other's presence at only one temperature, the temperature of zero.

Now, if we attempt to heat such a mixture by a flame beneath it, the ice melts, but the temperature of the mixture is never raised above that of 0° so long as some of the ice remains unmelted. The heat

imparted changes ice at zero into water at zero, but the thermometer indicates no increase of temperature. Hence physicists say that heat has become *latent,* and that water contains a certain quantity of latent heat beyond that of ice at the same temperature.

On the other hand, when we withdraw more heat from the mixture of ice and water, the water gradually freezes; but as long as there is still liquid water, the temperature remains at zero. Water at 0° has given up its latent heat, and has become changed into ice at 0°.

Now a glacier is a mass of ice which is everywhere interpenetrated by water, and its internal temperature is therefore everywhere that of the freezing point. The deeper layers, even of the fields of névé, appear on the heights which occur in our Alpine chain to have everywhere the same temperature. For, though the freshly fallen snow of these heights is, for the most part, at a lower temperature than that of 0°, the first hours of warm sunshine melt its surface and form water, which trickles into the deeper colder layers, and there freezes, until it has throughout been brought to the temperature of the freezing point. This temperature then remains unchanged. For, though by the sun's rays the surface of the ice may be melted, it cannot be raised above zero, and the cold of winter penetrates as little into the badly conducting masses of snow and ice as it does into our cellars. Thus the interior of the masses of névé, as well as of the glacier, remains permanently at the melting point.

But the temperature at which water freezes may be altered by strong pressure. This was first deduced from the mechanical theory of heat by James Thomson of Belfast, and almost simultaneously by Clausius of Zürich; and, indeed, the amount of this change may be correctly predicted from the same reasoning. For each increase of a pressure of one atmosphere the freezing point is lowered by the 1-115th part of a degree Centigrade. The brother of the former, Sir W. Thomson, the celebrated Glasgow physicist, made an experimental confirmation of this theoretical deduction by compressing in a suitable vessel a mixture of ice and snow. This mixture became colder and colder as the pressure was increased, and to the extent required by the mechanical theory.

Now, if a mixture of ice and water becomes colder when it is

subjected to increased pressure without the withdrawal of heat, this can only be effected by some free heat becoming latent; that is, some ice in the mixture must melt and be converted into water. In this is found the reason why mechanical pressure can influence the freezing point. You know that ice occupies more space than the water from which it is formed. When water freezes in closed vessels, it can burst not only glass vessels, but even iron shells. Inasmuch, therefore, as in the compressed mixture of ice and water some of the ice melts and is converted into water, the volume of the mass diminishes, and the mass can yield more to the pressure upon it than it could have done without such an alteration of the freezing point. Pressure furthers in this case, as is usual in the interaction of various natural forces, the occurrence of a change, that is fusion, which is favourable to the development of its own activity.

In Sir W. Thomson's experiments water and ice were confined in a closed vessel from which nothing could escape. The case is somewhat different when, as with glaciers, the water disseminated in the compressed ice can escape through fissures. The ice is then compressed, but not the water which escapes. The compressed ice becomes colder in conformity with the lowering of its freezing point by pressure; but the freezing point of water which is not compressed is not lowered. Thus under these circumstances we have ice colder than 0° in contact with water at 0°. The consequence is that around the compressed ice water continually freezes and forms new ice, while on the other hand part of the compressed ice melts.

This occurs, for instance, when only two pieces of ice are pressed against each other. By the water which freezes at their surfaces of contact they are firmly joined into one coherent piece of ice. With powerful pressure, and the chilling therefore great, this is quickly effected; but even with a feeble pressure it takes place, if sufficient time be given. Faraday, who discovered this property, called it the *regelation of ice;* the explanation of this phenomenon has been much controverted; I have detailed to you that which I consider most satisfactory.

This freezing together of two pieces of ice is very readily effected by pieces of any shape, which must not, however, be at a lower temperature than 0°, and the experiment succeeds best when the

pieces are already in the act of melting.[1] They need only be strongly pressed together for a few minutes to make them adhere. The more plane are the surfaces in contact, the more complete is their union. But a very slight pressure is sufficient if the two pieces are left in contact for some time.[2]

This property of melting ice is also utilised by boys in making snowballs and snowmen. It is well known that this only succeeds either when the snow is already melting, or at any rate is only so much lower than 0° that the warmth of the hand is sufficient to raise it to this temperature. Very cold snow is a dry loose powder which does not stick together.

The process which children carry out on a small scale in making snowballs takes place in glaciers on the very largest scale. The deeper layers of what was originally fine loose névé are compressed by the huge masses resting on them, often amounting to several hundred feet, and under this pressure they cohere with an ever firmer and closer structure. The freshly fallen snow originally consisted of delicate microscopically fine ice spicules, united and forming delicate six-rayed, feathery stars of extreme beauty. As often as the upper layers of the snow fields are exposed to the sun's rays, some of the snow melts; water permeates the mass, and on reaching the lower layers of still colder snow, it again freezes; thus it is that the firn first becomes granular and acquires the temperature of the freezing point. But as the weight of the superincumbent masses of snow continually increases by the firmer adherence of its individual granules, it ultimately changes into a dense and perfectly hard mass.

This transformation of snow into ice may be artificially effected by using a corresponding pressure.

We have here (Fig. 113) a cylindrical cast iron vessel, A A; the base, B B, is held by three screws, and can be detached, so as to remove the cylinder of ice which is formed. After the vessel has lain for a while in ice water, so as to reduce it to the temperature of 0°, it is packed full of snow, and then the cylindrical plug, C C, which fits the inner aperture, but moves in it with gentle friction, is forced

[1] In the Lecture a series of small cylinders of ice, which had been prepared by a method to be afterwards described, were pressed with their plane ends against each other, and thus a cylindrical bar of ice produced.

[2] Vide the additions at the end of this Lecture.

in with the aid of an hydraulic press. The press used was such that the pressure to which the snow was exposed could be increased to fifty atmospheres. Of course the looser snow contracts to a very small volume under such a powerful pressure. The pressure is removed, the cylindrical plug taken out, the hollow again filled up with snow, and the process repeated until the entire form is filled with the mass of ice, which no longer gives way to pressure. The compressed snow which I now take out, you will see, has been transformed into a hard, angular, and translucent cylinder of ice; and how hard it is appears from the crash which ensues when I throw it to the ground. Just as the loose snow in the glaciers is pressed together to solid ice, so also in many places ready-formed irregular pieces of ice are joined and form clear and compact ice. This is most remarkable at the base of the glacier cascades. These are glacier falls where the upper

FIG. 113

part of the glacier ends at a steep rocky wall, and blocks of ice shoot down as avalanches over the edge of this wall. The heap of shattered blocks of ice which accumulate become joined at the foot of the rock-wall to a compact, dense mass, which then continues its way downwards as glacier. More frequent than such cascades, where the glacier-stream is quite dissevered, are places where the base of the valley has a steeper slope, as, for instance, the places in the Mer de Glace (FIG. 105), at g, of the Cascade of the Glacier du Géant, and at i and h of the great terminal cascade of the Glacier des Bois. The ice splits there into thousands of banks and cliffs, which then recombine towards the bottom of the steeper slope and form a coherent mass.

This also we may imitate in our ice mould. Instead of the snow I take irregular pieces of ice, press them together; add new pieces of ice, press them again, and so on, until the mould is full. When the mass is taken out it forms a compact coherent cylinder of tolerably clear ice, which has a perfectly sharp edge, and is an accurate copy of the mould.

This experiment, which was first made by Tyndall, shows that a block of ice may be pressed into any mould just like a piece of wax. It might, perhaps, be thought that such a block had, by the pressure in the interior, been first reduced to powder so fine that it readily penetrated every crevice of the mould, and then that this powdered ice, like snow, was again combined by freezing. This suggests itself the more readily, since while the press is being worked a continual creaking and cracking is heard in the interior of the mould. Yet the mere aspect of the cylinders pressed from blocks of ice shows us that it has not been formed in this manner; for they are generally clearer than the ice which is produced from snow, and the individual larger pieces of ice which have been used to produce them are recognised, though they are somewhat changed and flattened. This is most beautiful when clear pieces of ice are laid in the form and the rest of the space stuffed full of snow. The cylinder is then seen to consist of alternate layers of clear and opaque ice, the former arising from the pieces of ice, and the latter from the snow; but here also the pieces of ice seem pressed into flat discs.

These observations teach, then, that ice need not be completely smashed to fit into the prescribed mould, but that it may give way without losing its coherence. This can be still more completely proved, and we can acquire a still better insight into the cause of the pliability of ice, if we press the ice between two plane wooden boards, instead of in the mould, into which we cannot see.

I place first an irregular cylindrical piece of natural ice, taken from the frozen surface of the river, with its two plane terminal surfaces between the plates of the press. If I begin to work, the block is broken by pressure; every crack which forms extends through the entire mass of the block; this splits into a heap of larger fragments, which again crack and are broken the more the press is worked. If the pressure is relaxed, all these fragments are, indeed, reunited by

freezing, but the aspect of the whole indicates that the shape of the block has resulted less from pliability than from fracture, and that the individual fragments have completely altered their mutual positions.

The case is quite different when one of the cylinders which we have formed from snow or ice is placed between the plates of the

FIG. 114 FIG. 115

press. As the press is worked the creaking and cracking is heard, but it does not break; it gradually changes its shape, becomes lower and at the same time thicker; and only when it has been changed into a tolerably flat circular disc does it begin to give way at the edges and form cracks, like crevasses on a small scale. FIG. 114 shows the height and diameter of such a cylinder in its original condition; FIG. 115 represents its appearance after the action of the press.

A still stronger proof of the pliability of ice is afforded when one of our cylinders is forced through a narrow aperture. With this view I place a base on the previously described mould, which has a conical perforation, the external aperture of which is only two thirds the diameter of the cylindrical aperture of the form. FIG. 116 gives a section of the whole. If now I insert into this one of the compressed cylinders of ice, and force down the plug a, the ice is forced through the narrow aperture in the base. It at first emerges as a solid cylinder of the same diameter as the aperture; but as the ice follows more rapidly in the centre than at the edges, the free terminal

surface of the cylinder becomes curved, the end thickens, so that it
could not be brought back through the aperture, and it ultimately

FIG. 116

splits off. FIG. 117 exhibits a series
of shapes which have resulted in this
manner.[3]

Here also the cracks in the emerg-
ing cylinder of ice exhibit a surpris-
ing similarity with the longitudinal
rifts which divide a glacier current
where it presses through a narrow
rocky pass into a wider valley.

In the cases which we have de-
scribed we see the change in shape of
the ice taking place before our eyes,
whereby the block of ice retains its

coherence without breaking into individual pieces. The brittle mass
of ice seems rather to yield like a piece of wax.

A closer inspection of a clear cylinder of ice compressed from clear
pieces of ice, while the pressure is being applied, shows us what takes
place in the interior; for we then see an innumerable quantity of
extremely fine radiating cracks shoot through it like a turbid cloud,
which mostly disappear, though not completely, the moment the

FIG. 117

pressure is suspended. Such a compressed block is distinctly more
opaque immediately after the experiment than it was before; and
the turbidity arises, as may easily be observed by means of a lens,
from a great number of whitish capillary lines crossing the interior

[3] In this experiment the lower temperature of the compressed ice sometimes
extended so far through the iron form, that the water in the slit between the base
plate and the cylinder froze and formed a thin sheet of ice, although the pieces of
ice as well as the iron mould had previously laid in ice water, and could not be
colder than 0°.

of the mass of what is otherwise clear. These lines are the optical expression of extremely fine cracks[4] which interpenetrate the mass of the ice. Hence we may conclude that the compressed block is traversed by a great number of fine cracks and fissures which render it pliable; that its particles become a little dispersed, and are therefore withdrawn from pressure, and that immediately afterwards the greater part of the fissures disappear, owing to their sides freezing. Only in those places in which the surfaces of the small displaced particles do not accurately fit to each other some fissured spaces remain open, and are discovered as white lines and surfaces by the reflection of the light.

These cracks and laminæ also become more perceptible when the ice—which, as I before mentioned, is below zero immediately after pressure has been applied—is again raised to this temperature and begins to melt. The crevices then fill with water, and such ice then consists of a quantity of minute granules from the size of a pin's head to that of a pea, which are closely pushed into one another at the edges and projections, and in part have coalesced, while the narrow fissures between them are full of water. A block of ice thus formed of ice granules adheres firmly together; but if particles be detached from its corners they are seen to consist of these angular granules. Glacier ice, when it begins to melt, is seen to possess the same structure, except that the pieces of which it consists are mostly larger than in artificial ice, attaining the size of a pigeon's egg.

Glacier ice and compressed ice are thus seen to be substances of a granular structure, in opposition to regularly crystallised ice, such as is formed on the surface of still water. We here meet with the same differences as between calcareous spar and marble, both of which consist of carbonate of lime; but while the former is in large, regular crystals, the latter is made up of irregularly agglomerated crystalline grains. In calcareous spar, as well as in crystallised ice, the cracks

[4] These cracks are probably quite empty and free from air, for they are also formed when perfectly clear and air-free pieces of ice are pressed in the form which has been previously filled with water, and where, therefore, no air could gain access to the pieces of ice. That such air-free crevices occur in glacier ice has been already demonstrated by Tyndall. When the compressed ice afterwards melts, these crevices fill up with water, no air being left. They are then, however, far less visible, and the whole block is therefore clearer. And just for this reason they could not originally have been filled with water.

produced by inserting the point of a knife extend through the mass, while in granular ice a crack which arises in one of the bodies where it must yield does not necessarily spread beyond the limits of the granule.

Ice which has been compressed from snow, and has thus from the outset consisted of innumerable very fine crystalline needles, is seen to be particularly plastic. Yet in appearance it materially differs from glacier ice, for it is very opaque, owing to the great quantity of air which was originally inclosed in the flaky mass of snow, and which remains there as extremely minute bubbles. It can be made clearer by pressing a cylinder of such ice between wooden boards; the air bubbles appear then on the top of the cylinder as a light foam. If the discs are again broken, placed in the mould, and pressed into a cylinder, the air may gradually be more and more eliminated, and the ice be made clearer. No doubt in glaciers the originally whitish mass of névé is thus gradually transformed into the clear, transparent ice of the glacier.

Lastly, when streaked cylinders of ice formed from pieces of snow and ice are pressed into discs, they become finely streaked, for both their clear and their opaque layers are uniformly extended.

Ice thus striated occurs in numerous glaciers, and is no doubt caused, as Tyndall maintains, by snow falling between the blocks of ice; this mixture of snow and clear ice is again compressed in the subsequent path of the glacier, and gradually stretched by the motion of the mass: a process quite analogous to the artificial one which we have demonstrated.

Thus to the eye of the natural philosopher the glacier, with its wildly heaped ice blocks, its desolate, stony, and muddy surface, and its threatening crevasses, has become a majestic stream whose peaceful and regular flow has no parallel; which according to fixed and definite laws, narrows, expands, is heaped up, or, broken and shattered, falls down precipitous heights. If we trace it beyond its termination we see its waters, uniting to a copious brook, burst through its icy gate and flow away. Such a brook, on emerging from the glacier, seems dirty and turbid enough, for it carries away as powder the stone which the glacier has ground. We are disenchanted at seeing the wondrously beautiful and transparent ice converted

into such muddy water. But the water of the glacier streams is as pure and beautiful as the ice, though its beauty is for the moment concealed and invisible. We must search for these waters after they have passed through a lake in which they have deposited this powdered stone. The Lakes of Geneva, of Thun, of Lucerne, of Constance, the Lago Maggiore, the Lake of Como, and the Lago di Garda are chiefly fed with glacier waters; their clearness and their wonderfully beautiful blue or blue-green colour are the delight of all travellers.

Yet, leaving aside the beauty of these waters, and considering only their utility, we shall have still more reason for admiration. The unsightly mud which the glacier streams wash away forms a highly fertile soil in the places where it is deposited; for its state of mechanical division is extremely fine, and it is moreover an utterly unexhausted virgin soil, rich in the mineral food of plants. The fruitful layers of fine loam which extend along the whole Rhine plain as far as Belgium, and are known as Loess, are nothing more than the dust of ancient glaciers.

Then, again, the irrigation of a district, which is effected by the snow fields and glaciers of the mountains, is distinguished from that of other places by its comparatively greater abundancy, for the moist air which is driven over the cold mountain peaks deposits there most of the water it contains in the form of snow. In the second place, the snow melts most rapidly in summer, and thus the springs which flow from the snow fields are most abundant in that season of the year in which they are most needed.

Thus we ultimately get to know the wild, dead ice wastes from another point of view. From them trickles in thousands of rills, springs, and brooks the fructifying moisture which enables the industrious dwellers of the Alps to procure succulent vegetation and abundance of nourishment from the wild mountain slopes. On the comparatively small surface of the Alpine chain they produce the mighty streams the Rhine, the Rhone, the Po, the Adige, the Inn, which for hundreds of miles form broad, rich river valleys, extending through Europe to the German Ocean, the Mediterranean, the Adriatic, and the Black Sea. Let us call to mind how magnificently Goethe, in "Mahomet's Song," has depicted the course of the rocky

spring, from its origin beyond the clouds to its union with Father Ocean. It would be presumptuous after him to give such a picture in other than his own words:—

> And along, in triumph rolling,
> Names he gives to regions; cities
> Grow amain beneath his feet.
>
> On and ever on he rushes;
> Spire and turret fiery crested
> Marble palaces, the creatures
> Of his wealth, he leaves behind.
>
> Pine-built houses bears the Atlas
> On his giant shoulders. O'er his
> Head a thousand pennons rustle,
> Floating far upon the breezes,
> Tokens of his majesty.
>
> And so beareth he his brothers,
> And his treasures, and his children,
> To their primal sire expectant,
> All his bosom throbbing, heaving,
> With a wild tumultuous joy.

THEODORE MARTIN's Translation.

ADDITIONS

The theory of the regulation of ice has led to scientific discussions between Faraday and Tyndall on the one hand, and James and Sir W. Thomson on the other. In the text I have adopted the theory of the latter, and must now accordingly defend it.

Faraday's experiments show that a very slight pressure, not more than that produced by the capillarity of the layer of water between two pieces of ice, is sufficient to freeze them together. James Thomson observed that in Faraday's experiments pressure which could freeze them together was not utterly wanting. I have satisfied myself by my own experiments that only very slight pressure is necessary. It must, however, be remembered that the smaller the pressure the longer will be the time required to freeze the two pieces, and that then the junction will be very narrow and very fragile. Both these points are readily explicable on Thomson's theory. For under a feeble pressure the difference in temperature between ice and water will be very small, and the latent heat will only be slowly abstracted from the layers of water in contact with the pressed parts of the ice, so that a long time is necessary before they freeze. We must further take into account that we cannot in general consider that the two surfaces are quite in contact; under a feeble pressure which does not appreciably alter their shape, they will only touch in what are practically three points. A feeble total pressure on the pieces of ice concentrated on such narrow surfaces will always produce a tolerably great local pressure under the influence of which some ice will melt, and the water thus formed will freeze. But the bridge which joins them will never be otherwise than narrow.

Under stronger pressure, which may more completely alter the shape of the pieces of ice, and fit them against each other, and which will melt more of the surfaces that are first in contact, there will be a greater difference between the temperature of the ice and water, and the bridges will be more rapidly formed, and be of greater extent.

In order to show the slow action of the small differences of temperature which here come into play, I made the following experiments.

A glass flask with a drawn-out neck was half filled with water, which was boiled until all the air in the flask was driven out. The neck of the flask was then hermetically sealed. When cooled, the flask was void of air, and the water within it freed from the pressure of the atmosphere. As the water thus prepared can be cooled considerably below $0°$ C. before the first ice is formed, while when ice is in the flask it freezes at $0°$ C., the flask was in the first instance placed in a freezing mixture until the water was changed into ice. It was afterwards permitted to melt slowly in a place the temperature of which was $+2°$ C., until the half of it was liquefied.

The flask thus half filled with water, having a disc of ice swimming upon it, was placed in a mixture of ice and water, being quite surrounded by the mixture. After an hour, the disc within the flask was frozen to the glass. By shaking the flask the disc was liberated, but it froze again. This occurred as often as the shaking was repeated.

The flask was permitted to remain for eight days in the mixture, which was kept throughout at a temperature of $0°$ C. During this time a number of very regular and sharply defined ice crystals were formed, and augmented very slowly in size. This is perhaps the best method of obtaining beautifully formed crystals of ice.

While, therefore, the outer ice which had to support the pressure of the atmosphere slowly melted, the water within the flask, whose freezing point, on account of a defect of pressure, was $0.0075°$ C. higher, deposited crystals of ice. The heat abstracted from the water in this operation had, moreover, to pass through the glass of the flask, which, together with the small difference of temperature, explains the slowness of the freezing process.

Now as the pressure of one atmosphere on a square millimetre amounts to about ten grammes, a piece of ice weighing ten grammes, which lies upon another and touches it in three places, the total surface of which is a square millimetre, will produce on these surfaces a pressure of an atmosphere. Ice will therefore be formed more rapidly in the surrounding water than it was in the flask, where the

side of the glass was interposed between the ice and the water. Even with a much smaller weight the same result will follow in the course of an hour. The broader the bridges become, owing to the freshly formed ice, the greater will be the surfaces over which the pressure exerted by the upper piece of ice is distributed, and the feebler it will become; so that with such feeble pressure the bridges can only slowly increase, and therefore they will be readily broken when we try to separate the pieces.

It cannot, moreover, be doubted that in Faraday's experiments, in which two perforated discs of ice were placed in contact on a horizontal glass rod, so that gravity exerted no pressure, capillary attraction is sufficient to produce a pressure of some grammes between the plates, and the preceding discussions show that such a pressure, if adequate time be given, can form bridges between the plates.

If, on the other hand, two of the above-described cylinders of ice are powerfully pressed together by the hands, they adhere in a few minutes so firmly that they can only be detached by the exertion of a considerable force, for which indeed that of the hands is sometimes inadequate.

In my experiments I found that the force and rapidity with which the pieces of ice united were so entirely proportional to the pressure that I cannot but assign this as the actual and sufficient cause of their union.

In Faraday's explanation, according to which regelation is due to a contact action of ice and water, I find a theoretical difficulty. By the water freezing, a considerable quantity of latent heat must be set free, and it is not clear what becomes of this.

Finally, if ice in its change into water passes through an intermediate viscous condition, a mixture of ice and water which was kept for days at a temperature of 0° must ultimately assume this condition in its entire mass, provided its temperature was uniform throughout; this however is never the case.

As regards what is called the plasticity of ice, James Thomson has given an explanation of it in which the formation of cracks in the interior is not presupposed. No doubt when a mass of ice in different parts of the interior is exposed to different pressures, a portion of the more powerfully compressed ice will melt; and the latent

heat necessary for this will be supplied by the ice which is less strongly compressed, and by the water in contact with it. Thus ice would melt at the compressed places, and water would freeze in those which are not pressed: ice would thus be gradually transformed and yield to pressure. It is also clear that, owing to the very small conductivity for heat which ice possesses, a process of this kind must be extremely slow, if the compressed and colder layers of ice, as in glaciers, are at considerable distances from the less compressed ones, and from the water which furnishes the heat for melting.

To test this hypothesis, I placed in a cylindrical vessel, between two discs of ice of three inches in diameter, a smaller cylindrical piece of an inch in diameter. On the uppermost disc I placed a wooden disc, and this I loaded with a weight of twenty pounds. The section of the narrow piece was thus exposed to a pressure of more than an atmosphere. The whole vessel was packed between pieces of ice, and left for five days in a room the temperature of which was a few degrees above the freezing point. Under these circumstances the ice in the vessel, which was exposed to the pressure of the weight, should melt, and it might be expected that the narrow cylinder on which the pressure was most powerful should have been most melted. Some water was indeed formed in the vessel, but mostly at the expense of the larger discs at the top and bottom, which being nearest the outside mixture of ice and water, could acquire heat through the sides of the vessel. A small welt, too, of ice, was formed round the surface of contact of the narrower with the lower broad piece, which showed that the water, which had been formed in consequence of the pressure, had again frozen in places in which the pressure ceased. Yet under these circumstances there was no appreciable alteration in the shape of the middle piece which was most compressed.

This experiment shows that although changes in the shape of the pieces of ice must take place in the course of time in accordance with J. Thomson's explanation, by which the more strongly compressed parts melt, and new ice is formed at the places which are freed from pressure, these changes must be extremely slow when the thickness of the pieces of ice through which the heat is conducted is at all considerable. Any marked change in shape by melting in a medium the

temperature of which is everywhere 0°, could not occur without access of external heat, or from the uncompressed ice and water; and with the small differences in temperature which here come into play, and from the badly conducting power of ice, it must be extremely slow.

That on the other hand, especially in granular ice, the formation of cracks, and the displacement of the surfaces of those cracks, render such a change of form possible, is shown by the above-described experiments on pressure; and that in glacier ice changes of form thus occur, follows from the banded structure, and the granular aggregation which is manifest on melting, and also from the manner in which the layers change their position when moved, and so forth. Hence, I doubt not that Tyndall has discovered the essential and principal cause of the motion of glaciers, in referring it to the formation of cracks and to regelation.

I would at the same time observe that a quantity of heat, which is far from inconsiderable, must be produced by friction in the larger glaciers. It may be easily shown by calculation that when a mass of firn moves from the Col du Géant to the source of the Arveyron, the heat due to the mechanical work would be sufficient to melt a fourteenth part of the mass. And as the friction must be greatest in those places that are most compressed, it will at any rate be sufficient to remove just those parts of the ice which offer most resistance to motion.

I will add, in conclusion, that the above-described granular structure of ice is beautifully shown in polarised light. If a small clear piece is pressed in the iron mould, so as to form a disc of about five inches in thickness, this is sufficiently transparent for investigation. Viewed in the polarising apparatus, a great number of variously coloured small bands and rings are seen in the interior; and by the arrangement of their colours it is easy to recognise the limits of the ice granules, which, heaped on one another in irregular order of their optical axes, constitute the plate. The appearance is essentially the same when the plate has just been taken out of the press, and the cracks appear in it as whitish lines, as afterwards when these crevices have been filled up in consequence of the ice beginning to melt.

In order to explain the continued coherence of the piece of ice during its change of form, it is to be observed that in general the cracks in the granular ice are only superficial, and do not extend throughout its entire mass. This is directly seen during the pressing of the ice. The crevices form and extend in different directions, like cracks produced by a heated wire in a glass tube. Ice possesses a certain degree of elasticity, as may be seen in a thin flexible plate. A fissured block of ice of this kind will be able to undergo a displacement at the two sides which form the crack, even when these continue to adhere in the unfissured part of the block. If then part of the fissure at first formed is closed by regelation, the fissure can extend in the opposite direction without the continuity of the block being at any time disturbed. It seems to me doubtful, too, whether in compressed ice and in glacier ice, which apparently consists of interlaced polyhedral granules, these granules, before any attempt is made to separate them, are completely detached from each other, and are not rather connected by ice bridges which readily give way; and whether these latter do not produce the comparatively firm coherence of the apparent heap of granules.

The properties of ice here described are interesting from a physical point of view, for they enable us to follow so closely the transition from a crystalline body to a granular one; and they give the causes of the alteration of its properties better than in any other well-known example. Most natural substances show no regular crystalline structure; our theoretical ideas refer almost exclusively to crystallised and perfectly elastic bodies. It is precisely in this relationship that the transition from fragile and elastic crystalline ice into plastic granular ice is so very instructive.

THE WAVE THEORY OF LIGHT

THE TIDES

BY

SIR WILLIAM THOMSON

(LORD KELVIN)

INTRODUCTORY NOTE

WILLIAM THOMSON, Baron Kelvin of Largs, was born in Belfast, Ireland, June 24, 1824. He was the son of the professor of mathematics at Glasgow University, and himself entered that institution at the age of eleven. By the time he was twenty-one he graduated from Cambridge as Second Wrangler, and, after studying in Paris, he returned to Scotland to become, as professor of natural philosophy, the colleague of his father and elder brother. The story of his life thenceforth is the record of amazingly brilliant and fruitful scientific work, recognized by the award of almost all the honors appropriate to such service, from learned societies, universities, and governments at home and abroad. His part in laying the Atlantic Cable was the occasion of his receiving knighthood, and in 1892 he was raised to the peerage. He held his professorship at Glasgow for fifty-three years, and later was chosen its Chancellor. He died on December 17, 1907, and was buried in Westminster Abbey.

Lord Kelvin's activities were remarkable for both profundity and range. A large number of his results are to be appreciated only by the highly skilled mathematician and physicist; but his speculations on the ultimate constitution of matter; his statement of the principle of the dissipation of energy, with its bearing upon the age of life on the earth; his calculations as to the age of the earth itself, and much more, are of great general interest. His fertility in practical invention was no less notable. He contrived a large number of instruments; his services to navigation and ocean telegraphy being especially valuable. Long before his death he was recognized as the most distinguished man of science of his time and country, and he was also the most loved.

The lectures which follow are favorable examples of his power of exposition in subjects in which he had no superior.

THE WAVE THEORY OF
LIGHT

[A LECTURE DELIVERED AT THE ACADEMY OF MUSIC,
PHILADELPHIA, UNDER THE AUSPICES OF
THE FRANKLIN INSTITUTE,
SEPTEMBER 29th, 1884.]

THE subject upon which I am to speak to you this evening is happily for me not new in Philadelphia. The beautiful lectures on light which were given several years ago by President Morton, of the Stevens' Institute, and the succession of lectures on the same subject so admirably illustrated by Professor Tyndall, which many now present have heard, have fully prepared you for anything I can tell you this evening in respect to the wave theory of light.

It is indeed my humble part to bring before you only some mathematical and dynamical details of this great theory. I cannot have the pleasure of illustrating them to you by anything comparable with the splendid and instructive experiments which many of you have already seen. It is satisfactory to me to know that so many of you, now present, are so thoroughly prepared to understand anything I can say, that those who have seen the experiments will not feel their absence at this time. At the same time I wish to make them intelligible to those who have not had the advantages to be gained by a systematic course of lectures. I must say, in the first place, without further preface, as time is short and the subject is long, simply that sound and light are both due to vibrations propagated in the manner of waves; and I shall endeavour in the first place to define the manner of propagation and the mode of motion that constitute those two subjects of our senses, the sense of sound and the sense of light.

Each is due to vibrations, but the vibrations of light differ widely from the vibrations of sound. Something that I can tell you more easily than anything in the way of dynamics or mathematics respecting the two classes of vibrations is, that there is a great difference in the frequency of the vibrations of light when compared with the frequency of the vibrations of sound. The term "frequency" applied to vibrations is a convenient term, applied by Lord Rayleigh in his book on sound to a definite number of full vibrations of a vibrating body per unit of time. Consider, then, in respect to sound, the frequency of the vibrations of notes, which you all know in music represented by letters, and by the syllables for singing, the do, re, mi, &c. The notes of the modern scale correspond to different frequencies of vibrations. A certain note and the octave above it, correspond to a certain number of vibrations per second, and double that number.

I may conveniently explain in the first place the note called 'C'; I mean the middle 'C'; I believe it is the C of the tenor voice, that most nearly approaches the tones used in speaking. That note corresponds to two hundred and fifty-six full vibrations per second—two hundred and fifty-six times to and fro per second of time.

Think of one vibration per second of time. The seconds pendulum of the clock performs one vibration in two seconds, or a half vibration in one direction per second. Take a ten-inch pendulum of a drawing-room clock, which vibrates twice as fast as the pendulum of an ordinary eight-day clock, and it gives a vibration of one per second, a full period of one per second to and fro. Now think of three vibrations per second. I can move my hand three times per second easily, and by a violent effort I can move it to and fro five times per second. With four times as great force, if I could apply it, I could move it twice five times per second.

Let us think, then, of an exceedingly muscular arm that would cause it to vibrate ten times per second, that is, ten times to the left and ten times to the right. Think of twice ten times, that is, twenty times per second, which would require four times as much force; three times ten, or thirty times a second, would require nine times as much force. If a person were nine times as strong as the most muscular arm can be, he could vibrate his hand to and fro thirty

times per second, and without any other musical instrument could make a musical note by the movement of his hand which would correspond to one of the pedal notes of an organ.

If you want to know the length of a pedal pipe, you can calculate it in this way. There are some numbers you must remember, and one of them is this. You, in this country, are subjected to the British insularity in weights and measures; you use the foot and inch and yard. I am obliged to use that system, but I apologise to you for doing so, because it is so inconvenient, and I hope all Americans will do everything in their power to introduce the French metrical system. I hope the evil action performed by an English minister whose name I need not mention, because I do not wish to throw obloquy on any one, may be remedied. He abrogated a useful rule, which for a short time was followed, and which I hope will soon be again enjoined, that the French metrical system be taught in all our national schools. I do not know how it is in America. The school system seems to be very admirable, and I hope the teaching of the metrical system will not be let slip in the American schools any more than the use of the globes. I say this seriously: I do not think any one knows how seriously I speak of it. I look upon our English system as a wickedly brain-destroying piece of bondage under which we suffer. The reason why we continue to use it is the imaginary difficulty of making a change, and nothing else; but I do not think in America that any such difficulty should stand in the way of adopting so splendidly useful a reform.

I know the velocity of sound in feet per second. If I remember rightly, it is 1,089 feet per second in dry air at the freezing temperature, and 1,115 feet per second in air of what we would call moderate temperature, 59 or 60 degrees—(I do not know whether that temperature is ever attained in Philadelphia or not; I have had no experience of it, but people tell me it is sometimes 59 or 60 degrees in Philadelphia, and I believe them)—in round numbers let us call the speed 1,000 feet per second. Sometimes we call it a thousand musical feet per second, it saves trouble in calculating the length of organ pipes; the time of vibration in an organ pipe is the time it takes a vibration to run from one end to the other and back. In an organ pipe 500 feet long the period would be one per second; in an

organ pipe ten feet long the period would be 50 per second; in an organ pipe twenty feet long the period would be 25 per second at the same rate. Thus 25 per second, and 50 per second of frequencies correspond to the periods of organ pipes of 20 feet and 10 feet.

The period of vibration of an organ pipe, open at both ends, is approximately the time it takes sound to travel from one end to the other and back. You remember that the velocity in dry air in a pipe 10 feet long is a little more than 50 periods per second; going up to 256 periods per second, the vibrations correspond to those of a pipe two feet long. Let us take 512 periods per second; that corresponds to a pipe about a foot long. In a flute, open at both ends, the holes are so arranged that the length of the sound-wave is about one foot, for one of the chief "open notes." Higher musical notes correspond to greater and greater frequency of vibration, viz., 1,000, 2,000, 4,000, vibrations per second; 4,000 vibrations per second correspond to a piccolo flute of exceedingly small length; it would be but one and a half inches long. Think of a note from a little dog-call, or other whistle, one and a half inches long, open at both ends, or from a little key having a tube three quarters of an inch long, closed at one end; you will then have 4,000 vibrations per second.

A wave-length of sound is the distance traversed in the period of vibration. I will illustrate what the vibrations of sound are by this condensation travelling along our picture on the screen. Alternate condensations and rarefactions of the air are made continuously by a sounding body. When I pass my hand vigorously in one direction, the air before it becomes dense, and the air on the other side becomes rarefied. When I move it in the other direction these things become reversed; there is a spreading out of condensation from the place where my hand moves in one direction and then in the reverse. Each condensation is succeeded by a rarefaction. Rarefaction succeeds condensation at an interval of one-half what we call "wave-lengths." Condensation succeeds condensation at the full interval of a wave-length.

We have here these luminous particles on this scale,[1] representing portions of air close together, more dense; a little higher up, por-

[1] Alluding to a moving diagram of wave motion of sound produced by a working slide for lantern projection.

tions of air less dense. I now slowly turn the handle of the apparatus in the lantern, and you see the luminous sectors showing condensation travelling slowly upwards on the screen; now you have another condensation making one wave-length.

This picture or chart represents a wave-length of four feet. It represents a wave of sound four feet long. The fourth part of a thousand is 250. What we see now of the scale represents the lower note C of the tenor voice. The air from the mouth of a singer is alternately condensed and rarefied just as you see here. But that process shoots forward at the rate of about one thousand feet per second; the exact period of the motion being 256 vibrations per second for the actual case before you.

Follow one particle of the air forming part of a sound wave, as represented by these moving spots of light on the screen; now it goes down, then another portion goes down rapidly; now it stops going down; now it begins to go up; now it goes down and up again. As the maximum of condensation is approached it is going up with diminishing maximum velocity. The maximum of rarefaction has now reached it, and the particle stops going up and begins to move down. When it is of mean density the particles are moving with maximum velocity, one way or the other. You can easily follow these motions, and you will see that each particle moves to and fro and the thing that we call *condensation* travels along.

I shall show the distinction between these vibrations and the vibrations of light. Here is the fixed appearance of the particles when displaced but not in motion. You can imagine particles of something, the thing whose motion constitutes light. This thing we call the luminiferous ether. That is the only substance we are confident of in dynamics. One thing we are sure of, and that is the reality and substantiality of the luminiferous ether. This instrument is merely a method of giving motion to a diagram designed for the purpose of illustrating wave motion of light. I will show you the same thing in a fixed diagram, but this arrangement shows the mode of motion.

Now follow the motion of each particle. This represents a particle of the luminiferous ether, moving at the greatest speed when it is at the middle position.

You see the two modes of vibration,[2] sound and light now moving together; the travelling of the wave of condensation and rarefaction, and the travelling of the wave of transverse displacement. Note the direction of propagation. Here it is from your left to your right, as you look at it. Look at the motion when made faster. We have now the direction reversed. The propagation of the wave is from right to left, again the propagation of the wave is from left to right; each particle moves perpendicularly to the line of propagation.

I have given you an illustration of the vibration of sound waves, but I must tell you that the movement illustrating the condensation and rarefaction represented in that moving diagram are necessarily very much exaggerated, to let the motion be perceptible, whereas the greatest condensation in actual sound motion is not more than one or two per cent. or a small fraction of a per cent. Except that the amount of condensation was exaggerated in the diagram for sound, you have in the chart a correct representation of what actually takes place in sounding the low note C.

On the other hand, in the moving diagram representing light waves what had we? We had a great exaggeration of the inclination of the line of particles. You must first imagine a line of particles in a straight line, and then you must imagine them disturbed into a wave-curve, the shape of the curve corresponding to the disturbance. Having seen what the propagation of the wave is, look at this diagram and then look at that one. This, in light, corresponds to the different sounds I spoke of at first. The wave-length of light is the distance from crest to crest of the wave, or from hollow to hollow. I speak of crests and hollows, because we have a diagram of ups and downs as the diagram is placed.

Here, then, you have a wave-length.[3] In this lower diagram (Fig. 119) you have a wave-length of violet light. It is but one-half the length of the upper wave of red light; the period of vibration is but half as long. Now there, on an enormous scale, exaggerated not only as to slope, but immensely magnified as to wave-length, we have an

[2] Showing two moving diagrams, simultaneously, on the screen, one depicting a wave motion of light, the other a sound vibration.

[3] Exhibiting a large drawing, or chart, representing a red and a violet wave of light (reproduced in Figs. 118 and 119).

illustration of the waves of violet light. The drawing marked "red" (Fig. 118) corresponds to red light, and this lower diagram corresponds to violet light. The upper curve really corresponds to something a little below the red ray of light in the spectrum, and the lower curve to something beyond the violet light. The variation in wave-length between the most extreme rays is in the proportion of four and a half of red to eight of the violet, instead of four and eight; the red waves are nearly as one to two of the violet.

To make a comparison between the number of vibrations for each wave of sound and the number of vibrations constituting light waves, I may say that 30 vibrations per second is about the smallest number which will produce a musical sound; 50 per second gives one of the

Fig. 118—Waves of Red Light

Fig. 119—Waves of Violet Light

grave pedal notes of an organ, 100 or 200 per second give the low notes of the bass voice, higher notes with 250 per second, 300 per second, 1,000, 4,000 up to 8,000 per second give about the shrillest notes audible to the human ear.

Instead of the numbers, which we have, say in the most commonly used part of the musical scale, *i. e.,* from 200 or 300 to 600 or 700 per second, we have millions of millions of vibrations per second in light waves: that is to say, 400 per second, instead of 400 million million per second, which is the number of vibrations performed when we have red light produced.

An exhibition of red light travelling through space from the remotest star is due to propagation by waves or vibrations, in which each individual particle of the transmitting medium vibrates to and fro 400 million million times in a second.

Some people say they cannot understand a million million. Those people cannot understand that twice two makes four. That is the way I put it to people who talk to me about the incomprehensibility of such large numbers. I say *finitude* is incomprehensible, the infinite in the universe *is* comprehensible. Now apply a little logic to this. Is the negation of infinitude incomprehensible? What would you think of a universe in which you could travel one, ten, or a thousand miles, or even to California, and then find it come to an end? Can you suppose an end of matter or an end of space? The idea is incomprehensible. Even if you were to go millions and millions of miles the idea of coming to an end is incomprehensible. You can understand one thousand per second as easily as you can understand one per second. You can go from one to ten, and ten times ten and then to a thousand without taxing your understanding and then you can go on to a thousand million and a million million. You can all understand it.

Now 400 million million vibrations per second is the kind of thing that exists as a factor in the illumination by red light. Violet light, after what we have seen and have had illustrated by that curve (FIG. 119), I need not tell you corresponds to vibrations of about 800 million million per second. There are recognisable qualities of light caused by vibrations of much greater frequency and much less frequency than this. You may imagine vibrations having about twice the frequency of violet light, and others having about one-fifteenth the frequency of red light, and still you do not pass the limit of the range of continuous phenomena, only a part of which constitutes *visible* light.

When we go below visible red light what have we? We have something we do not see with the eye, something that the ordinary photographer does not bring out on his photographically sensitive plates. It is light, but we do not see it. It is something so closely continuous with *visible* light, that we may define it by the name of *invisible* light. It is commonly called radiant heat; invisible radiant heat. Perhaps, in this thorny path of logic, with hard words flying in our faces, the least troublesome way of speaking of it is to call it radiant heat. The heat effect you experience when you go near a bright hot coal fire, or a hot steam boiler; or when you go near, but

not over, a set of hot water pipes used for heating a house; the thing we perceive in our faces and hands when we go near a boiling pot and hold the hand on a level with it, is radiant heat; the heat of the hands and face caused by a hot fire, or by a hot kettle when held *under* the kettle, is also radiant heat.

You might readily make the experiment with an earthen teapot; it radiates heat better than polished silver. Hold your hands below the teapot and you perceive a sense of heat; above it you get more heat; either way you perceive heat. If held over the teapot you readily understand that there is a little current of hot air rising; if you put your hand under the teapot you find cold air rising, and the upper side of your hand is heated by radiation while the lower side is fanned and is actually cooled by virtue of the heated kettle above it.

That perception by the sense of heat, is the perception of something actually continuous with light. We have knowledge of rays of radiant heat perceptible down to (in round numbers) about four times the wave-length, or one-fourth the period, of visible or red light. Let us take red light at 400 million million vibrations per second, then the lowest radiant heat, as yet investigated, is about 100 million million per second of frequency of vibration.

I had hoped to be able to give you a lower figure. Professor Langley has made splendid experiments on the top of Mount Whitney, at the height of 15,000 feet above the sea-level, with his "Bolometer," and has made actual measurements of the wave-length of radiant heat down to exceedingly low figures. I will read you one of the figures; I have not got it by heart yet, because I am expecting more from him.[4] I learned a year and a half ago that the lowest radiant heat observed by the diffraction method of Professor Langley corresponds to 28 one hundred thousandths of a centimetre of wavelength, 28 as compared with red light, which is 7.3; or nearly fourfold. Thus wave-lengths of four times the amplitude, or one-fourth

[4] Since my lecture I have heard from Professor Langley that he has measured the refrangibility by a rock salt prism, and inferred the wave-length of heat rays from a "Leslie cube" (a metal vessel filled with hot water and radiating heat from a blackened side). The greatest wave-length he has thus found is one-thousandth of a centimetre, which is seventeen times that of sodium light—the corresponding period being about thirty million million per second.

November, 1884.—W. T.

the frequency per second of red light, have been experimented on by Professor Langley and recognised as radiant heat.

Everybody knows the "photographer's light," and has heard of *invisible* light producing visible effects upon the chemically prepared plate in the camera. Speaking in round numbers, I may say that, in going up to about twice the frequency I have mentioned for violet light, you have gone to the extreme end of the range of known light of the highest rates of vibration; I mean to say that you have reached the greatest frequency that has yet been observed. Photographic, or actinic light, as far as our knowledge extends at present, takes us to a little less than one-half the wave-length of violet light.

You will thus see that while our acquaintance with wave motion below the red extends down to one quarter of the slowest rate which affects the eye, our knowledge of vibrations at the other end of the scale only comprehends those having twice the frequency of violet light. In round numbers we have 4 octaves of light, corresponding to 4 octaves of sound in music. In music the octave has a range to a note of double frequency. In light we have one octave of visible light, one octave above the visible range and two octaves below the visible range. We have 100 per second, 200 per second, 400 per second (million million understood) for invisible radiant heat; 800 per second for visible light, and 1,600 per second for invisible or actinic light.

One thing common to the whole is the heat effect. It is extremely small in moonlight, so small that until recently nobody knew there was any heat in the moon's rays. Herschel thought it was perceptible in our atmosphere by noticing that it dissolved away very light clouds, an effect which seemed to show in full moonlight more than when we have less than full moon. Herschel, however, pointed this out as doubtful; but now, instead of its being a doubtful question, we have Professor Langley giving as a fact that the light from the moon drives the indicator of his sensitive instrument clear across the scale, showing a comparatively prodigious heating effect!

I must tell you that if any of you want to experiment with the heat of the moonlight, you must measure the heat by means of apparatus which comes within the influence of the moon's rays only. This is a very necessary precaution; if, for instance, you should take

your Bolometer or other heat detector from a comparatively warm room into the night air, you would obtain an indication of a fall in temperature owing to this change. You must be sure that your apparatus is in thermal equilibrium with the surrounding air, then take your burning-glass, and first point it to the moon and then to space in the sky beside the moon; you thus get a differential measurement in which you compare the radiation of the moon with the radiation of the sky. You will then see that the moon has a distinctly heating effect.

To continue our study of visible light, that is undulations extending from red to violet in the spectrum (which I am going to show

A a B C D E b F G H
FIG. 120—The Solar Spectrum

you presently), I would first point out on this chart (FIG. 120) that in the section from letter A to letter D we have visual effect and heating effect only; but no ordinary chemical or photographic effect. Photographers can leave their usual sensitive chemically prepared plates exposed to yellow light and red light without experiencing any sensible effect; but when you get toward the blue end of the spectrum the photographic effect begins to tell, and more and more strongly as you get towards the violet end. When you get beyond the violet there is the invisible light known chiefly by its chemical action. From yellow to violet we have visual effect, heating effect, and chemical effect, all three; above the violet only chemical and heating effects, and so little of the heating effect that it is scarcely perceptible.

The prismatic spectrum is Newton's discovery of the composition of white light. White light consists of every variety of colour from red to violet. Here, now, we have Newton's prismatic spectrum, produced by a prism. I will illustrate a little in regard to the nature of colour by putting something before the light which is like coloured glass; it is coloured gelatin. I will put in a plate of red gelatin which is carefully prepared of chemical materials and see what that will do. Of all the light passing to it from violet to red it only lets through the red and orange, giving a mixed reddish colour. Here is a plate

of green gelatin: the green absorbs all the red, giving only green. Here is a plate absorbing something from each portion of the spectrum, taking away a great deal of the violet and giving a yellow or orange appearance to the light. Here is another absorbing the green and all the violet, leaving red, orange, and a very little faint green.

When the spectrum is very carefully produced, far more carefully than Newton knew how to show it, we have a homogeneous spectrum. It must be noticed that Newton did not understand what we call a homogeneous spectrum; he did not produce it, and does not point out in his writings the conditions for producing it. With an exceedingly fine line of light we can bring it out as in sunlight, like this upper picture—red, orange, yellow, green, blue, indigo, and violet, according to Newton's nomenclature. Newton never used a narrow beam of light, and so could not have had a homogeneous spectrum.

This is a diagram painted on glass and showing the colours as we know them. It would take two or three hours if I were to explain the subject of spectrum analysis to-night. We must tear ourselves away from it. I will just read out to you the wave-lengths corresponding to the different positions of the sun's spectrum of certain dark lines commonly called "Fraunhofer's lines." I will take as a unit the one hundred thousandth of a centimetre. A centimetre is .4 of an inch; it is a rather small half an inch. I take the thousandth of a centimetre and the hundredth of that as a unit. At the red end of the spectrum the light in the neighbourhood of that black line A (Fig. 120) has for its wave-length 7.6; B has 6.87; D has 5.89; the "frequency" for A is 3.9 times 100 million million, the frequency of D light is 5.1 times 100 million million per second.

Now what force is concerned in those vibrations as compared with sound at the rate of 400 vibrations per second? Suppose for a moment the same matter was to move to and fro through the same range but 400 million million times per second. The force required is as the square of the number expressing the frequency. Double frequency would require quadruple force for the vibration of the same body. Suppose I vibrate my hand again, as I did before. If I move it once per second a moderate force is required; for it to vibrate ten times per second 100 times as much force is required; for

400 vibrations per second 160,000 times as much force. If I move my hand once per second through a space of a quarter of an inch a very small force is required; it would require very considerable force to move it ten times a second, even through so small a range; but think of the force required to move a tuning fork 400 times a second, and compare that with the force required for a motion of 400 million million times a second. If the mass moved is the same, and the range of motion is the same, then the force would be one million million million million times as great as the force required to move the prongs of the tuning fork—it is as easy to understand that number as any number like 2, 3, or 4. Consider now what that number means and what we are to infer from it. What force is there in the space between my eye and that light? What forces are there in the space between our eyes and the sun, and our eyes and the remotest visible star? There is matter and there is motion, but what magnitude of force may there be?

I move through this "luminiferous ether" as if it were nothing. But were there vibrations with such frequency in a medium of steel or brass, they would be measured by millions and millions and millions of tons' action on a square inch of matter. There are no such forces in our air. Comets make a disturbance in the air, and perhaps the luminiferous ether is split up by the motion of a comet through it. So when we explain the nature of electricity, we explain it by a motion of the luminiferous ether. We cannot say that it is electricity. What can this luminiferous ether be? It is something that the planets move through with the greatest ease. It permeates our air; it is nearly in the same condition, so far as our means of judging are concerned, in our air and in the inter-planetary space. The air disturbs it but little; you may reduce air by air-pumps to the hundred thousandth of its density, and you make little effect in the transmission of light through it. The luminiferous ether is an elastic solid, for which the nearest analogy I can give you is this jelly which you see,[5] and the nearest analogy to the waves of light is the motion, which you can imagine, of this elastic jelly, with a ball of wood floating in the middle of it. Look there, when with my hand I

[5] Exhibiting a large bowl of clear jelly with a small red wooden ball embedded in the surface near the centre.

vibrate the little red ball up and down, or when I turn it quickly round the vertical diameter, alternately in opposite directions;—that is the nearest representation I can give you of the vibrations of luminiferous ether.

Another illustration is Scottish shoemakers' wax or Burgundy pitch, but I know Scottish shoemakers' wax better. It is heavier than water, and absolutely answers my purpose. I take a large slab of the wax, place it in a glass jar filled with water, place a number of corks on the lower side and bullets on the upper side. It is brittle like the Trinidad pitch or Burgundy pitch which I have in my hand—you can see how hard it is—but when left to itself it flows like a fluid. The shoemakers' wax breaks with a brittle fracture, but it is viscous and gradually yields.

What we know of the luminiferous ether is that it has the rigidity of a solid and gradually yields. Whether or not it is brittle and cracks we cannot yet tell, but I believe the discoveries in electricity and the motions of comets and the marvellous spurts of light from them, tend to show cracks in the luminiferous ether—show a correspondence between the electric flash and the aurora borealis and cracks in the luminiferous ether. Do not take this as an assertion, it is hardly more than a vague scientific dream: but you may regard the existence of the luminiferous ether as a reality of science; that is, we have an all-pervading medium, an elastic solid, with a great degree of rigidity—a rigidity so prodigious in proportion to its density that the vibrations of light in it have the frequencies I have mentioned, with the wave-lengths I have mentioned. The fundamental question as to whether or not luminiferous ether has gravity has not been answered. We have no knowledge that the luminiferous ether is attracted by gravity; it is sometimes called imponderable because some people vainly imagine that it has no weight: I call it matter with the same kind of rigidity that this elastic jelly has.

Here are two tourmalines; if you look through them toward the light you see the white light all round, *i. e.* they are transparent. If I turn round one of these tourmalines the light is extinguished, it is absolutely black, as though the tourmalines were opaque. This is an illustration of what is called polarisation of light. I cannot speak to you about qualities of light without speaking of the polarisation of

light. I want to show you a most beautiful effect of polarising light, before illustrating a little further by means of this large mechanical illustration which you have in the bowl of jelly. What you saw first were two plates of the crystal tourmaline (which came from Brazil, I believe) having the property of letting light pass when both plates are placed in one particular direction as regards their axes of crystallisation, and extinguishing it when it passes through them with one of the plates held in another direction. Now I put in the lantern an instrument called a "Nicol prism," which also gives rays of polarised light. A Nicol prism is a piece of Iceland spar, cut in two and turned one part relatively to the other in a very ingenious way, and put together again and cemented into one by Canada balsam. The Nicol prism takes advantage of the property which the spar has of double refraction, and produces the phenomenon which I now show you. I turn one prism round in a certain direction and you get light—a maximum of light. I turn it through a right angle and you get blackness. I turn it one quarter round again, and get maximum light; one quarter more, maximum blackness; one quarter more, and bright light. We rarely have a grand specimen of a Nicol prism as this.

There is another way of producing polarised light. I stand before that light and look at its reflection in a plate of glass on the table through one of the Nicol prisms, which I turn round, so. Now if I incline that plate of glass at a particular angle—rather more than fifty-five degrees—I find a particular position in which, if I look at it and then turn the prism round in the hand, the effect is absolutely to extinguish the light in one position of the prism and to give it maximum brightness in another position. I use the term "absolute" somewhat rashly. It is only a reduction to a very small quantity of light, not an absolute annulment as we have in the case of the two Nicol prisms used conjointly. As to the mechanics of the thing, those of you who have never heard of this before would not know what I was talking about; it could only be explained to you by a course of lectures in physical optics. The thing is this, vibrations of light must be in a definite direction relatively to the line in which the light travels.

Look at this diagram, the light goes from left to right; we have

vibrations perpendicular to the line of transmission. There is a line up and down which is the line of vibration. Imagine here a source of light, violet light, and here in front of it is the line of propagation. Sound-vibrations are to and fro in, this is transverse to, the line of propagation. Here is another, perpendicular to the diagram, still following the law of transverse vibration; here is another, circular vibration. Imagine a long rope, you whirl one end of it and you see a screw-like motion running along, and you can get this circular motion in one direction or in the opposite.

Plane-polarised light is light with the vibrations all in a single plane, perpendicular to the plane through the ray which is technically called the "plane of polarisation." Circularly polarised light consists of undulations of luminiferous ether having a circular motion. Elliptically polarised light is something between the two, not in a straight line, and not in a circular line; the course of vibration is an ellipse. Polarised light is light that performs its motions continually in one mode or direction. If in a straight line it is plane-polarised; if in a circular direction it is circularly polarised light; when elliptical it is elliptically polarised light.

With Iceland spar, one unpolarised ray of light divides on entering it into two rays of polarised light, by reason of its power of double refraction, and the vibrations are perpendicular to one another in the two emerging rays. Light is always polarised when it is reflected from a plate of unsilvered glass, or from water, at a certain definite angle of fifty-six degrees for glass, fifty-two degrees for water, the angle being reckoned in each case from a perpendicular to the surface. The angle for water is the angle whose tangent is 1.4. I wish you to look at the polarisation with your own eyes. Light from glass at fifty-six degrees and from water at fifty-two degrees goes away vibrating perpendicularly to the plane of incidence and plane of reflection.

We can distinguish it without the aid of an instrument. There is a phenomenon well known in physical optics as "Haidinger's Brushes." The discoverer is well known in Philadelphia as a mineralogist, and the phenomenon I speak of goes by his name. Look at the sky in a direction of ninety degrees from the sun, and you will see a yellow and blue cross, with the yellow toward the sun, and

from the sun, spreading out like two foxes' tails with blue between, and then two red brushes in the space at right angles to the blue. If you do not see it, it is because your eyes are not sensitive enough, but a little training will give them the needed sensitiveness. If you cannot see it in this way try another method. Look into a pail of water with a black bottom; or take a clear glass dish of water, rest it on a black cloth, and look down at the surface of the water on a day with a white cloudy sky (if there is such a thing ever to be seen in Philadelphia). You will see the white sky reflected in the basin of water at an angle of about fifty degrees. Look at it with the head tipped on one side and then again with the head tipped to the other side, keeping your eyes on the water, and you will see Haidinger's brushes. Do not do it fast or you will make yourself giddy. The explanation of this is the refreshing of the sensibility of the retina. The Haidinger's brush is always there, but you do not see it because your eye is not sensitive enough. After once seeing it you always see it; it does not thrust itself inconveniently before you when you do not want to see it. You can also readily see it in a piece of glass with a dark cloth below it, or in a basin of water.

I am going to conclude by telling you how we know the wavelengths of light, and how we know the frequency of the vibrations, and we shall actually make a measurement of the wave-length of yellow light. I am now going to show you the diffraction spectrum.

You see on the screen,[6] on each side of a central white bar of light, a set of bars of light, of variegated colours, the first one on each side showing blue or indigo colour, about four inches from the central white bar, and red about four inches farther, with vivid green between the blue and the red. That effect is produced by a grating with 400 lines to the centimetre, engraved on glass, which I now hold in my hand. The next grating that we shall try has 3,000 lines on a Paris inch. You see the central space and on each side a large number of spectrums, blue at one end and red at the other. The fact that, in the first spectrum, red is about twice as far from the centre as the blue, proves that a wave-length of red light is double that of blue light.

I will now show you the operation of measuring the length of a

[6] Showing the chromatic bands thrown upon the screen from a diffraction grating.

wave of sodium light, that is a light like that marked D on the spectrum (FIG. 120), a light produced by a spirit-lamp with salt in it. The sodium vapour is heated up to several thousand degrees, when it becomes self-luminous and gives such a light as we get by throwing salt upon a spirit-lamp in the game of snap-dragon.

I hold in my hand a beautiful grating of glass silvered by Liebig's process with metallic silver, a grating with 6,480 lines to the inch, belonging to my friend Professor Barker, which he has kindly brought here for us this evening. You will see the brilliancy of colour as I turn the light reflected from the grating toward you and pass the beam round the room. You have now seen directly with your own eyes these brilliant colours reflected from the grating, and you have also seen them thrown upon the screen from a grating placed in the lantern. Now with a grating of 17,000 lines per inch—a much greater number than the other—you will see how much further from the central bright space the first spectrum is; how much more this grating changes the direction, or diffraction, of the beam of light. Here is the centre of the grating, and there is the first spectrum. You will note that the violet light is least diffracted and the red light is most diffracted. This diffraction of light first proved to us definitely the reality of the undulatory theory of light.

You ask why does not light go round a corner as sound does. Light does go round a corner in these diffraction spectrums; and it is shown going round a corner, since it passes through these bars and is turned round an angle of thirty degrees. The phenomena of light going round a corner seen by means of instruments adapted to show the result and to measure the angles through which it is turned, is called the diffraction of light.

I can show you an instrument which will measure the wave-lengths of light. Without proving the formula, let me tell it to you. A spirit-lamp with salt sprinkled on the wick gives very nearly homogeneous light, that is to say, light of one wave-length, or all of the same period. I have here a little grating which I take in my hand. I look through this grating and see that candle before me. Close behind it you see a blackened slip of wood with two white marks on it ten inches asunder. The line on which they are marked is placed perpendicular to the line at which I shall go from it. When I look at this salted

spirit-lamp I see a series of spectrums of yellow light. As I am some-
what short-sighted I am making my eye see with this eye-glass and
the natural lenses of the eye what a long-sighted person would make
out without an eye-glass. On that screen you saw a succession of
spectrums. I now look direct at the candle and what do I see? I see
a succession of five or six brilliantly coloured spectrums on each side
of the candle. But when I look at the salted spirit-lamp, now I see
ten spectrums on one side and ten on the other, each of which is a
monochromatic band of light.

I will measure the wave-length of the light thus. I walk away to a
considerable distance and look at the spirit-lamp and marks. I see a
set of spectrums. The first white line is exactly behind the flame. I
want the first spectrum to the right of that white line to fall exactly
on the other white line, which is ten inches from the first. As I walk
away from it I see it is now very near it; it is now on it. Now the
distance from my eye is to be measured, and the problem is again to
reduce feet to inches. The distance from the spectrum of the flame
to my eye is thirty-four feet nine inches. Mr. President, how many
inches is that? 417 inches, in round numbers 420 inches. Then we
have the proportion, as 420 is to 10 so is the length from bar to bar
of the grating to the wave-length of sodium light. That is to say as
forty-two is to one. The distance from bar to bar is the four hun-
dredth of a centimetre: therefore the forty-second part of the four
hundredth of a centimetre is the wave-length according to our
simple, and easy and hasty experiment. The true wave-length of
sodium light, according to the most accurate measurement, is about
a 17,000th of a centimetre, which differs by scarcely more than one
per cent. from our result!

The only apparatus you see is this little grating—a piece of glass
having a space four-tenths of an inch wide ruled with 400 fine lines.
Any of you who will take the trouble to buy one may measure the
wave-length of a candle flame himself. I hope some of you will be
induced to make the experiment for yourselves.

If I put salt on the flame of a spirit-lamp, what do I see through
this grating? I see merely a sharply defined yellow light, constituting
the spectrum of vaporised sodium, while from the candle flame I see
an exquisitely coloured spectrum, far more beautiful than that I

showed you on the screen. I see in fact a series of spectrums on the two sides with the blue toward the candle flame and the red further out. I cannot get one definite thing to measure from in the spectrum from the candle flame, as I can with the flame of a spirit-lamp with the salt thrown on it, which gives as I have said a simple yellow light. The highest blue light I see in the candle flame is now exactly on the line. Now measure to my eye, it is forty-four feet four inches, or 532 inches. The length of this wave then is the 532d part of the four hundredth of a centimetre which would be the 21,280th of a centimetre, say the 21,000th of a centimetre. Then measure for the red and you will find something like the 11,000th for the lowest of the red light.

Lastly, how do we know the frequency of vibration?

Why, by the velocity of light. How do we know that? We know it in a number of different ways, which I cannot explain now because time forbids, and I can now only tell you shortly that the frequency of vibration for any particular ray is equal to the velocity of light divided by the wave-length for that ray. The velocity of light is about 187,000 British statute miles per second, but it is much better to take the kilometre—which is about six-tenths of a mile—for the unit, when we find the velocity is very accurately 300,000 kilometres, or 30,000,000,000 centimetres, per second. Take now the wave-length of sodium light, as we have just measured it by means of the salted spirit-lamp, to be one 17,000th of a centimetre, and we find the frequency of vibration of the sodium light to be 510 million million per second. There, then, you have a calculation of the frequency from a simple observation which you all can make for yourselves.

Lastly, I must tell you about the colour of the blue sky which is illustrated by this spherule imbedded in an elastic solid (Fig. 121). I want to explain to you in two minutes the mode of vibration. Take the simplest plane-polarised light. Here is a spherule which is producing it in an elastic solid. Imagine the solid to extend miles horizontally and miles up and down, and imagine this spherule to vibrate up and down. It is quite clear that it will make transverse vibrations similarly in all horizontal directions. The plane of polarisation is defined as a plane perpendicular to the line of vibration. Thus, light produced by a molecule vibrating up and down, as this

red globe in the jelly before you, is polarised in a horizontal plane because the vibrations are vertical.

Here is another mode of vibration. Let me twist this spherule in the jelly as I am now doing, and that will produce vibrations, also spreading out equally in all horizontal directions. When I twist this globe round it draws the jelly round with it; twist it rapidly back and the jelly flies back. By the inertia of the jelly the vibrations spread in all directions and the lines of vibration are horizontal all through the jelly. Everywhere, miles away that solid is placed in

FIG. 121—Vibrating Spherule Imbedded in an Elastic Solid

vibration. You do not see the vibrations, but you must understand that they are there. If it flies back it makes vibration, and we have waves of horizontal vibrations travelling out in all directions from the exciting molecule.

I am now causing the red globe to vibrate to and fro horizontally. That will cause vibrations to be produced which will be parallel to the line of motion at all places of the plane perpendicular to the range of the exciting molecule. What makes the blue sky? These are exactly the motions that make the blue light of the sky, which is due to spherules in the luminiferous ether, but little modified by the air. Think of the sun near the horizon, think of the light of the sun streaming through and giving you the azure blue and violet overhead. Think first of any one particle and think of it moving in such a way as to give horizontal and vertical vibrations and circular and elliptic vibrations.

You see the blue sky in high pressure steam blown into the air; you see it in the experiment of Tyndall's blue sky in which a delicate condensation of vapour gives rise to exactly the azure blue of the sky.

Now the motion of the luminiferous ether relatively to the spherule gives rise to the same effect as would an opposite motion impressed upon the spherule quite independently by an independent force. So

you may think of the blue colour coming from the sky as being produced by to and fro vibrations of matter in the air, which vibrates much as this little globe vibrates imbedded in the jelly.

The result in a general way is this: The light coming from the blue sky is polarised in a plane through the sun, but the blue light of the sky is complicated by a great number of circumstances and one of them is this, that the air is illuminated not only by the sun but by the earth. If we could get the earth covered by a black cloth then we could study the polarised light of the sky with a simplicity which we cannot do now. There are, in nature, reflections from the seas and rocks and hills and waters in an infinitely complicated manner.

Let observers observe the blue sky not only in winter when the earth is covered with snow, but in summer when it is covered with dark green foliage. This will help to unravel the complicated phenomena in question. But the azure blue of the sky is light produced by the reaction on the vibrating ether of little spherules of water, of perhaps a fifty thousandth or a hundred thousandth of a centimetre diameter, or perhaps little motes, or lumps, or crystals of common salt, or particles of dust, or germs of vegetable or animal species wafted about in the air. Now what is the luminiferous ether? It is matter prodigiously less dense than air—millions and millions and millions of times less dense than air. We can form some sort of idea of its limitations. We believe it is a real thing, with great rigidity in comparison with its density: it may be made to vibrate 400 million million times per second; and yet be of such density as not to produce the slightest resistance to any body going through it.

Going back to the illustration of the shoemakers' wax; if a cork will, in the course of a year, push its way up through a plate of that wax when placed under water, and if a lead bullet will penetrate downwards to the bottom, what is the law of the resistance? It clearly depends on time. The cork slowly in the course of a year works its way up through two inches of that substance; give it one or two thousand years to do it and the resistance will be enormously less; thus the motion of a cork or bullet, at the rate of one inch in 2,000 years, may be compared with that of the earth, moving at the rate of six times ninety-three million miles a year, or nineteen miles

per second, through the luminiferous ether; but when we can have actually before us a thing elastic like jelly and yielding like pitch, surely we have a large and solid ground for our faith in the speculative hypothesis of an elastic luminiferous ether, which constitutes the wave theory of light.

THE TIDES

[EVENING LECTURE TO THE BRITISH ASSOCIATION
AT THE SOUTHAMPTON MEETING, FRIDAY,
AUGUST 25, 1882]

THE subject on which I have to speak this evening is the tides, and at the outset I feel in a curiously difficult position. If I were asked to tell what I mean by the Tides I should feel it exceedingly difficult to answer the question. The tides have something to do with motion of the sea. Rise and fall of the sea is sometimes called a tide; but I see, in the Admiralty Chart of the Firth of Clyde, the whole space between Ailsa Craig and the Ayrshire coast marked "very little tide here." Now, we find there a good ten feet rise and fall, and yet we are authoritatively told there is very little tide. The truth is, the word "tide" as used by sailors at sea means *horizontal* motion of the water; but when used by landsmen or sailors in port, it means *vertical* motion of the water. I hope my friend Sir Frederick Evans will allow me to say that we must take the designation in the chart, to which I have referred, as limited to the instruction of sailors navigating that part of the sea, and to say that there is a very considerable landsman's tide there—a rise and fall of the surface of the water relatively to the land—though there is exceedingly little current.

One of the most interesting points of tidal theory is the determination of the currents by which the rise and fall is produced, and so far the sailor's idea of what is most noteworthy as to tidal motion is correct: because before there can be a rise and fall of the water anywhere it must come from some other place, and the water cannot pass from place to place without moving horizontally, or nearly horizontally, through a great distance. Thus the primary phenomenon of the tides is after all the tidal current; and it is the tidal currents that are referred to on charts where we have arrow-heads

marked with the statement that we have "very little tide here," or that we have "strong tides" there.

One instance of great interest is near Portland. We hear of the "race of Portland" which is produced by an exceedingly strong tidal current; but in Portland harbour there is exceedingly little rise and fall, and that little is much confused, as if the water did not know which way it was going to move. Sometimes the water rises, sinks, seems to think a little while about it, and then rises again. The rise of the tide at Portland is interesting to the inhabitants of Southampton in this, that whereas here, at Southampton, there is a double high water, there, at Portland, there is a double low water. The double high water seems to extend across the Channel. At Havre, and on the bar off the entrance to Havre, there is a double high water very useful to navigation; but Southampton I believe is pre-eminent above all the ports in the British Islands with respect to this convenience. There is here (at Southampton) a good three hours of high water;—a little dip after the first high water, and then the water rises again a very little more for an hour and a half or two hours, before it begins to fall to low water.

I shall endeavour to refer to this subject again. It is not merely the Isle of Wight that gives rise to the phenomenon. The influence extends to the east as far as Christchurch, and is reversed at Portland, and we have the double or the prolonged high water also over at Havre; therefore, it is clearly not, as it has been supposed to be, due to the Isle of Wight.

But now I must come back to the question, What are the "Tides"? Is a "tidal wave" a tide? What is called in the newspapers a "tidal wave" rises sometimes in a few minutes, does great destruction, and goes down again, somewhat less rapidly. There are frequent instances in all parts of the world of the occurrence of that phenomenon. Such motions of the water, however, are not tides; they are usually caused by earthquakes. But we are apt to call any not *very* short-time rise and fall of the water a tide, as when standing on the coast of a slanting shore where there are long ocean waves, we see the gradual sinkings and risings produced by them, and say that it is a wave we see, not a tide, till one comes which is exceptionally slow, and then we say "that is liker a tide than a wave." The fact is,

there is something perfectly continuous in the species of motion called wave, from the smallest ripple in a musical glass, whose period may be a thousandth of a second, to a "lop of water" in the Solent, whose period is one or two seconds, and thence on to the great ocean wave with a period of from fifteen to twenty seconds, where end the phenomenon which we commonly call waves (Fɪɢ. 122), and

FIG. 122—Wave forms

not tides. But any rise and fall which is manifestly of longer period, or slower in its rise from lowest to highest, than a wind wave, we are apt to call a tide; and some of the phenomena that are analysed for, and worked out in this very tidal analysis that I am going to explain, are in point of fact more properly wind waves than true tides.

Leaving these complicated questions, however, I will make a short cut, and assuming the cause without proving it, define the thing by the cause. I shall therefore define tides thus: Tides are motions of water on the earth, due to the attractions of the sun and of the moon. I cannot say tides are motions due to the *actions* of the sun and of the moon; for so I would include, under the designation of tide, every ripple that stirs a puddle or a millpond, and waves in the Solent or in the English Channel, and the long Atlantic wind waves, and the great swell of the ocean from one hemisphere to the other and back again (under the name which I find in the harmonic reduction of *tidal* observations), proved to take place once a year, and which I can only explain as the result of the sun's heat.

But while the action of the sun's heat by means of the wind produces ripples and waves of every size, it also produces a heaping-up of the water as illustrated by this diagram (Fɪɢ. 123). Suppose we have wind blowing across one side of a sheet of water, the wind ruffles the surface, the waves break if the wind is strong, and the

result is a strong tangential force exerted by the wind on the surface water. If a ship is sailing over the water there is strong tangential force; thus the water is found going fast to leeward for a long distance astern of a great ship sailing with a side wind: and, just as the sails of a ship standing high above the sea give a large area for the wind to act upon, every wave standing up gives a surface, and we have horizontal tangential force over the whole surface of a troubled sea. The result is that water is dragged along the surface from one side of the ocean to the other—from one side of the Atlantic to the other—and is heaped up on the side towards which the wind is blowing. To understand the dynamics of this phenomenon, think of a long straight canal with the wind blowing lengthwise along it. In virtue of the tangential force exerted on the surface of the water by the wind, and which increases with the speed of the wind, the water will become heaped up at one end of the canal, as shown in the diagram (Fig. 123), while the surface water throughout the

FIG. 123—Showing the heaping-up of water produced by wind.

whole length will be observed moving in the direction of the wind—say in the direction of the two arrows near to the surface of the water above and below it. But to re-establish the disturbed hydrostatic equilibrium, the water so heaped up will tend to flow back to the end from which it has been displaced, and as the wind prevents this taking place by a surface current, there will be set up a return current along the bottom of the canal, in a direction opposite to that of the wind, as indicated by the lowermost arrow in the diagram (Fig. 123). The return current in the ocean, however, is not always an under current, such as I have indicated in the diagram, but may sometimes be a lateral current. Thus a gale of wind blowing over ten degrees of latitude will cause a drag of water at the surface, but the return current may be not an under current but a current on

one side or the other of the area affected by the wind. Suppose, for instance, in the Mediterranean there is a strong east wind blowing along the African coast, the result will be a current from east to west along that coast, and return current along the northern coasts of the Mediterranean.

The rise and fall of the water due to these motions are almost inextricably mixed up with the true tidal rise and fall.

There is another rise and fall, also connected with the heating effect of the sun, that I do not call a true tide, and that is a rise and fall due to change of atmospheric pressure. When the barometer is high over a large area of ocean, then, there and in neighboring places, the tendency to hydrostatic equilibrium causes the surface of the water to be lower, where it is pushed down by the greater weight of air, and to be higher where there is less weight over it. It does not follow that in every case it is lower, because there may not be time to produce the effect, but there is this tendency. It is very well known that two or three days of low barometer make higher tides on our coast. In Scotland and England and Ireland, two or three days of low barometer generally produce all round the shore higher water than when the barometer is high; and this effect is chiefly noticed at the time of tidal high water, because people take less notice of low water—as at Portland where they think nothing of the double low water. Hence we hear continually of very high tides—very high water noticed at the time of high tides—when the barometer is low. We have not always, however, in this effect of barometric pressure really great tidal rise *and* fall. On the contrary we have the curious phenomenon that sometimes when the barometer is very low, and there are gales in the neighbourhood, there is very little *rise* and *fall,* as the water is *kept* heaped up and does not sink by anything like its usual amount from the extra high level that it has at high water. But I fear I have got into questions which are leading me away from my subject, and as I cannot get through them I must just turn back.

Now think of the definition which I gave of the "tides," and think of the sun alone. The *action* of the sun cannot be defined as the cause of the solar tides. Solar tides are due to action of the sun, but all risings and fallings of the water due to the action of the sun

are not tides. We want the quantification of the predicate here very badly. We have a true tide depending on the sun, the mean solar diurnal tide, having for its period twenty-four solar hours, which is inextricably mixed up with those meteorological tides that I have just been speaking of—tides depending on the sun's heat, and on the variation of the direction of the wind, and on the variation of barometric pressure according to the time of day. The consequence is that in tidal analysis, when we come to the solar tides, we cannot know how much of the analysed result is due to attraction, and how much to heating effect directly or indirectly, whether on water, or on air, or on water as affected by air. As to the lunar tides we are quite sure of them;—they are gravitational, and nothing but gravitational; but I hope to speak later of the supposed relation of the moon to the weather, and the relation that has to the tides.

I have defined the tides as motions of water on the earth due to the attractions of the sun and of the moon. How are we to find out whether an observed motion of the water is a tide or is not a tide as thus defined? Only by the combination of theory and observation: if these afford sufficient reason for believing that the motion is due to attraction of the sun or of the moon, or of both, then we must call it a tide.

It is curious to look back on the knowledge of the tides possessed in ancient times, and to find as early as two hundred years before the Christian era a very clear account given of the tides at Cadiz. But the Romans generally, knowing only the Mediterranean, had not much clear knowledge of the tides. At a much later time than that, we hear from the ancient Greek writers and explorers—Posidonius, Strabo, and others—that in certain remote parts of the world, in Thule, in Britain, in Gaul, and on the distant coasts of Spain, there were motions of the sea—a rising and falling of the water—which depended in some way on the moon. Julius Cæsar came to know something about it; but it is certain the Roman Admiralty did not supply Julius Cæsar's captains with tide tables when he sailed from the Mediterranean with his expeditionary force, destined to put down anarchy in Britain. He says, referring to the fourth day after his first landing in Britain—"That night it happened to be full moon, which time is accustomed to give the

greatest risings of water in the ocean, though our people did not know it." It has been supposed however that some of his people did know it—some of his quartermasters had been in England before and did know—but that the discipline in the Roman navy was so good that they had no right to obtrude their knowledge; and so, although a storm was raging at the time, he was not told that the water would rise in the night higher than usual, and nothing was done to make his transports secure higher up on the shore while he was fighting the Britons. After the accident Cæsar was no doubt told—"Oh, we knew that before, but it might have been ill taken if we had said so."

Strabo says—"Soon after moonrise the sea begins to swell up and flow over the earth till the moon reaches mid heaven. As she descends thence the sea recedes till about moonset, when the water is lowest. It then rises again as the moon, below the horizon, sinks to mid heaven under the earth." It is interesting here to find the tides described simply with reference to the moon. But there is something more in this ancient account of Strabo; he says, quoting Posidonius—"This is the daily circuit of the sea. Moreover, there is a regular monthly course, according to which the greatest rise and fall takes place about new moon, then diminishing rise and fall till half moon, and again increasing till full moon." And lastly he refers to a hearsay report of the Gaditani (Cadizians) regarding an annual period in the amount of the daily rise and fall of the sea, which seems to be not altogether right, and is confessedly in part conjectural. He gave no theory, of course, and he avoided the complication of referring to the sun. But the mere mention of an annual period is interesting in the history of tidal theory, as suggesting that the rises and falls are due not to the moon alone but to the sun also. The account given by Posidonius is fairly descriptive of what occurs at the present day at Cadiz. Exactly the opposite would be true at many places; but at Cadiz the time of high water at new and full moon is nearly twelve o'clock. Still, I say we have only definition to keep us clear of ambiguities and errors; and yet, to say that those motions of the sea which we call tides depend on the moon, was considered, even by Galileo, to be a lamentable piece of mysticism which he read with regret in the writings of so renowned an author as Kepler.

It is indeed impossible to avoid theorising. The first who gave a theory was Newton; and I shall now attempt to speak of it sufficiently to allow us to have it as a foundation for estimating the forces with which we are concerned, in dealing with some of the very perplexing questions which tidal phenomena present.

We are to imagine the moon as attracting the earth, subject to the forces that the different bodies exert upon each other. We are not to take Hegel's theory—that the Earth and the Planets do not move like stones, but move along like blessed gods, each an independent being. If Hegel had any grain of philosophy in his ideas of the solar system, Newton is all wrong in his theory of the tides. Newton considered the attraction of the sun upon the earth and the moon, of the earth upon the moon, and the mutual attractions of different parts of the earth; and left it for Cavendish to complete the discovery of gravitation, by exhibiting the mutual attraction of two pieces of lead in his balance. Tidal theory is one strong link in the grand philosophic chain of the Newtonian theory of gravitation. In explaining the tide-generating force we are brought face to face with some of the subtleties, and with some of the mere elements, of physical astronomy. I will not enter into details, as it would be useless for those who already understand the tidal theory, and unintelligible to those who do not.

I may just say that the moon attracts a piece of matter, for example a pound-weight, here on the earth, with a force which we compare with the earth's attraction thus. Her mass is $\frac{1}{80}$ of the earth's, and she is sixty times as far away from the earth's centre as we are here. Newton's theory of gravitation shows, that when you get outside the mass of the earth the resultant attraction of the earth on the pound weight, is the same as if the whole mass of the earth were collected at the centre, and that it varies inversely as the square of the distance from the centre. The same law is inferred regarding the moon's attraction from the general theory. The moon's attraction on this pound weight is therefore $\frac{\frac{1}{80}}{60 \times 60}$, or $\frac{1}{288,000}$ of the attraction of the earth on the same mass. But that is not the tide-generating force. The moon attracts any mass at the nearest parts of the earth's surface with greater force than an equal mass near the centre; and attracts a mass belonging to the remoter parts with less force.

Imagine a point where the moon is overhead, and imagine another point on the surface of the earth at the other end of a diameter passing through the first point and the centre of the earth (illustrated by B and A of FIG. 124, p. 284). The moon attracts the nearest point (B) with a force which is greater than that with which it attracts the farther point (A) in the ratio of the square of 59 to the square of 61. Hence the moon's attraction on equal masses at the nearest and farthest points differs by one fifteenth part of her attraction on an equal mass at the earth's centre, or about a 4,320,-000th, or, roughly, a four-millionth, of the earth's attraction on an equal mass at its surface. Consequently the water tends to protrude towards the moon and from the moon. If the moon and earth were held together by a rigid bar the water would be drawn to the side nearest to the moon—drawn to a prodigious height of several hundred feet. But the earth and moon are not so connected. We may imagine the earth as falling towards the moon, and the moon as falling towards the earth, but never coming nearer; the bodies, in reality, revolving round their common centre of gravity. A point nearest to the moon is as it were dragged away from the earth, and thus the result is that apparent gravity differs by about one four-millionth at the points nearest to and farthest from the moon. At the intermediate points of the circle C, D (FIG. 124, p. 284), there is a somewhat complicated action according to which gravitation is increased by about one 17-millionth, and its direction altered by about one 17-millionth, so that a pendulum 17,000 feet long, a plummet rather longer than from the top of Mont Blanc to sea level, would, if showing truly the lunar disturbing force, be deflected through a space of one thousandth of a foot. It seems quite hopeless by a plummet to exhibit the lunar disturbance of gravity. A spring balance to show the alteration of magnitude, and a plummet to show the change of direction are conceivable; but we can scarcely believe that either can ever be produced, with sufficient delicacy and consistency and accuracy to indicate these results.

A most earnest and persevering effort has been made by Mr. George Darwin and Mr. Horace Darwin to detect variations in gravity due to lunar disturbance, and they have made apparatus which, notwithstanding the prodigious smallness of the effect to be observed,

is in point of delicacy and consistency capable of showing it; but when they had got their delicate pendulum—their delicate plummet about the length of an ordinary seconds' pendulum—and their delicate multiplying gear to multiply the motion of its lower end by about a million times, and to show the result on a scale by the reflection of a ray of light, they found the little image incessantly moving backward and forward on the scale with no consistency or regularity; and they have come to the conclusion that there are continual local variations of apparent gravity taking place for which we know no rule, and which are considerably greater than the lunar disturbance for which they were seeking. That which they found—continual motions of the surface of the earth, and which was not the primary object of their investigation—is in some respects more interesting than what they sought and did not find. The delicate investigation thus opened up promises a rich harvest of knowledge. These disturbances are connected with earthquakes such as have been observed in a very scientific and accurate manner by Milne, Thomas Gray, and Ewing in Japan, and in Italy by many accurate observers. All such observations agree in showing continual tremor and palpitation of the earth in every part.

One other phenomenon that I may just refer to now as coming out from tide-gauge observations, is a phenomenon called *seiches* by Forel, and described by him as having been observed in the lakes of Geneva and Constance. He attributes them to differences of barometric pressure at the ends of the lake, and it is probable that part of the phenomenon is due to such differences. I think it is certain, however, that the whole is not due to such differences. The Portland tide curve and those of many other places, notably the tide curve for Malta, taken about ten years ago by Sir Cooper Key, and observations on the Atlantic coasts and in many other parts of the world, show something of these phenomena; a ripple or roughness on the curve traced by the tide gauge, which, when carefully looked to, indicates a variation not regular but in some such period as twenty or twenty-five minutes. It has been suggested that they are caused by electric action! Whenever the cause of a thing is not known it is immediately put down as electrical!

I would like to explain to you the equilibrium theory, and the

kinetic theory, of the tides, but I am afraid I must merely say there are such things; and that Laplace in his great work, his *Mécanique Céleste,* first showed that the equilibrium theory was utterly insufficient to account for the phenomena, and gave the true principles of the dynamic action on which they depend. The resultant effect of the tide-generating force is to cause the water to tend to become protuberant towards the moon and the sun and from them, when they are in the same straight line, and to take a regular spheroidal

FIG. 124—Spring Tides

FIG. 125—Spring Tides

form, in which the difference between the greatest and the least semi-diameter is about 2 feet for lunar action alone, and 1 foot for the action of the sun alone—that is a tide which amounts to 3 feet when the sun and moon act together (FIGS. 124 and 125), and to 1 foot only when they act at cross purposes (FIGS. 126 and 127), so as to produce opposite effects. These diagrams, FIGS. 124 to 127, illustrate spring and neap tides: the dark shading around the globe, E, representing a water envelope surrounding the earth. There has been much discussion on the origin of the word *neap.* It seems to be an Anglo-Saxon word meaning scanty. *Spring* seems to be the same as when we speak of plants *springing* up. I well remember at the meeting of the British Association at Edinburgh a French member who, meaning spring tides, spoke of the *grandes marées du printemps.* Now you laugh at this; and yet, though he did not mean it, he was quite right, for the spring tides in the spring time are greater

on the whole than those at other times, and we have the greatest
spring-tides in the spring of the year. For then the moon is nearest
the sun also very high spring tides is enquire. So, interpreting
of the two words, it the same reprehensible. Nean tid at the spring
tides, and spring tides are tides which swing on to correspondingly
great heights.

The equilibrium theory of the tide is a way of getting tidal
phenomena... We see the tides would be so and so if the water took
the figure of equilibrium. Now the water does not have the tidal
wave, as we have deduced in the elsewhere (First, 1841-3), but
the tides of the water may be imagined to exhibit when as figure,
or, as the water, that it would take if there what figure over
the whole water of the earth. For have a diff...

FIG. 126—Neap Tides

FIG. 127—Neap Tides

on the whole than those at other times, and we have the greatest spring tides in the spring of the year. But there the analogy ceases, for we have also very high spring tides in autumn. Still the meaning of the two words is the same etymologically. Neap tides are scanty tides, and spring tides are tides which spring up to remarkably great heights.

The equilibrium theory of the tides is a way of putting tidal phenomena. We say the tides would be so and so if the water took the figure of equilibrium. Now the water does not cover the whole earth, as we have assumed in the diagrams (FIGS. 124-127), but the surface of the water may be imagined as taking the same figure, so far as there is water, that it would take if there were water over the whole surface of the earth. But here a difficult question comes in—namely, the attraction of the water for parts of itself. If we consider the water flowing over the whole earth this attraction must be taken into account. If we imagine the water of exceedingly small density so that its attraction on itself is insensible compared with that of the earth, we have thus to think of the equilibrium theory. But, on the other hand, if the water had the same density as the earth, the result would be that the solid nucleus would be almost ready to float; and now imagine that the water is denser than the earth, and we put the tides out of consideration altogether. Think of the earth covered over with mercury instead of water—a layer of mercury a foot deep. The solid earth would tend to float, and would float, and the result would be that the denser liquid would run to, and cover one side up to a certain depth, and the earth would be as it were floating out of the sea. That explains one curious result that Laplace seems to have been much struck with: the stability of the ocean requires that the density of the water should be less than that of the solid earth. But take the sea as having the specific gravity of water, the mean density of the earth is only 5.6 times that of water, and this is not enough to prevent the attraction of water for water from being sensible. Owing therefore to the attraction of the water for parts of itself the tidal phenomena are somewhat larger than they would be without it, but neglecting this, and neglecting the deformation of the solid earth, we have the ordinary equilibrium theory.

Why does the water not follow the equilibrium theory? Why have we tides of 20 feet or 30 feet or 40 feet in some places, and only of 2 or 3 feet in others? Because the water has not time in the course of 12 hours to take the equilibrium figure, and because after tending towards it, the water runs beyond it.

I ask you to think of the oscillations of water in a trough. Look at this diagram (Fig. 128), which will help you to understand how the

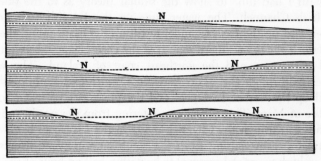

FIG. 128—Oscillations of Water in a Trough

tidal effect is prodigiously magnified by a dynamical action due to the inertia of the water. The tendency of water in motion to keep its motion prevents it from taking the figure of equilibrium. [A chart showing the tides of the English Channel was exhibited, from which it was seen that while at Dover there were tides of 21 feet, there was at Portland very little rise and fall.] Imagine a canal instead of the English Channel, a canal stopped at the Straits of Dover and at the opposite end at Land's End, and imagine somehow a disturbing force causing the water to be heaped up at one end. There would be a swing of water from one end to the other, and if the period of the disturbing force approximately agreed with the period of free oscillation, the effect would be that the rise and fall would go vastly above and below the range due to equilibrium action. Hence it is we have the 21 feet rise and fall at Dover. The very little rise and fall at Portland is also illustrated in the uppermost figure of this diagram (Fig. 128). Thus high water at Dover is low water at Land's End, and the water seesaws as it were about a line going across from Portland to Havre (represented by N in the figure); not a line going

directly across, however, for on the other side of the Channel there is a curious complication.

At the time of high water at Dover there is hardly any current in the Channel. As soon as the water begins to fall at Dover the current begins to flow west through the whole of the Channel. When it is mid-tide at Dover the tide is flowing fastest in the Channel. This was first brought to light by Admiral Beechey.

I wish I had time to show the similar theory as to the tides in the Irish Channel. The water runs up the English Channel to Dover, and up the Irish Channel to fill up the basin round the Isle of Man. Take the northern mouth of the Irish Channel between the Mull of Cantire and the northeast coast of Ireland. The water rushes in through the straits between Cantire and Rathlin Island, to fill up the Bay of Liverpool and the great area of water round the Isle of Man. This tidal wave entering from the north, running southward through the Channel, meets in the Liverpool basin with the tidal stream coming from the south entrance, and causes the time of high water at Liverpool to be within half-an-hour of the time of no currents in the northern and southern parts of the Channel.

I would like to read you the late Astronomer-Royal's appreciation of Laplace's splendid work on the tides.

Airy says of Laplace: "If now, putting from our thoughts the details of the investigation, we consider its general plan and objects, we must allow it to be one of the most splendid works of the greatest mathematician of the past age. To appreciate this, the reader must consider, first, the boldness of the writer, who, having a clear understanding of the gross imperfections in the methods of his predecessors, had also the courage deliberately to take up the problem on grounds fundamentally correct (however it might be limited by suppositions afterwards introduced); secondly, the general difficulty of treating the motion of fluids; thirdly, the peculiar difficulty of treating the motions when the fluids cover an area which is not plane but convex; and fourthly, the sagacity of perceiving that it was necessary to consider the earth as a revolving body, and the skill of correctly introducing this consideration. This last point alone, in our opinion, gives a greater claim for reputation than the boasted explanation of the long inequality of Jupiter and Saturn."

Tidal theory must be carried on along with tidal observations. Instruments for measuring and recording the height of the water at any

FIG. 129—Tide Gauge

time give us results of observations.[1] Here is such an instrument—a tide gauge (FIG. 129). The floater is made of thin sheet copper, and

[1] The various instruments and tide-curves referred to in this lecture are fully described and illustrated in a paper on "The Tide Gauge, Tidal Harmonic Analyser, and Tide Predicter," read before the Institution of Civil Engineers, on 1st March, 1881, and published in their *Proceedings* for that date.

is suspended by a fine platinum wire. The vertical motion of the floater, as the water rises and falls, is transmitted, in a reduced proportion by a single pinion and wheel, to this frame or marker, which carries a small marking pencil. The paper on which the pencil marks the recording curve, is stretched on this cylinder, which, by means of the clockwork, is caused to make one revolution every twenty-four hours. The leaning-tower-of-Pisa arrangement of the paper-cylinder, and the extreme simplicity of the connection between

FIG. 130—Facsimile of weekly sheet of curves traced by Tide Gauge

marker and floater, constitute the chief novelty. This tide gauge is similar to one now in actual use, recording the rise and fall of the water in the River Clyde, at the entrance to the Queen's Dock, Glasgow. A sheet bearing the curves (FIG. 130) traced by that machine during a week is exhibited.

After the observations have been taken, the next thing is to make use of them. Hitherto this has been done by laborious arithmetical calculation. I hold in my hand the Reports of the late Tidal Committee of the British Association with the results of the harmonic analysis—about eight years' work carried on with great labour, and by aid of successive grants from the British Association. The Indian Government has continued the harmonic analysis for the seaports of India. The *Tide Tables for Indian Ports for the Year* 1882, issued under the authority of the Indian Government, show this analysis as in progress for the following ports, viz.: Aden, Kurrachee, Okha Point and Beyt Harbour at the entrance to the Gulf of Cutch, Bombay, Karwar, Beypore, Paumben Pass, Madras, Vizagapatam, Dia-

mond Harbour, Fort Gloster and Kidderpore on the River Hooghly, Rangoon, Moulmein, and Port Blair. Mr. Roberts, who was first employed as calculator by the Committee of the British Association, has been asked to carry on the work for the Indian Government, and latterly, in India, native calculators under Major Baird, have worked by the methods and forms by which Mr. Roberts had worked in England for the British Association.[2] The object is to find the values of the different tidal constituents. We want to separate out from the whole rise and fall of the ocean the part due to the sun,

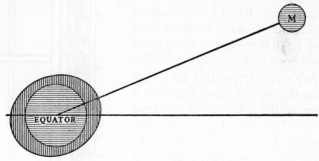

Fig. 131—Declinational Tide

the part due to the moon, the part due to one portion of the moon's effect, and the part due to another. There are complications depending on the moon's position—declinational tides according as the moon is or is not in the plane of the earth's equator—and also on that of the sun. Thus we have the diurnal declinational tides. When the moon is in the north declination (Fig. 131) we have (in the equilibrium theory) higher water at lunar noon than at lunar midnight. That difference in the height of high water, and the corresponding solar noon tides and solar midnight tides, due to the sun not being in the earth's equator, constitute the lunar and solar diurnal declinational tides. In summer the noon high water might be

[2] Note of September 17, 1887. On the subject of Tidal Harmonic Analysis see "Manual of Instructions for Tidal Observation," by Major Baird, published by Messrs. Taylor and Francis, London, 1886; also the Reports of the British Association Committee "On Harmonic Analysis of Tidal Observations."—W. T.

expected to be higher than the midnight high water, because the sun is nearer overhead to us than to our Antipodes.

By kind permission of Sir Frederick Evans, I am able to place before you these diagrams of curves drawn by Captain Harris, R. N., of the Hydrographic Department of the Admiralty, exhibiting the rise and fall of tides in Princess Royal Harbour, King George Sound, Western Australia, from January 1st to December 31st, 1877, and in Broad Sound, Queensland, Australia, from July 15th, 1877, to July 23rd, 1878. Look at this one of these diagrams, a diagram of the tides at the northeast corner of Australia. For several days high water always at noon. When the tides are noticeable at all we have high water at noon, and when the tides are not at noon they are so small that they are not taken notice of at all. It thus appears as if the tides were irrespective of the moon, but they are not really so. When we look more closely, it is a *full* moon if we have a great tide at noon; or else it is *new* moon. It is at half moon that we have the small tides, and when they are smallest we have high water at six. There is also a great difference between day and night high water; the difference between them is called the diurnal tide. A similar phenomenon is shown on a smaller scale in this curve, drawn by the first tide-predict-

Fig. 132—Tidal Harmonic Analyser

ing machine. At a certain time the two high waters become equalised, and the two low waters very unequal (see p. 290 for real examples).

The object of the harmonic analysis is to analyse out from the complicated curve traced by the tide gauge the simplest harmonic elements. A simple harmonic motion may be imagined as that of a body which moves simply up and down in a straight line, keeping level with the end of a clock hand, moving uniformly round. The exceedingly complicated motion that we have in the tides is analysed into a series of simple harmonic motions in different periods and with different amplitudes or ranges; and these simple harmonic constituents added together give the complicated tides.

All the work hitherto done has been accomplished by sheer calculation; but calculation of so methodical a kind that a machine ought to be found to do it. The Tidal Harmonic Analyser consists of an application of Professor James Thomson's disk-globe-and-cylinder integrator to the evaluation of the integrals required for the harmonic analysis. The principle of the machine and the essential details are fully described and explained in papers communicated by Professor James Thomson and the author to the Royal Society, in 1876 and 1878, and published in the *Proceedings* for those years;[3] also reprinted, with a postscript dated April, 1879, in Thomson and Tait's *Natural Philosophy,* Second Edition, Appendix B. It remains now to describe and explain the actual machine referred to in the last of these communications, which is the only tidal harmonic analyser hitherto made. It may be mentioned, however, in passing, that a similar instrument, with the simpler construction wanted for the simpler harmonic analysis of ordinary meteorological phenomena, has been constructed for the Meteorological Committee, and is now regularly at work at their office, harmonically analysing the results of meteorological observations, under the superintendence of Mr. R. H. Scott.

FIG. 132 represents the tidal harmonic analyser, constructed under the author's direction, with the assistance of a grant from the Gov-

[3] *Vide* vol. xxiv. p. 262, and vol. xxvii. p. 371.

ernment Grant Fund of the Royal Society. The eleven cranks of this instrument are allotted as follows:—

Cranks.	Object.	Distinguishing Letter.	Speed.
1 and 2	To find the mean lunar semi-diurnal tide . . .	M	$2\,(\gamma-\sigma)$
3 ,, 4	,, mean solar ,, ,, . .	S	$2\,(\gamma-\eta)$
5 ,, 6	,, luni-solar declinational diurnal tide	K_1	γ
7 ,, 8	,, slower lunar ,, ,,	O	$(\gamma-2\sigma)$
9 ,, 10	,, slower solar ,, ,,	P	$(\gamma-2\eta)$
11	,, mean water level	A_o	. . .

The general arrangement of the several parts may be seen from Fig. 132. The large circle at the back, near the center, is merely a counter to count the days, months, and years for four years, being the leap year period. It is driven by a worm carried on an intermediate shaft, with a toothed wheel geared on another on the solar shaft. In front of the centre is the paper drum, which is on the solar shaft, and goes round in the period corresponding to twelve mean solar hours. On the extreme left, the first pair of disks, with globes and cylinders, and crank shafts with cranks at right angles between them, driving their two cross-heads, corresponds to the K_1, or luni-solar diurnal tide. The next pair of disk-globe-and-cylinders corresponds to M, or the mean lunar semi-diurnal tide, the chief of all the tides. The next pair lie on the two sides of the main shaft carrying the paper drum, and correspond to S, the mean solar semi-diurnal tide. The first pair on the right correspond to O, or the lunar diurnal tide. The second pair on the right correspond to P, the solar diurnal tide. The last disk on the extreme right is simply Professor James Thomson's disk-globe-and-cylinder integrator, applied to measure the area of the curve as it passes through the machine.

The idle shafts for the M and the O tides are seen in front respectively on the left and right of the centre. The two other longer idle shafts for the K and the P tides are behind, and therefore not seen. That for the P tide serves also for the simple integrator on the extreme right.

The large hollow square brass bar, stretching from end to end

along the top of the instrument, and carrying the eleven forks rigidly attached to it, projecting downwards, is moved to and fro through the requisite range by a rack and pinion, worked by a handle and crank in front above the paper cylinder, a little to the right of its centre. Each of these eleven forks moves one of the eleven globes of the eleven disk-globe-and-cylinder integrators of which the machine is composed. The other handle and crank in front, lower down and a little to the left of the centre, drives by a worm, at a conveniently slow speed, the solar shaft, and through it, and the four idle shafts, the four other tidal shafts.

To work the machine the operator turns with his left hand the driving crank, and with his right hand the tracing crank, by which the fork-bar is moved. His left hand he turns always in one direction, and at as nearly constant a speed as is convenient to allow his right hand, alternately in contrary directions, to trace exactly with the steel pointer the tidal curve on the paper, which is carried across the line of to-and-fro motion of the pointer by the revolution of the paper drum, of which the speed is in simple proportion to the speed of the operator's left hand.

The eleven little counters of the cylinders in front of the disks are to be set each at zero at the commencement of an operation, and to be read off from time to time during the operation, so as to give the value of the eleven integrals for as many particular values of the time as it is desired to have them.

A first working model harmonic analyser, which served for model and for the meteorological analyser, now at work in the Meteorological Office, is here before you. It has five disk-globe-and-cylinders, and shafting geared for the ratio $1:2$. Thus it serves to determine, from the deviation curve, the celebrated "A B C D E" of the *Admiralty Compass Manual,* this is to say, the coefficients in the harmonic expression

$$A + B \sin \theta + C \cos \theta + D \sin 2\theta + E \cos 2\theta.$$

for the deviation of the compass in an iron ship.

The first instrument which I designed and constructed for use as a Tide Predictor was described in the Catalogue of the Loan Collection of Scientific Apparatus at South Kensington in 1876; and the

instrument itself was presented by the British Association to the South Kensington Museum, where it now is. The second instrument constructed on the same principle is in London, and is being worked under the direction of Mr. Roberts, analysing the tides for the Indian ports. The result of this work is these books (*Tide Tables for In-*

FIG. 133—Tide Predictor

dian Ports) in which we have, for the first time, tables of the times and heights of high water and low water for fourteen of the Indian ports.

To predict the tides for the India and China Seas and Australia we have a much more difficult thing to do than for the British ports. The Admiralty Tide Tables give all that is necessary for the British ports, practically speaking; but for other parts of the world generally the diurnal tide comes so much into play that we have exceedingly complicated action. The most complete thing would be a table showing the height of the water every hour of the twenty-four. No one has yet ventured to do that generally for all parts of

the world; but for the comparatively complicated tides of the India Seas, the curves traced by the Tide Predictor from which is obtained the information given in these Indian tide tables, do actually tell the height of the water for every instant of the twenty-four hours.

The mechanical method which I have utilised in this machine is primarily due to the Rev. F. Bashforth who, in 1845, when he was a Bachelor of Arts and Fellow of St. John's College, Cambridge, described it to Section A of the 1845 (Cambridge) meeting of the British Association in a communication entitled "A Description of a Machine for finding the Numerical Roots of Equations and tracing a Variety of Useful Curves," of which a short notice appears in the British Association Report for that year. The same subject was taken up by Mr. Russell in a communication to the Royal Society in 1869, "On the Mechanical Description of Curves," [4] which contains a drawing showing mechanism substantially the same as that of the Tide Predictor. Here is the principle as embodied in No. 3 Tide Predictor (represented in Fig. 133, p. 296), now actually before you:—

A long cord of which one end is held fixed passes over one pulley, under another, and so on. These eleven pulleys are all moved up and down by cranks, and each pulley takes in or lets out cord according to the direction in which it moves. These cranks are all moved by trains of wheels gearing into the eleven wheels fixed on this driving shaft. The greatest number of teeth on any wheel is 802 engaging with another of 423. All the other wheels have comparatively small numbers of teeth. The machine is finished now, except a cast-iron sole and cast-iron back. A flywheel of great inertia enables me to turn the machine fast, without jerking the pulleys, and so to run off a year's curve in about twenty-five minutes. This machine is arranged for fifteen constituents in all and besides that there is an arrangement for analysing out the long period tides.

The following table shows how close an approximation to astronomical accuracy is given by the numbers chosen for the teeth of the several wheels. These numbers I have found by the ordinary arithmetical progress of converging fractions.

[4] *Proc. Royal Society,* June 17, 1869; (vol. xviii. p. 72).

Tidal Constituents.	Speed in Degrees per Mean Solar Hour.		Losses of Angle in Machine.	
	Accurate.	As given by Machine.	Per Mean Solar Hour	Per Half Year.
M_2	$28°\cdot9841042$	$15 \times \dfrac{485}{251} = 28°\cdot9840630$	$+\ 0°\cdot0000412$	$0°\cdot180$
K_1	$15°\cdot0410686$	$15 \times \dfrac{366}{365} = 15°\cdot0410959$	$-\ 0°\cdot0000267$	$0°\cdot117$
O	$13°\cdot9430356$	$15 \times \dfrac{343}{369} = 13°\cdot9430894$	$-\ 0°\cdot0000538$	$0°\cdot237$
P	$14°\cdot9589314$	$15 \times \dfrac{364}{365} = 14°\cdot9589040$	$+\ 0°\cdot0000242$	$0°\cdot119$
N	$28°\cdot4397296$	$15 \times \dfrac{802}{423} = 28°\cdot4397163$	$+\ 0°\cdot0000133$	$0°\cdot059$
L	$29°\cdot5284788$	$15 \times \dfrac{313}{159} = 29°\cdot5283018$	$+\ 0°\cdot000177$	$0°\cdot78$
v	$28°\cdot5125830$	$15 \times \dfrac{230}{121} = 28°\cdot5123966$	$+\ 0°\cdot0001864$	$0°\cdot82$
$M\,S$	$58°\cdot9841042$	$15 \times \dfrac{230}{121} \times \dfrac{271}{131} = 58°\cdot9836600$	$+\ 0°\cdot000444$	$1°\cdot95$
μ	$27°\cdot9682084$	$15 \times \dfrac{468}{251} = 27°\cdot9681275$	$+\ 0°\cdot0000809$	$0°\cdot36$
λ	$29°\cdot4556254$	$15 \times \dfrac{487}{248} = 29°\cdot4556451$	$-\ 0°\cdot0000197$	$0°\cdot087$
Ω	$13°\cdot3986609$	$15 \times \dfrac{410}{459} = 13°\cdot3986928$	$-\ 0°\cdot0000318$	$0°\cdot14$

To-day (Aug. 25, 1882), a committee, consisting of only two members, Mr. George Darwin and Professor Adams of Cambridge, have been appointed, and one of their chief objects will be to examine the long period tides.

There is one very interesting point I said I would endeavour to speak of if I had time; I have not time, but still I must speak of it—the influence of the moon on the weather. "We almost laugh when we hear of the influence of the moon on the weather," Sir F. Evans said to me, "but there is an influence." Gales of wind are remarkably

prevalent in Torres Straits and the neighbourhood about the time
of new and full moon. This was noticed by Dr. Rattray, a surgeon
in the navy, in connection with observations made by the surveying
ship, *Fly,* during the three years 1841–44. Dr. Rattray noticed that
at those times there was a large area of coral reef uncovered at the
very low water of the spring tides, extending out some sixty or
seventy miles from land. This large area becomes highly heated,
and the great heating of that large portion of land gives rise to a
tendency to gales at the full and change, that is at the new and full
moon. This indirect effect of the moon upon the weather through
the tides is exceedingly interesting; but it does not at all invalidate
the scientific conclusion that there is no direct influence, and the
general effect of the moon on the weather—the changes in the moon
and the changes in the weather, and their supposed connection—
remains a mere chimæra.

The subject of elastic tides in which the yielding of the solid earth
is taken into account is to be one of the primary objects of Mr. G.
Darwin's committee. The tide-generating force which tends to pull

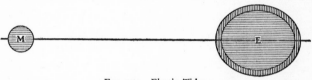

FIG. 134—Elastic Tides

the water to and from the moon, tends to pull the earth also.
Imagine the earth made of india-rubber and pulled out to and from
the moon. It will be made prolate (FIG. 134). If the earth were of
india-rubber the tides would be nothing, the rise and fall of the
water relatively to the solid would be practically nil. If the earth
(as has long been a favourite hypothesis of geologists) had a thin
shell 20 or 30 miles thick with liquid inside, there would be no such
thing as tides of water rising and falling relatively to land, or sea-
bottom. The earth's crust would yield to and from the moon, and the
water would not move at all relatively to the crust. If the earth were
even as rigid as glass all through, calculation shows that the solid
would yield so much that the tides could only be about one third of
what they would be if the earth were perfectly rigid. Again, if the

earth were two or three times as rigid as glass, about as rigid as a solid globe of steel, it would still, considering its great dimensions, yield two or three feet to that great force, which elastic yielding would be enough to make the tides only two thirds of what they would be if the earth were perfectly rigid. Mr. G. Darwin has made the investigation by means of the lunar fortnightly tides, and the general conclusion, subject to verification, is that the earth does seem to yield somewhat, and may have something like the rigidity of a solid globe of steel.

APPENDIX A

[Extracts from a Lecture on "The Tides," given to the Glasgow Science Lectures Association, not hitherto published, and now included as explaining in greater detail certain paragraphs of the preceding Lecture.]

(1) *Gravitation.*—The great theory of gravitation put before us by Newton asserts that every portion of matter in the universe attracts every other portion; and that the force depends on the masses of the two portions considered, and on the distance between them. Now, the first great point of Newton's theory is, that bodies which have equal masses are equally attracted by any other body, a body of double mass experiencing double force. This may seem only what is to be expected. It would take more time than we have to spare were I to point out *all* that is included in this statement; but let me first explain to you how the motions of different kinds of matter depend on a property called *inertia*. I might show you a mass of iron as here. Consider that if I apply force to it, it gets into a state of motion; greater force applied to it, during the same time, gives it increased velocity, and so on. Now, instead of a mass of iron, I might hang up a mass of lead, or a mass of wood, to test the equality of the mass by the equality of the motion which is produced in the same time by the action of the same force, or in equal times by the action of equal forces. Thus, quite irrespectively of the kind of matter concerned, we have a test of the quantity of matter. You might weigh a pound of tea against a pound of brass without ever putting them into the balance at all. You might hang up one body by a proper suspension, and you might, by a spring, measure the force applied, first to the one body, and then to the other. If the one body is found to acquire equal velocity under the influence of equal force for equal times as compared with the other body, then the mass of the one is said to be equal to the mass of the other.

I have spoken of mutual forces between any two masses. Let us consider the weight or heaviness of a body on the earth's surface. Newton explained that the attraction of the whole earth upon a body —for example, this 56 pounds mass of iron—causes its heaviness or weight. Well, now, take 56 pounds of iron here, and take a mass of lead, which, when put in the balance, is found to be of equal weight. You see we have quite a new idea here. You weigh this mass of iron against a mass of lead, or to weigh out a commodity for sale; as, for instance, to weigh out pounds of tea, to weigh them with brass weights is to compare their gravitations towards the earth—to compare the heavinesses of the different bodies. But the first subject that I asked you to think of had nothing to do with heaviness. The first subject was the mass of the different bodies as tested by their resistance to force tending to set them in motion. I may just say that the property of resistance against being set into motion, and again against resistance to being stopped when in motion, is the property of matter called *inertia*.

The first great point in Newton's discovery shows, then, that if the property of *inertia* is possessed to an equal degree by two different substances, they have equal heaviness. One of his proofs was founded on the celebrated guinea and feather experiment, showing that the guinea and feather fall at the same rate when the resistance of the air is removed. Another was founded upon making pendulums of different substances—lead, iron, and wood—to vibrate, and observing their times of vibration. Newton thus discovered that bodies which have equal heaviness have equal inertia.

The other point of the law of gravitation is, that the force between any two bodies diminishes as the distance increases, according to the law of the inverse square of the distance. That law expresses that, with double distance, the force is reduced one quarter, at treble distance the force is reduced to one-ninth part. Suppose we compare forces at the distance of one million miles, then again at the distance of two and a half million miles, we have to square the one number, then square the other, and find the proportion of the square of the one number to the square of the other. The forces are inversely as the squares of the distance, that is the most commonly quoted part of the law of gravitation; but the law is incomplete without the first

part, which establishes the relation between two apparently different properties of matter. Newton founded this law upon a great variety of different natural phenomena. The motion of the planets round the sun, and the moon round the earth, proved that for each planet the force varies inversely as the square of its distance from the sun; and that from planet to planet the forces on equal portions of their masses are inversely as the squares of their distances. The last link in the great chain of this theory is the tides.

(2) *Tide-Generating Force.*—And now we are nearly ready to complete the theory of tide-generating force. The first rough view of the case, which is not always incorrect, is that the moon attracts the waters of the earth towards herself and heaps them up, therefore, on one side of the earth. It is not so. It would be so if the earth and moon were at rest and prevented from falling together by a rigid bar or column. If the earth and moon were stuck on the two ends of a strong bar, and put at rest in space, then the attraction of the moon would draw the waters of the earth to the side of the earth next to the moon. But in reality things are very different from that supposition. There is no rigid bar connecting the moon and the earth. Why then does not the moon fall towards the earth? According to Newton's theory, the moon is always falling towards the earth. Newton compared the fall of the moon, in his celebrated statement, with the fall of a stone at the earth's surface, as he recounted, after the fall of an apple from the tree, which he perceived when sitting in his garden musing on his great theory. The moon is falling towards the earth, and falls in an hour as far as a stone falls in a second. It chances that the number 60 is nearly enough, as I have said before, a numerical expression for the distance of the moon from the earth in terms of the earth's radius. It is only by that chance that the comparison between the second and hour can be here introduced. Since there are 60 times 60 seconds in an hour, and about 60 radii of the earth in the distance from the moon, we are led to the comparison now indicated, but I am inverting the direction of Newton's comparison. He found by observation that the moon falls as far in an hour as a stone falls in a second, and hence inferred that the force on the moon is a 60th of the 60th of the force per equal mass on the earth's surface. Then he learned from accurate observations, and

from the earth's dimensions, what I have mentioned as the moon's distance, and perceived the law of variation between the weight of a body at the earth's surface and the force that keeps the moon in her orbit. The moon in Newton's theory was always falling towards the earth. Why does it not come down? Can it be always falling and never come down? That seems impossible. It *is* always falling, but it has also a motion perpendicular to the direction in which it is falling, and the result of that continual falling is simply a change of direction of this motion.

It would occupy too much of our time to go into this theory. It is simply the dynamical theory of centrifugal force. There is a continual falling away from the line of motion, as illustrated in a stone thrown from the hand describing an ordinary curve. You know that if a stone is thrown horizontally it describes a parabola—the stone falling away from the line in which it was thrown. The moon is continually falling away from the line in which it moves at any instant, falling away towards the point of the earth's centre, and falling away towards that point in the varying direction from itself. You can see it may be always falling, now from the present direction, now from the altered direction, now from the farther altered direction in a further altered line; and so it may be always falling and never coming down. The parts of the moon nearest to the earth tend to fall most rapidly, the parts furthest from the earth, least rapidly; in its own circle, each is falling away and the result is as if we had the moon falling directly.

But while the moon is always falling towards the earth, the earth is always falling towards the moon; and each preserves a constant distance, or very nearly a constant distance from the common centre of gravity of the two. The parts of the earth nearest to the moon are drawn towards the moon with more force than an equal mass at the average distance; the most distant parts are drawn towards the moon with less force than corresponds to the average distance. The solid mass of the earth, as a whole, experiences, according to its mass, a force depending on the average distance; while each portion of the water on the surface of the earth experiences an attractive force due to its own distance from the moon. The result clearly is, then, a tendency to protuberance towards the moon and from the moon;

and thus, in a necessarily most imperfect manner, I have explained to you how it is that the waters are not heaped up on the side next the moon, but are drawn up towards the moon and left away from the moon so as to tend to form an oval figure. The diagram (FIG. 125, p. 284) shows the protuberance of water towards and from the moon. It shows also the sun on the far side, I need scarcely say, with an enormous distortion of proportions, because without that it would be impossible in a diagram to show the three bodies. This illustrates the tendency of the tide-generating forces.

(3) *Elastic Tides.*—But another question arises. This great force of gravity operating in different directions, pulling at one place, pressing in at another, will it not squeeze the earth out of shape? I perceive signs of incredulity; you think it impossible it can produce any sensible effect. Well, I will just tell you that instead of being impossible, instead of it not producing any such effect, we have to suppose the earth to be of exceedingly rigid material, in order that the effect of these distorting influences on it may not mask the phenomenon of the tides altogether.

There is a very favourite geological hypothesis which I have no doubt many here present have heard, which perhaps till this moment many here present have believed, but which I hope no one will go out of this room believing, and that is that the earth is a mere crust, a solid shell thirty, or forty, or fifty miles thick at the most, and that it is filled with molten liquid lava. This is not a supposition to be dismissed as absurd, as ludicrous, as absolutely unfounded and un-reasonable. It is a theory based on hypothesis which requires most careful weighing. But it has been carefully weighed and found wanting in conformity to the truth. On a great many different essential points it has been found at variance with the truth. One of these points is, that unless the material of this supposed shell were preternaturally rigid, were scores of times more rigid than steel, the shell would yield so freely to the tide-generating forces that it would take the figure of equilibrium, and there would be no rise and fall of the water, relatively to the solid land, left to show us the phenomena of the tides.

Imagine that this (FIG. 134, p. 299) represents a solid shell with water outside, you can understand if the solid shell yields with suf-

ficiently great freedom, there will be exceedingly little tidal yielding left for the water to show. It may seem strange when I say that hard steel would yield so freely. But consider the great hardness of steel and the smaller hardness of india-rubber. Consider the greatness of the earth, and think of a little hollow india-rubber ball, how freely it yields to the pressure of the hand, or even to its own weight when laid on a table. Now, take a great body like the earth: the greater the mass the more it is disposed to yield to the attraction of distorting forces when these forces increase with the whole mass. I cannot just now fully demonstrate to you this conclusion; but I say that a careful calculation of the forces shows that in virtue of the greatness of the mass it would require an enormously increased rigidity in order to keep in shape. So that if we take the actual dimensions of the earth at forty-two million feet diameter, and the crust at fifty miles thick, or two hundred and fifty thousand feet, and with these proportions make the calculation, we find that something scores of times more rigid than steel would be required to keep the shape so well as to leave any appreciable degree of difference from the shape of hydrostatic equilibrium, and allow the water to indicate, by *relative* displacement, its tendency to take the figure of equilibrium; that is to say, to give us the phenomena of tides. The geological inference from this conclusion is, that not only must we deny the fluidity of the earth and the assertion that it is encased by a thin shell, but we must say that the earth has, on the whole, a rigidity greater than that of a solid globe of glass of the same dimensions; and perhaps greater than that of a globe of steel of the same dimensions. But that it cannot be less rigid than a globe of glass, we are assured. It is not to be denied that there may be a very large space occupied by liquid. We know there are large spaces occupied by lava; but we do not know how large they may be, although we can certainly say that there are no such spaces, as can in volume be compared with the supposed hollow shell, occupied by liquid constituting the interior of the earth. The earth as a whole must be rigid, and perhaps exceedingly rigid, probably rendered more rigid than it is at the surface strata by the greater pressure in the greater depths.

The phenomena of underground temperature, which led geologists to that supposition, are explained otherwise than by their assumption of a thin shell full of liquid; and further, every view we can take of underground temperature, in the past history of the earth, confirms the statement that we have no right to assume interior fluidity.

THE EXTENT OF THE UNIVERSE

BY
SIMON NEWCOMB

INTRODUCTORY NOTE

In spite of the fertility of America in mechanical invention and applied science, there are few branches of pure science in which she can be regarded as among the leading nations. Her nearest approach to pre-eminence has probably been in astronomy; and in this field Simon Newcomb was, at his death, the most distinguished figure.

Newcomb was born in the village of Wallace, Nova Scotia, March 12, 1835. His father, who was a teacher, gave him his elementary education; and at the age of eighteen we find him teaching a country school in Maryland. Two years later, a position as computer on the "Nautical Almanac" brought him to Cambridge, Mass., where he studied in Harvard University till 1861, when he was appointed professor of mathematics in the United States Navy. He remained in the government service till he was retired as a rear admiral in 1897, having served besides as professor of mathematics and astronomy in Johns Hopkins University, Baltimore, from 1884.

Newcomb's chief labors were in the department of mathematical astronomy, and were directed toward the explanation of the observed movements of the heavenly bodies. The difficulty and complexity of the calculations involved are beyond the conception of the layman; and the achievements which brought Newcomb honors from the learned of almost all civilized countries have to be taken on trust by the general. He had, nevertheless, an admirable power of clear exposition of those parts of his subject which were capable of popularization; and the accompanying paper is a good example of the simple treatment of a large subject.

Newcomb's interests extended beyond his special field, and he wrote with vigor and originality on finance and economics, and played a leading part in the general intellectual life of his time. When he died in the midst of his labors on July 11, 1909, he left a place at the head of American science that will not easily be filled.

THE EXTENT OF THE UNIVERSE

WE cannot expect that the wisest men of our remotest posterity, who can base their conclusions upon thousands of years of accurate observation, will reach a decision on this subject without some measure of reserve. Such being the case, it might appear the dictate of wisdom to leave its consideration to some future age, when it may be taken up with better means of information than we now possess. But the question is one which will refuse to be postponed so long as the propensity to think of the possibilities of creation is characteristic of our race. The issue is not whether we shall ignore the question altogether, like Eve in the presence of Raphael; but whether in studying it we shall confine our speculations within the limits set by sound scientific reasoning. Essaying to do this, I invite the reader's attention to what science may suggest, admitting in advance that the sphere of exact knowledge is small compared with the possibilities of creation, and that outside this sphere we can state only more or less probable conclusions.

The reader who desires to approach this subject in the most receptive spirit should begin his study by betaking himself on a clear, moonless evening, when he has no earthly concern to disturb the serenity of his thoughts, to some point where he can lie on his back on bench or roof, and scan the whole vault of heaven at one view. He can do this with the greatest pleasure and profit in late summer or autumn—winter would do equally well were it possible for the mind to rise so far above bodily conditions that the question of temperature should not enter. The thinking man who does this under circumstances most favorable for calm thought will form a new conception of the wonder of the universe. If summer or autumn be

chosen, the stupendous arch of the Milky Way will pass near the zenith, and the constellation Lyra, led by its beautiful blue Vega of the first magnitude, may be not very far from that point. South of it will be seen the constellation Aquila, marked by the bright Altair, between two smaller but conspicuous stars. The bright Arcturus will be somewhere in the west, and, if the observation is not made too early in the season, Aldebaran will be seen somewhere in the east. When attention is concentrated on the scene the thousands of stars on each side of the Milky Way will fill the mind with the consciousness of a stupendous and all-embracing frame, beside which all human affairs sink into insignificance. A new idea will be formed of such a well-known fact of astronomy as the motion of the solar system in space, by reflecting that, during all human history, the sun, carrying the earth with it, has been flying towards a region in or just south of the constellation Lyra, with a speed beyond all that art can produce on earth, without producing any change apparent to ordinary vision in the aspect of the constellation. Not only Lyra and Aquila, but every one of the thousand stars which form the framework of the sky, were seen by our earliest ancestors just as we see them now. Bodily rest may be obtained at any time by ceasing from our labors, and weary systems may find nerve rest at any summer resort; but I know of no way in which complete rest can be obtained for the weary soul—in which the mind can be so entirely relieved of the burden of all human anxiety—as by the contemplation of the spectacle presented by the starry heavens under the conditions just described. As we make a feeble attempt to learn what science can tell us about the structure of this starry frame, I hope the reader will allow me to at least fancy him contemplating it in this way.

The first question which may suggest itself to the inquiring reader is: How is it possible by any methods of observation yet known to the astronomer to learn anything about the universe as a whole? We may commence by answering this question in a somewhat comprehensive way. It is possible only because the universe, vast though it is, shows certain characteristics of a unified and bounded whole. It is not a chaos, it is not even a collection of things, each of which came into existence in its own separate way. If it were, there would be nothing in common between two widely separate regions of the

universe. But, as a matter of fact, science shows unity in the whole structure, and diversity only in details. The Milky Way itself will be seen by the most ordinary observer to form a single structure. This structure is, in some sort, the foundation on which the universe is built. It is a girdle which seems to span the whole of creation, so far as our telescopes have yet enabled us to determine what creation is; and yet it has elements of similarity in all its parts. What has yet more significance, it is in some respects unlike those parts of the universe which lie without it, and even unlike those which lie in that central region within it where our system is now situated. The minute stars, individually far beyond the limits of visibility to the naked eye, which form its cloudlike agglomerations, are found to be mostly bluer in color, from one extreme to the other, than the general average of the stars which make up the rest of the universe.

In the preceding essay on the structure of the universe, we have pointed out several features of the universe showing the unity of the whole. We shall now bring together these and other features with a view of showing their relation to the question of the extent of the universe.

The Milky Way being in a certain sense the foundation on which the whole system is constructed, we have first to notice the symmetry of the whole. This is seen in the fact that a certain resemblance is found in any two opposite regions of the sky, no matter where we choose them. If we take them in the Milky Way, the stars are more numerous than elsewhere; if we take opposite regions in or near the Milky Way, we shall find more stars in both of them than elsewhere; if we take them in the region anywhere around the poles of the Milky Way, we shall find fewer stars, but they will be equally numerous in each of the two regions. We infer from this that whatever cause determined the number of the stars in space was of the same nature in every two antipodal regions of the heavens.

Another unity marked with yet more precision is seen in the chemical elements of which stars are composed. We know that the sun is composed of the same elements which we find on the earth and into which we resolve compounds in our laboratories. These same elements are found in the most distant stars. It is true that some of these bodies seem to contain elements which we do not find

on earth. But as these unknown elements are scattered from one extreme of the universe to the other, they only serve still further to enforce the unity which runs through the whole. The nebulæ are composed, in part at least, of forms of matter dissimilar to any with which we are acquainted. But, different though they may be, they are alike in their general character throughout the whole field we are considering. Even in such a feature as the proper motions of the stars, the same unity is seen. The reader doubtless knows that each of these objects is flying through space on its own course with a speed comparable with that of the earth around the sun. These speeds range from the smallest limit up to more than one hundred miles a second. Such diversity might seem to detract from the unity of the whole; but when we seek to learn something definite by taking their average, we find this average to be, so far as can yet be determined, much the same in opposite regions of the universe. Quite recently it has become probable that a certain class of very bright stars known as Orion stars—because there are many of them in the most brilliant of our constellations—which are scattered along the whole course of the Milky Way, have one and all, in the general average, slower motions than other stars. Here again we have a definable characteristic extending through the universe. In drawing attention to these points of similarity throughout the whole universe, it must not be supposed that we base our conclusions directly upon them. The point they bring out is that the universe is in the nature of an organized system; and it is upon the fact of its being such a system that we are able, by other facts, to reach conclusions as to its structure, extent, and other characteristics.

One of the great problems connected with the universe is that of its possible extent. How far away are the stars? One of the unities which we have described leads at once to the conclusion that the stars must be at very different distances from us; probably the more distant ones are a thousand times as far as the nearest; possibly even farther than this. This conclusion may, in the first place, be based on the fact that the stars seem to be scattered equally throughout those regions of the universe which are not connected with the Milky Way. To illustrate the principle, suppose a farmer to sow a wheat field of entirely unknown extent with ten bushels of wheat.

We visit the field and wish to have some idea of its acreage. We may do this if we know how many grains of wheat there are in the ten bushels. Then we examine a space two or three feet square in any part of the field and count the number of grains in that space. If the wheat is equally scattered over the whole field, we find its extent by the simple rule that the size of the field bears the same proportion to the size of the space in which the count was made that the whole number of grains in the ten bushels sown bears to the number of grains counted. If we find ten grains in a square foot, we know that the number of square feet in the whole field is one-tenth that of the number of grains sown. So it is with the universe of stars. If the latter are sown equally through space, the extent of the space occupied must be proportional to the number of stars which it contains.

But this consideration does not tell us anything about the actual distance of the stars or how thickly they may be scattered. To do this we must be able to determine the distance of a certain number of stars, just as we suppose the farmer to count the grains in a certain small extent of his wheat field. There is only one way in which we can make a definite measure of the distance of any one star. As the earth swings through its vast annual circuit round the sun, the direction of the stars must appear to be a little different when seen from one extremity of the circuit than when seen from the other. This difference is called the parallax of the stars; and the problem of measuring it is one of the most delicate and difficult in the whole field of practical astronomy.

The nineteenth century was well on its way before the instruments of the astronomer were brought to such perfection as to admit of the measurement. From the time of Copernicus to that of Bessel many attempts had been made to measure the parallax of the stars, and more than once had some eager astronomer thought himself successful. But subsequent investigation always showed that he had been mistaken, and that what he thought was the effect of parallax was due to some other cause, perhaps the imperfections of his instrument, perhaps the effect of heat and cold upon it or upon the atmosphere through which he was obliged to observe the star, or upon the going of his clock. Thus things went on until 1837,

when Bessel announced that measures with a heliometer—the most refined instrument that has ever been used in measurement—showed that a certain star in the constellation Cygnus had a parallax of one-third of a second. It may be interesting to give an idea of this quantity. Suppose one's self in a house on top of a mountain looking out of a window one foot square, at a house on another mountain one hundred miles away. One is allowed to look at that distant house through one edge of the pane of glass and then through the opposite edge; and he has to determine the change in the direction of the distant house produced by this change of one foot in his own position. From this he is to estimate how far off the other mountain is. To do this, one would have to measure just about the amount of parallax that Bessel found in his star. And yet this star is among the few nearest to our system. The nearest star of all, Alpha Centauri, visible only in latitudes south of our middle ones, is perhaps half as far as Bessel's star, while Sirius and one or two others are nearly at the same distance. About 100 stars, all told, have had their parallax measured with a greater or less degree of probability. The work is going on from year to year, each successive astronomer who takes it up being able, as a general rule, to avail himself of better instruments or to use a better method. But, after all, the distances of even some of the 100 stars carefully measured must still remain quite doubtful.

Let us now return to the idea of dividing the space in which the universe is situated into concentric spheres drawn at various distances around our system as a centre. Here we shall take as our standard a distance 400,000 times that of the sun from the earth. Regarding this as a unit, we imagine ourselves to measure out in any direction a distance twice as great as this—then another equal distance, making one three times as great, and so indefinitely. We then have successive spheres of which we take the nearer one as the unit. The total space filled by the second sphere will be 8 times the unit; that of the third space 27 times, and so on, as the cube of each distance. Since each sphere includes all those within it, the volume of space between each two spheres will be proportional to the difference of these numbers—that is, to 1, 7, 19, etc. Comparing these volumes with the number of stars probably within them, the general

result up to the present time is that the number of stars in any of these spheres will be about equal to the units of volume which they comprise, when we take for this unit the smallest and innermost of the spheres, having a radius 400,000 times the sun's distance. We are thus enabled to form some general idea of how thickly the stars are sown through space. We cannot claim any numerical exactness for this idea, but in the absence of better methods it does afford us some basis for reasoning.

Now we can carry on our computation as we supposed the farmer to measure the extent of his wheat field. Let us suppose that there are 125,000,000 stars in the heavens. This is an exceedingly rough estimate, but let us make the supposition for the time being. Accepting the view that they are nearly equally scattered throughout space, it will follow that they must be contained within a volume equal to 125,000,000 times the sphere we have taken as our unit. We find the distance of the surface of this sphere by extracting the cube root of this number, which gives us 500. We may, therefore, say, as the result of a very rough estimate, that the number of stars we have supposed would be contained within a distance found by multiplying 400,000 times the distance of the sun by 500; that is, that they are contained within a region whose boundary is 200,000,000 times the distance of the sun. This is a distance through which light would travel in about 3,300 years.

It is not impossible that the number of stars is much greater than that we have supposed. Let us grant that there are eight times as many, or 1,000,000,000. Then we should have to extend the boundary of our universe twice as far, carrying it to a distance which light would require 6,600 years to travel.

There is another method of estimating the thickness with which stars are sown through space, and hence the extent of the universe, the result of which will be of interest. It is based on the proper motion of the stars. One of the greatest triumphs of astronomy of our time has been the measurement of the actual speed at which many of the stars are moving to or from us in space. These measures are made with the spectroscope. Unfortunately, they can be best made only on the brighter stars—becoming very difficult in the case of stars not plainly visible to the naked eye. Still the motions of

several hundreds have been measured and the number is constantly increasing.

A general result of all these measures and of other estimates may be summed up by saying that there is a certain average speed with which the individual stars move in space; and that this average is about twenty miles per second. We are also able to form an estimate as to what proportion of the stars move with each rate of speed from the lowest up to a limit which is probably as high as 150 miles per second. Knowing these proportions we have, by observation of the proper motions of the stars, another method of estimating how thickly they are scattered in space; in other words, what is the volume of space which, on the average, contains a single star. This method gives a thickness of the stars greater by about twenty-five per cent. than that derived from the measures of parallax. That is to say, a sphere like the second we have proposed, having a radius 800,000 times the distance of the sun, and therefore a diameter 1,600,000 times this distance, would, judging by the proper motions, have ten or twelve stars contained within it, while the measures of parallax only show eight stars within the sphere of this diameter having the sun as its centre. The probabilities are in favor of the result giving the greater thickness of the stars. But, after all, the discrepancy does not change the general conclusion as to the limits of the visible universe. If we cannot estimate its extent with the same certainty that we can determine the size of the earth, we can still form a general idea of it.

The estimates we have made are based on the supposition that the stars are equally scattered in space. We have good reason to believe that this is true of all the stars except those of the Milky Way. But, after all, the latter probably includes half the whole number of stars visible with a telescope, and the question may arise whether our results are seriously wrong from this cause. This question can best be solved by yet another method of estimating the average distance of certain classes of stars.

The parallaxes of which we have heretofore spoken consist in the change in the direction of a star produced by the swing of the earth from one side of its orbit to the other. But we have already remarked that our solar system, with the earth as one of its bodies, has been

journeying straightforward through space during all historic times. It follows, therefore, that we are continually changing the position from which we view the stars, and that, if the latter were at rest, we could, by measuring the apparent speed with which they are moving in the opposite direction from that of the earth, determine their distance. But since every star has its own motion, it is impossible, in any one case, to determine how much of the apparent motion is due to the star itself, and how much to the motion of the solar system through space. Yet, by taking general averages among groups of stars, most of which are probably near each other, it is possible to estimate the average distance by this method. When an attempt is made to apply it, so as to obtain a definite result, the astronomer finds that the data now available for the purpose are very deficient. The proper motion of a star can be determined only by comparing its observed position in the heavens at two widely separate epochs. Observations of sufficient precision for this purpose were commenced about 1750 at the Greenwich Observatory, by Bradley, then Astronomer Royal of England. But out of 3,000 stars which he determined, only a few are available for the purpose. Even since his time, the determinations made by each generation of astronomers have not been sufficiently complete and systematic to furnish the material for anything like a precise determination of the proper motions of stars. To determine a single position of any one star involves a good deal of computation, and if we reflect that, in order to attack the problem in question in a satisfactory way, we should have observations of 1,000,000 of these bodies made at intervals of at least a considerable fraction of a century, we see what an enormous task the astronomers dealing with this problem have before them, and how imperfect must be any determination of the distance of the stars based on our motion through space. So far as an estimate can be made, it seems to agree fairly well with the results obtained by the other methods. Speaking roughly, we have reason, from the data so far available, to believe that the stars of the Milky Way are situated at a distance between 100,000,000 and 200,000,000 times the distance of the sun. At distances less than this it seems likely that the stars are distributed through space with some approach to uniformity. We may state as a general conclusion, indicated by several methods of making the

estimate, that nearly all the stars which we can see with our tele-
scopes are contained within a sphere not likely to be much more than
200,000,000 times the distance of the sun.

The inquiring reader may here ask another question. Granting
that all the stars we can see are contained within this limit, may
there not be any number of stars outside the limit which are invisible
only because they are too far away to be seen?

This question may be answered quite definitely if we grant that
light from the most distant stars meets with no obstruction in reach-
ing us. The most conclusive answer is afforded by the measure of
starlight. If the stars extended out indefinitely, then the number of
those of each order of magnitude would be nearly four times that
of the magnitude next brighter. For example, we should have nearly
four times as many stars of the sixth magnitude as of the fifth; nearly
four times as many of the seventh as of the sixth, and so on indefi-
nitely. Now, it is actually found that while this ratio of increase is
true for the brighter stars, it is not so for the fainter ones, and that
the increase in the number of the latter rapidly falls off when we
make counts of the fainter telescopic stars. In fact, it has long been
known that, were the universe infinite in extent, and the stars equally
scattered through all space, the whole heavens would blaze with
the light of countless millions of distant stars separately invisible
even with the telescope.

The only way in which this conclusion can be invalidated is by
the possibility that the light of the stars is in some way extinguished
or obstructed in its passage through space. A theory to this effect
was propounded by Struve nearly a century ago, but it has since
been found that the facts as he set them forth do not justify the con-
clusion, which was, in fact, rather hypothetical. The theories of
modern science converge towards the view that, in the pure ether of
space, no single ray of light can ever be lost, no matter how far it
may travel. But there is another possible cause for the extinction
of light. During the last few years discoveries of dark and there-
fore invisible stars have been made by means of the spectroscope
with a success which would have been quite incredible a very few
years ago, and which, even to-day, must excite wonder and admira-
tion. The general conclusion is that, besides the shining stars which

exist in space, there may be any number of dark ones, forever invisible in our telescopes. May it not be that these bodies are so numerous as to cut off the light which we would otherwise receive from the more distant bodies of the universe? It is, of course, impossible to answer this question in a positive way, but the probable conclusion is a negative one. We may say with certainty that dark stars are not so numerous as to cut off any important part of the light from the stars of the Milky Way, because, if they did, the latter would not be so clearly seen as it is. Since we have reason to believe that the Milky Way comprises the more distant stars of our system, we may feel fairly confident that not much light can be cut off by dark bodies from the most distant region to which our telescopes can penetrate. Up to this distance we see the stars just as they are. Even within the limit of the universe as we understand it, it is likely that more than one-half the stars which actually exist are too faint to be seen by human vision, even when armed with the most powerful telescopes. But their invisibility is due only to their distance and the faintness of their intrinsic light, and not to any obstructing agency.

The possibility of dark stars, therefore, does not invalidate the general conclusions at which our survey of the subject points. The universe, so far as we can see it, is a bounded whole. It is surrounded by an immense girdle of stars, which, to our vision, appears as the Milky Way. While we cannot set exact limits to its distance, we may yet confidently say that it is bounded. It has uniformities running through its vast extent. Could we fly out to distances equal to that of the Milky Way, we should find comparatively few stars beyond the limits of that girdle. It is true that we cannot set any definite limit and say that beyond this nothing exists. What we can say is that the region containing the visible stars has some approximation to a boundary. We may fairly anticipate that each successive generation of astronomers, through coming centuries, will obtain a little more light on the subject—will be enabled to make more definite the boundaries of our system of stars, and to draw more and more probable conclusions as to the existence or non-existence of any object outside of it. The wise investigator of to-day will leave to them the task of putting the problem into a more positive shape.

GEOGRAPHICAL EVOLUTION

BY
SIR ARCHIBALD GEIKIE

INTRODUCTORY NOTE

SIR ARCHIBALD GEIKIE was born in Edinburgh, Scotland, in 1835, and educated at the university in that city. He became a member of the Geological Survey of Scotland, of which, in 1867, he was made director; and from 1871 to 1882 was Murchison professor of geology and mineralogy in his own university. At the latter date he resigned to take up the general directorship of the Geological Survey of the United Kingdom, which he held till 1901. He has been an extremely productive investigator, and his achievements have brought him many distinctions from learned societies at home and abroad, including the honor of knighthood, the presidency of the British Association, and the secretaryship of the Royal Society.

Among his more important writings may be mentioned "The Scenery of Scotland, Viewed in Connection With its Physical Geography" (1865), "Text-book of Geology" (1882), "Ancient Volcanoes of Britain" (1897), "Types of Scenery and Their Influence on Literature" (1898), and "Landscape in History" (1905).

The following paper on "Geographical Evolution," published among his "Geological Sketches at Home and Abroad" (1882), might be entitled with less ambiguity "Geological Evolution," since it is in this sense rather than in the broader modern signification that the word "geographical" is employed throughout the essay.

The interest in literature indicated by the names of several of Geikie's books has not been without influence on his writings, for there are few scientific authors to-day who can command so fascinating a style. His power of exposition is shown by the skill with which, in the present paper, he maps out in comparatively few pages, the views of his school as to the geological history of the earth.

GEOGRAPHICAL EVOLUTION[1]

IN the quaint preface to his *Navigations and Voyages of the English Nation,* Hakluyt calls geography and chronology "the sunne and moone, the right eye and the left of all history." The position thus claimed for geography three hundred years ago by the great English chronicler was not accorded by his successors, and has hardly been admitted even now. The functions of the geographer and the traveller, popularly assumed to be identical, have been supposed to consist in descriptions of foreign countries, their climate, productions, and inhabitants, bristling on the one hand with dry statistics, and relieved on the other by as copious an introduction as may be of stirring adventure and personal anecdote. There has indeed been much to justify this popular assumption. It was not until the key-note of its future progress was struck by Karl Ritter, within the present century, that geography advanced beyond the domain of travellers' tales and desultory observation into that of orderly, methodical, scientific progress. This branch of inquiry, however, is now no longer the pursuit of mere numerical statistics, nor the chronicle of marvellous and often questionable adventures by flood and fell. It seeks to present a luminous picture of the earth's surface, its various forms of configuration, its continents, islands, and oceans, its mountains, valleys, and plains, its rivers and lakes, its climates, plants, and animals. It thus endeavours to produce a picture which shall not be one of mere topographical detail. It ever looks for a connection between scattered facts, tries to ascertain the relations which subsist between the different parts of the globe, their reactions on each other and the function of each in the general economy of the whole. Modern geography studies the distribution of vegetable and animal life over the earth's surface, with the action and reaction between it and the surrounding inorganic

[1] A Lecture delivered at the Evening Meeting of the Royal Geographical Society, 24th March, 1879.

world. It traces how man, alike unconsciously and knowingly, has changed the face of nature, and how, on the other hand, the conditions of his geographical environment have moulded his own progress.

With these broad aims geography comes frankly for assistance to many different branches of science. It does not, however, claim in any measure to occupy their domain. It brings to the consideration of their problems a central human interest in which these sciences are sometimes apt to be deficient; for it demands first of all to know how the problems to be solved bear upon the position and history of man and of this marvellously-ordered world wherein he finds himself undisputed lord. Geography freely borrows from meteorology, physics, chemistry, geology, zoology, and botany; but the debt is not all on one side. Save for the impetus derived from geographical research, many of these sciences would not be in their present advanced condition. They gain in vast augmentation of facts, and may cheerfully lend their aid in correlating these for geographical requirements.

In no respect does modern geography stand out more prominently than in the increased precision and fulness of its work. It has fitted out exploratory expeditions, and in so doing has been careful to see them provided with the instruments and apparatus necessary to enable them to contribute accurate and definite results. It has guided and fostered research, and has been eager to show a generous appreciation of the labours of those by whom our knowledge of the earth has been extended. Human courage and endurance are not less enthusiastically applauded than they once were; but they must be united to no common powers of observation before they will now raise a traveller to the highest rank. When we read a volume of recent travel, while warmly appreciating the spirit of adventure, fertility of resource, presence of mind, and other moral qualities of its author, we instinctively ask ourselves, as we close its pages, what is the sum of its additions to our knowledge of the earth? From the geographical point of view—and it is to this point alone that these remarks apply—we must rank an explorer according to his success in widening our knowledge and enlarging our views regarding the aspects of nature.

The demands of modern geography are thus becoming every year more exacting. It requires more training in its explorers abroad, more knowledge on the part of its readers at home. The days are drawing to a close when one can gain undying geographical renown by struggling against man and beast, fever and hunger and drought, across some savage and previously unknown region, even though little can be shown as the outcome of the journey. All honour to the pioneers by whom this first exploratory work has been so nobly done! They will be succeeded by a race that will find its laurels more difficult to win—a race from which more will be expected, and which will need to make up in the variety, amount, and value of its detail, what it lacks in the freshness of first glimpses into new lands.

With no other science has geography become more intimately connected than with geology, and the connection is assuredly destined to become yet deeper and closer. These two branches of human knowledge are, to use Hakluyt's phrase, "the sunne and moone, the right eye and the left," of all fruitful inquiry into the character and history of the earth's surface. As it is impossible to understand the genius and temperament of a people, its laws and institutions, its manners and customs, its buildings and its industries, unless we trace back the history of that people, and mark the rise and effect of each varied influence by which its progress has been moulded in past generations; so it is clear that our knowledge of the aspect of a continent, its mountains and valleys, rivers and plains, and all its surface-features, cannot be other than singularly feeble and imperfect, unless we realise what has been the origin of these features. The land has had a history, not less than the human races that inhabit it.

One can hardly consider attentively the future progress of geography without being convinced that in the wide development yet in store for this branch of human inquiry, one of its main lines of advance must be in the direction of what may be termed geographical evolution. The geographer will no longer be content to take continents and islands, mountain chains and river valleys, table-lands and plains, as initial or aboriginal outlines of the earth's surface. He will insist on knowing what the geologist can tell him regarding the growth of these outlines. He will try to trace out the gradual evolu-

tion of a continent, and may even construct maps to show its successive stages of development. At the same time, he will seek for information regarding the history of the plants and animals of the region, and may find much to reward his inquiry as to the early migrations of the fauna and flora, including those even of man himself. Thus his pictures of the living world of to-day, as they become more detailed and accurate, will include more and more distinctly a background of bygone geographical conditions, out of which, by continuous sequence, the present conditions will be shown to have arisen.

I propose this evening to sketch in mere outline the aspects of one side of this evolutional geography. I wish to examine, in the first place, the evidence whereby we establish the fundamental fact that the present surface of any country or continent is not that which it has always borne, and the data by which we may trace backward the origin of the land; and, in the second place, to consider, by way of illustration, some of the more salient features in the gradual growth of the framework of Europe.

The first of these two divisions of the subject deals with general principles, and may be conveniently grouped into two parts: 1st, The Materials of the Land. 2d, The Building of the Land.

I. General Principles of Continental Evolution.

i.—*The Materials of the Land.*

Without attempting to enter into detailed treatment of this branch of the subject, we may, for the immediate purpose in view, content ourselves with the broad, useful classification of the materials of the land into two great series—Fragmental and Crystalline.

§ 1. *Fragmental.*—A very cursory examination of rocks in almost any part of the world suffices to show that by far the larger portion of them consists of compacted fragmentary materials. Shales, sandstones, and conglomerates, in infinite variety of texture and colour, are piled above each other to form the foundation of plains and the structure of mountains. Each of these rocks is composed of distinct particles, worn by air, rain, frost, springs, rivers, glaciers, or the sea, from previously existing rocks. They are thus derivative formations, and their source, as well as their mode of origin, can be determined.

Their component grains are for the most part rounded, and bear evidence of having been rolled about in water. Thus we easily and rapidly reach a first and fundamental conclusion—that the substance of the main part of the solid land has been originally laid down and assorted under water.

The mere extent of the area covered by these water-formed rocks would of itself suggest that they must have been deposited in the sea. We cannot imagine rivers or lakes of magnitude sufficient to have spread over the sites of the present continents. The waters of the ocean, however, may easily be conceived to have rolled at different times over all that is now dry land. The fragmental rocks contain, indeed, within themselves proof that they were mainly of marine, and not of lacustrine or fluviatile origin. They have preserved in abundance the remains of foraminifera, corals, crinoids, molluscs, annelides, crustaceans, fishes, and other organisms of undoubtedly marine habitat, which must have lived and died in the places where their traces remain still visible.

But not only do these organisms occur scattered through sedimentary rocks; they actually themselves form thick masses of mineral matter. The Carboniferous or Mountain Limestone of Central England and Ireland, for example, reaches a thickness of from 2,000 to 3,000 feet, and covers thousands of square miles of surface. Yet it is almost entirely composed of congregated stems and joints and plates of crinoids, with foraminifera, corals, bryozoans, brachiopods, lamellibranchs, gasteropods, fish-teeth, and other unequivocally marine organisms. It must have been for ages the bottom of a clear sea, over which generation after generation lived and died, until their accumulated remains had gathered into a deep and compact sheet of rock. From the internal evidence of the stratified formations we thus confidently announce a second conclusion—that a great portion of the solid land consists of materials which have been laid down on the floor of the sea.

From these familiar and obvious deductions we may proceed further to inquire under what conditions these marine formations, spreading so widely over the land, were formed. According to a popular belief, shared in perhaps by not a few geologists, land and sea have been continually changing places. It is supposed that while,

on the one hand, there is no part of a continent over which sea waves may not have rolled, so, on the other hand, there is no lonely abyss of the ocean where a wide continent may not have bloomed. That this notion rests upon a mistaken interpretation of the facts may be shown from an examination—(1) of the rocks of the land, and (2) of the bottom of the present ocean.

(1) Among the thickest masses of sedimentary rock—those of the ancient palæozoic systems—no features recur more continually than alterations of different sediments, and surfaces of rock covered with well-preserved ripple-marks, trails and burrows of annelides, polygonal and irregular desiccation marks, like the cracks at the bottom of a sun-dried muddy pool. These phenomena unequivocally point to shallow and even littoral waters. They occur from bottom to top of deposits which reach a thickness of several thousand feet. They can be interpreted only in one way, viz., that their deposition began in shallow water; that during their formation the area of deposit gradually subsided for thousands of feet; yet that the rate of accumulation of sediment kept pace on the whole with this depression; and hence, that the original shallow water character of the deposits remained, even after the original sea bottom had been buried under a vast mass of sedimentary matter. Now, if this explanation be true, even for the enormously thick and comparatively uniform systems of older geological periods, the relatively thin and much more varied stratified groups of later date can offer no difficulty. In short, the more attentively the stratified rocks of the crust of the earth are studied, the more striking becomes the absence of any deposits among them which can legitimately be considered those of a deep sea. They have all been deposited in comparatively shallow water.

The same conclusion may be arrived at from a consideration of the circumstances under which the deposition must have taken place. It is evident that the sedimentary rocks of all ages have been derived from degradation of land. The gravel, sand, and mud, of which they consist, existed previously as part of mountains, hills, or plains. These materials carried down to the sea would arrange themselves there as they do still, the coarser portions nearest the shore, the finer silt and mud farthest from it. From the earliest geological times the great area of deposit has been, as it still is, the marginal belt of sea

floor skirting the land. It is there that nature has always strewn "the dust of continents to be." The decay of old rocks has been unceasingly in progress on the land, and the building up of new rocks has been unintermittently going on underneath the adjoining sea. The two phenomena are the complementary sides of one process, which belongs to the terrestrial and shallow oceanic parts of the earth's surface and not to the wide and deep ocean basins.

(2) Recent explorations of the bottom of the deep sea all over the world have brought additional light to this question. No part of the results obtained by the *Challenger* Expedition has a profounder interest for geologists and geographers than the proof which they furnish that the floor of the ocean basins has no real analogy among the sedimentary formations that form most of the framework of the land. We now know by actual dredging and inspection that the ordinary sediment washed off the land sinks to the sea bottom before it reaches the deeper abysses, and that, as a rule, only the finer particles are carried more than a few score of miles from the shore. Instead of such sandy and pebbly material as we find so largely among the sedimentary rocks of the land, wide tracts of the sea bottom at great depths are covered with various kinds of organic ooze, composed sometimes of minute calcareous foraminifera, sometimes of siliceous radiolaria or diatoms. Over other areas vast sheets of clay extend, derived apparently from the decomposition of volcanic detritus, of which large quantities are floated away from volcanic islands, and much of which may be produced by submarine volcanoes. On the tracts farthest removed from any land the sediment seems to settle scarcely so rapidly as the dust that gathers over the floor of a deserted hall. Mr. Murray of the *Challenger* staff, has described how from these remote depths large numbers of shark's teeth and ear-bones of whales were dredged up. We cannot suppose the number of sharks and whales to be much greater in these regions than in others where their relics were found much less plentifully. The explanation of the abundance of their remains was supplied by their varied condition of decay and preservation. Some were comparatively fresh, others had greatly decayed, and were incrusted with or even completely buried in a deposit of earthy manganese. Yet the same cast of the dredge brought up these different stages of decay

from the same surface of the sea floor. While generation after generation of sea creatures drops its bones to the bottom, now here, now there, so exceedingly feeble is the rate of deposit of sediment that they lie uncovered, mayhap for centuries, so that the remains which sink to-day may lie side by side with the mouldered and incrusted bones that found their way to the bottom hundreds of years ago.

Another striking indication of the very slow rate at which sedimentation takes place in these abysses has also been brought to notice by Mr. Murray. In the clay from the bottom he found numerous minute spherical granules of native iron, which, as he suggests, are almost certainly of meteoric origin—fragments of those falling stars which, coming to us from planetary space, burst into fragments when they rush into the denser layers of our atmosphere. In tracts where the growth of silt upon the sea floor is excessively tardy, the fine particles, scattered by the dissipation of these meteorites, may remain in appreciable quantity. In this case, again, it is not needful to suppose that meteorites have disappeared over these ocean depths more numerously than over other parts of the earth's surface. The iron granules have no doubt been as plentifully showered down elsewhere, though they cannot be so readily detected in accumulating sediment. I know no recent observation in physical geography more calculated to impress deeply the imagination than the testimony of this presumably meteoric iron from the most distant abysses of the ocean. To be told that mud gathers on the floor of these abysses at an extremely slow rate conveys but a vague notion of the tardiness of the process. But to learn that it gathers so slowly, that the very star-dust which falls from outer space forms an appreciable part of it, brings home to us, as hardly anything else could do, the idea of undisturbed and excessively slow accumulation.

From all this evidence we may legitimately conclude that the present land of the globe, though formed in great measure of marine formations, has never lain under the deep sea; but that its site must always have been near land. Even its thick marine limestones are the deposits of comparatively shallow water. Whether or not any trace of aboriginal land may now be discoverable, the characters of the most unequivocally marine formations bear emphatic testimony to this proximity of a terrestrial surface. The present continental

ridges have probably always existed in some form, and as a corollary we may infer that the present deep ocean basins likewise date from the remotest geological antiquity.

§ 2. *Crystalline.*—While the greater part of the framework of the land has been slowly built up of sedimentary materials, it is abundantly varied by the occurrence of crystalline masses, many of which have been injected in a molten condition into rents underground, or have been poured out in lava streams at the surface.

Without entering at all into geological detail, it will be enough for the present purpose to recognise the characters and origin of two great types of crystalline material which have been called respectively the Eruptive and Metamorphic.

(*a*) *Eruptive.*—As the name denotes, eruptive or igneous rocks have been ejected from the heated interior of the earth. In a modern volcano lava ascends the central funnel, and issuing from the lip of the crater or from lateral fissures pours down the slopes of the cone in sheets of melted rock. The upper surface of the lava column within the volcano is kept in constant ebullition by the rise of steam through its mass. Every now and then a vast body of steam rushes out with a terrific explosion, scattering the melted lava into impalpable dust, and filling the air with ashes and stones, which descend in showers upon the surrounding country. At the surface, therefore, igneous rocks appear, partly as masses of congealed lava, and partly as more or less consolidated sheets of dust and stones. But beneath the surface there must be a downward prolongation of the lava column, which no doubt sends out veins into rents of the subterranean rocks. We can suppose that the general aspect of the lava which consolidates at some depth will differ from that which solidifies above ground.

As a result of the revolutions which the crust of the earth has undergone, the roots of many ancient volcanoes have been laid bare. We have been, as it were, admitted into the secrets of these subterranean laboratories of nature, and have learned much regarding the mechanism of volcanic action which we could never have discovered from any modern volcano. Thus, while on the one hand we meet with beds of lava and consolidated volcanic ashes which were undoubtedly erupted at the surface of the ground in ancient periods,

and were subsequently buried deep beneath sedimentary accumulations now removed, on the other hand we find masses of igneous rock which certainly never came near the surface, but must have been arrested in their ascent from below while still at a great depth, and have been laid bare to the light after the removal of the pile of rock under which they originally lay.

By noting these and other characters, geologists have learnt that, besides the regions of still active volcanoes, there are few large areas of the earth's surface where proofs of former volcanic action or of the protrusion of igneous rocks may not be found. The crust of the earth, crumpled and fissured, has been, so to speak, perforated and cemented together by molten matter driven up from below.

(*b*) *Metamorphic.*—The sedimentary rocks of the land have undergone many changes since their formation, some of which are still far from being satisfactorily accounted for. One of these changes is expressed by the term *Metamorphism,* and the rocks which have undergone this process are called *Metamorphic*. It seems to have taken place under widely varied conditions, being sometimes confined to small local tracts, at other times extending across a large portion of the continent. It consists in the rearrangement of the component materials of rocks, and notably in their recrystallisation along particular lines or laminæ. It is usually associated with evidence of great pressure; the rocks in which it occurs having been corrugated and crumpled, not only in vast folds, which extend across whole mountains, but even in such minute puckerings as can only be observed with the microscope. It shows itself more particularly among the older geological formations, or those which have been once deeply buried under more recent masses of rock, and have been exposed as the result of the removal of these overlying accumulations. The original characters of the sandstones, shales, grits, conglomerates, and limestones, of which, no doubt, these metamorphic masses once consisted, have been more or less effaced, and have given place to that peculiar crystalline laminated or foliated structure so distinctively a result of metamorphism.

An attentive examination of a metamorphic region shows that here and there the alteration and recrystallisation have proceeded so far that the rocks graduate into granites and other so-called igneous rocks. A series of specimens may be collected showing unaltered or

at least quite recognisable sedimentary rocks at the one end, and thoroughly crystalline igneous rocks at the other. Thus the remarkable fact is brought home to the mind that ordinary sandstones, shales, and other sedimentary materials may, in the course of ages, be converted by underground changes into crystalline granite. The framework of the land, besides being knit together by masses of igneous rock intruded from below, has been strengthened by the welding and crystallisation of its lowest rocks. It is these rocks which rise along the central crests of mountain chains, where, after the lapse of ages, they have been uncovered and laid bare, to be bleached and shattered by frost and storm.

ii.—*The Architecture of the Land.*

Let us now proceed to consider how these materials, sedimentary and crystalline, have been put together, so as to constitute the solid land of the globe.

It requires but a cursory examination to observe that the sedimentary masses have not been huddled together at random; that, on the contrary, they have been laid down in sheets one over the other. An arrangement of this kind at once betokens a chronological sequence. The rocks cannot all have been formed simultaneously. Those at the bottom must have been laid down before those at the top. A truism of this kind seems hardly to require formal statement. Yet it lies at the very foundation of any attempt to trace the geological history of a country. Did the rocks everywhere lie undisturbed one above another as they were originally laid down, their clear order of succession would carry with it its own evident interpretation. But such have been the changes that have arisen, partly from the operation of forces from below, partly from that of forces acting on the surface, that the true order of a series of rocks is not always so easily determined. By starting, however, from where the succession is normal and unbroken, the geologist can advance with confidence into regions where it has been completely interrupted; where the rocks have been shattered, crumpled, and even inverted.

The clue which guides us through these labyrinths is a very simple one. It is afforded by the remains of once living plants and animals which have been preserved in the rocky framework of the land. Each well-marked series of sedimentary accumulations contains its

own characteristic plants, corals, crustaceans, shells, fishes, or other organic remains. By these it can be identified and traced from country to country across a whole continent. When, therefore, the true order of superposition of the rocks has been ascertained by observing how they lie upon each other, the succession of their fossils is at the same time fixed. In this way the sedimentary part of the earth's crust has been classified into different formations, each characterised by its distinct assemblage of organic remains. In the most recent formations, most of these remains are identical with still living species of plants and animals; but as we descend in the series and come into progressively older deposits the proportion of existing species diminishes until at last all the species of fossils are found to be extinct. Still lower and older rocks reveal types and assemblages of organisms which depart farther and farther from the existing order.

By noting the fossil contents of a formation, therefore, even in a district where the rocks have been so disturbed that their sequence is otherwise untraceable, the geologist can confidently assign their relative position to each of the fractured masses. He knows, for instance, using for our present purpose the letters of the alphabet to denote the sequence of the formations, that a mass of limestone containing fossils typical of the formation B must be younger than another mass of rock containing the fossils of A. A series of strata full of the fossils of H resting immediately on others charged with those of C, must evidently be separated from these by a great gap, elsewhere filled in by the intervening formations D, E, F, G. Nay, should the rocks in the upper part of a mountain be replete with the fossils proper to D, while those in the lower slopes showed only the fossils of E, F, and G, it could be demonstrated that the materials of the mountain had actually been turned upside down, for, as proved by its organic remains, the oldest and therefore lowest formation had come to lie at the top, and the youngest, and therefore highest, at the bottom.

Of absolute chronology in such questions science can as yet give no measure. How many millions of years each formation may have required for its production, and how far back in time may be the era of any given group of fossils, are problems to which no answer, other

than a mere guess, can be returned. But this is a matter of far less moment than the relative chronology, which can usually be accurately fixed for each country, and on which all attempts to trace back the history of the land must be based.

While, then, it is true that most of the materials of the solid land have been laid down at successive periods under the sea, and that the relative dates of their deposition can be determined, it is no less certain that the formation of these materials has not proceeded uninterruptedly, and that they have not finally been raised into land by a single movement. The mere fact that they are of marine origin shows, of course, that the land owes its origin to some kind of terrestrial disturbance. But when the sedimentary formations are examined in detail, they present a most wonderful chronicle of long-continued, oft-repeated, and exceedingly complex movements of the crust of the globe. They show that the history of every country has been long and eventful; that, in short, hardly any portion of the land has reached its present condition, save after a protracted series of geological revolutions.

One of the most obvious and not the least striking features in the architecture of the land is the frequency with which the rocks, though originally horizontal, or approximately so, have been tilted up at various angles, or even placed on end. At first it might be supposed that these disturbed positions have been assumed at random, according to the capricious operations of subterranean forces. They seem to follow no order, and to defy any attempt to reduce them to system. Yet a closer scrutiny serves to establish a real connection among them. They are found, for the most part, to belong to great, though fractured, curves, into which the crust of the earth has been folded. In low countries far removed from any great mountain range, the rocks often present scarcely a trace of disturbance, or if they have been affected, it is chiefly by having been thrown into gentle undulations. As we approach the higher grounds, however, they manifest increasing signs of commotion. Their undulations become more frequent and steeper, until, entering within the mountain region, we find the rocks curved, crumpled, fractured, inverted, tossed over each other into yawning gulf and towering crest, like billows arrested at the height of a furious storm.

Yet even in the midst of such apparent chaos it is not impossible to trace the fundamental law and order by which it is underlaid. The prime fact to be noted is the universal plication and crumpling of rocks which were at first nearly horizontal. From the gentle undulations of the strata beneath the plains to their violent contortion and inversion among the mountains, there is that insensible gradation which connects the whole of these disturbances as parts of one common process. They cannot be accounted for by any mere local movements, though such movements no doubt took place abundantly. The existence of a mountain chain is not to be explained by a special upheaval or series of upheavals caused by an expansive force acting from below. Manifestly the elevation is only one phase of a vast terrestrial movement which has extended over whole continents, and has affected plains as well as high grounds.

The only cause which, so far as our present knowledge goes, could have produced such widespread changes is a general contraction of the earth's mass. There can be no doubt that at one time our planet existed in a gaseous, then in a liquid condition. Since these early periods it has continued to lose heat, and consequently to contract and to grow more and more solid, until, as the physicists insist, it has now become practically as rigid as a globe of glass or of steel. But in the course of the contraction, after the solid external crust was formed, the inner hot nucleus has lost heat more rapidly than the crust, and has tended to shrink inward from it. As a consequence of this internal movement, the outer solid shell has sunk down upon the retreating nucleus. In so doing, it has of course had to accommodate itself to a diminished area, and this it could only accomplish by undergoing plication and fracture. Though the analogy is not a very exact one, we may liken our globe to a shrivelled apple. The skin of the apple does not contract equally. As the internal moisture passes off, and the bulk of the fruit is reduced, the once smooth exterior becomes here and there corrugated and dimpled.

Without entering into this difficult problem in physical geology, it may suffice if we carry with us the idea that our globe must once have had a greater diameter than it now possesses, and that the crumpling of its outer layers, whether due to mere contraction or, as has been suggested, to the escape also of subterranean vapours,

affords evidence of this diminution. A little reflection suffices to show us that, even without any knowledge of the actual history of the contraction, we might anticipate that the effects would neither be continuous nor everywhere uniform. The solid crust would not, we may be sure, subside as fast as the mass inside. It would, for a time at least, cohere and support itself, until at last, gravitation proving too much for its strength, it would sink down. And the areas and amount of descent would be greatly regulated by the varying thickness and structure of the crust. Subsidence would not take place everywhere; for, as a consequence of the narrower space into which the crust sank, some regions would necessarily be pushed up. These conditions appear to have been fulfilled in the past history of the earth. There is evidence that the terrestrial disturbance has been renewed again and again, after long pauses, and that, while the ocean basins have on the whole been the great areas of depression, the continents have been the lines of uprise or relief, where the rocks were crumpled and pushed out of the way. Paradoxical, therefore, as the statement may appear, it is nevertheless strictly true, that the solid land, considered with reference to the earth's surface as a whole, is the consequence of subsidence rather than of upheaval.

Grasping, then, this conception of the real character of the movements to which the earth owes its present surface configuration, we are furnished with fresh light for exploring the ancient history and growth of the solid land. The great continental ridges seem to lie nearly on the site of the earliest lines of relief from the strain of contraction. They were forced up between the subsiding oceanic basins at a very early period of geological history. In each succeeding epoch of movement they were naturally used over again, and received an additional push upward. Hence we see the meaning of the evidence supplied by the sedimentary rocks as to shallow seas and proximity of land. These rocks could not have been otherwise produced. They were derived from the waste of the land, and were deposited near the land. For it must be borne in mind that every mass of land as soon as it appeared above water was at once attacked by the ceaseless erosion of moving water and atmospheric influences, and immediately began to furnish materials for the construction of future lands to be afterwards raised out of the sea.

Each great period of contraction elevated anew the much-worn land, and at the same time brought the consolidated marine sediments above water as parts of a new terrestrial surface. Again a long interval would ensue, marked perhaps by a slow subsidence both of the land and sea bottom. Meanwhile the surface of the land was channelled and lowered, and its detritus was spread over the sea floor, until another era of disturbance raised it once more with a portion of the surrounding ocean bed. These successive upward and downward movements explain why the sedimentary formations do not occur as a continuous series, but often lie each upon the upturned and worn edges of its predecessors.

Returning now to the chronological sequence indicated by the organic remains preserved among the sedimentary rocks, we see how it may be possible to determine the relative order of the successive upheavals of a continent. If, for example, a group of rocks, which as before may be called A, were found to have been upturned and covered over by undisturbed beds C, the disturbance could be affirmed to have occurred at some part of the epoch represented elsewhere by the missing series B. If, again, the group C were observed to have been subsequently tilted, and to pass under gently-inclined or horizontal strata E, a second period of disturbance would be proved to have occurred between the time of C and E.

I have referred to the unceasing destruction of its surface which the land undergoes from the time when it emerges out of the sea. As a rule, our conceptions of the rate of this degradation are exceedingly vague. Yet they may easily be made more definite by a consideration of present changes on the surface of the land. Every river carries yearly to the sea an immense amount of sand and mud. But this amount is capable of measurement. It represents, of course, the extent to which the general level of the surface of the river's drainage basin is annually lowered. According to such measurements and computations as have been already made, it appears that somewhere about $\frac{1}{6,000}$ of a foot is every year removed from the surface of its drainage basin by a large river. This seems a small fraction, yet by the power of mere addition it soon mounts up to a large total. Taking the mean level of Europe to be 600 feet, its surface, if everywhere worn away at what seems to be the present

mean normal rate, would be entirely reduced to the sea-level in little more than three and a half millions of years.

But of course the waste is not uniform over the whole surface. It is greatest on the slopes and valleys, least on the more level grounds. A few years ago, in making some estimates of the ratios between the rates of waste on these areas, I assumed that the tracts of more rapid erosion occupy only one-ninth of the whole surface affected, and that in these the rate of destruction is nine times greater than on the more level spaces. Taking these proportions, and granting that $\frac{1}{6,000}$ of a foot is the actual ascertained amount of loss from the whole surface, we learn by a simple arithmetical process that $\frac{1}{12}$ of an inch is carried away from the plains and tablelands in seventy-five years, while the same amount is worn out of the valleys in eight and a half years. One foot must be removed from the former in 10,800 years, and from the latter in 1,200 years. Hence, at the present rate of erosion, a valley 1,000 feet deep may be excavated in 1,200,000 years—by no means a very long period in the conception of most geologists.

I do not offer these figures as more than tentative results. They are based, however, not on mere guesses, but on data which, though they may be corrected by subsequent inquiry, are the best at present available, and are probably not far from the truth. They are of value in enabling us more vividly to realise how the prodigious waste of the land, proved by the existence of such enormous masses of sedimentary rock, went quietly on age after age, until results were achieved which seem at first scarcely possible to so slow and gentle an agency.

It is during this quiet process of decay and removal that all the distinctive minor features of the land are wrought out. When first elevated from the sea, the land doubtless presents on the whole a comparatively featureless surface. It may be likened to a block of marble raised out of the quarry—rough and rude in outline, massive in solidity and strength, but giving no indication of the grace into which it will grow under the hand of the sculptor. What art effects upon the marble block, nature accomplishes upon the surface of the land. Her tools are many and varied—air, frost, rain, springs, torrents, rivers, avalanches, glaciers, and the sea—each producing its

own characteristic traces in the sculpture. With these implements, out of the huge bulk of the land she cuts the valleys and ravines, scoops the lake-basins, hews with bold hand the colossal outlines of the mountains, carves out peak and crag, crest and cliff, chisels the courses of the torrents, splinters the sides of the precipices, spreads out the alluvium of the rivers, and piles up the moraines of the glaciers. Patiently and unceasingly has this great earth-sculptor sat at her task since the land first rose above the sea, washing down into the ocean the *débris* of her labour, to form the materials for the framework of future countries; and there will she remain at work so long as mountains stand, and rain falls, and rivers flow.

II. THE GROWTH OF THE EUROPEAN CONTINENT.

Passing now from the general principles with which we have hitherto been dealing, we may seek an illustration of their application to the actual history of a large mass of land. For this purpose let me ask your attention to some of the more salient features in the gradual growth of Europe. This continent has not the simplicity of structure elsewhere recognisable; but without entering into detail or following a continuous sequence of events, our present purpose will be served by a few broad outlines of the condition of the European area at successive geological periods.

It is the fate of continents, no less than of the human communities that inhabit them, to have their first origin shrouded in obscurity. When the curtain of darkness begins to rise from our primeval Europe, it reveals to us a scene marvellously unlike that of the existing continent. The land then lay chiefly to the north and northwest, probably extending as far as the edge of the great submarine plateau by which the European ridge is prolonged under the Atlantic for 230 miles to the west of Ireland. Worn fragments of that land exist in Finland, Scandinavia, and the northwest of Scotland, and there are traces of what seem to have been some detached islands in Central Europe, notably in Bohemia and Bavaria. Its original height and extent can of course never be known; but some idea of them may be formed by considering the bulk of solid rock which was formed out of the waste of that land. I find that if we take merely one portion of the detritus washed from its surface and laid down in

the sea—viz. that which is comprised in what is termed the Silurian system—and if we assume that it spreads over 60,000 square miles of Britain with an average thickness of 16,000 feet, or 3 miles, which is probably under the truth, then we obtain the enormous mass of 180,000 cubic miles. The magnitude of this pile of material may be better realised if we reflect that it would form a mountain ridge three times as long as the Alps, or from the North Cape to Marseilles (1800), with a breadth of more than 33 miles, and an average height of 16,000 feet—that is, higher than the summit of Mont Blanc. All this vast pile of sedimentary rock was worn from the slopes and shores of the primeval northern land. Yet it represents but a small fraction of the material so removed, for the sea of that ancient time spread over nearly the whole of Europe eastwards into Asia, and everywhere received a tribute of sand and mud from the adjoining shores.

There is perhaps no mass of rock so striking in its general aspect as that of which this northern embryo of Europe consisted. It lacks the variety of composition, structure, colour, and form, which distinguishes rocks of more modern growth; but in dignity of massive strength it stands altogether unrivalled. From the headlands of the Hebrides to the far fjords of arctic Norway it rises up grim and defiant of the elements. Its veins of quartz, felspar, and hornblende project from every boss and crag like the twisted and knotted sinews of a magnificent torso. Well does the old gneiss of the north deserve to have been made the foundation-stone of a continent.

What was the character of the vegetation that clothed this earliest prototype of Europe is a question to which at present no definite answer is possible. We know, however, that the shallow sea which spread from the Atlantic southward and eastward over most of Europe was tenanted by an abundant and characteristic series of invertebrate animals—trilobites, graptolites, cystideans, brachiopods, and cephalopods, strangely unlike, on the whole, to anything living in our waters now, but which then migrated freely along the shores of the arctic land between what are now America and Europe.

The floor of this shallow sea continued to sink, until over Britain, at least, it had gone down several miles. Yet the water remained shallow because the amount of sediment constantly poured into it

from the northwest filled it up about as fast as the bottom subsided. This slow subterranean movement was varied by uprisings here and there, and notably by the outburst at successive periods of a great group of active submarine volcanoes over Wales, the Lake district, and the south of Ireland; but at the close of the Silurian period a vast series of disturbances took place, as the consequence of which the first rough outlines of the European continent were blocked out. The floor of the sea was raised into long ridges of land, among which were some on the site of the Alps, the Spanish peninsula, and the hills of the west and north of Britain. The thick mass of marine sediment was crumpled up, and here and there even converted into hard crystalline rock. Large enclosed basins, gradually cut off from the sea, like the modern Caspian and Sea of Aral, extended from beyond the west of Ireland across to Scandinavia and even into the west of Russia. These lakes abounded in bone-covered fishes of strange and now long-extinct types, while the land around was clothed with a club moss and reed-like vegetation—*Psilophyton, Sigillaria, Calamite,* etc.—the oldest terrestrial flora of which any abundant records have yet been found in Europe. The sea, dotted with numerous islands, appears to have covered most of the heart of the continent.

A curious fact deserves to be noticed here. During the convulsions by which the sediments of the Silurian sea floor were crumpled up, crystallised, and elevated into land, the area of Russia seems to have remained nearly unaffected. Not only so, but the same immunity from violent disturbance has prevailed over that vast territory during all subsequent geological periods. The Ural Mountains on the east have again and again served as a line of relief, and have been from time to time ridged up anew. The German domains on the west have likewise suffered extreme convulsion. But the wide intervening plateau of Russia has apparently always maintained its flatness either as sea-bottom or as terrestrial plains. As I have already remarked, there has been a remarkable persistence alike in exposure to and immunity from terrestrial disturbance. Areas that lay along lines of weakness have suffered repeatedly in successive geological revolutions, while tracts outside of these regions of convulsion have

simply moved gently up or down without material plication or fracture.

By the time of the coal growths, the aspect of the European area had still further changed. It then consisted of a series of low ridges or islands in the midst of a shallow sea or of wide salt-water lagoons. A group of islands occupied the site of some of the existing high grounds of Britain. A long, irregular ridge ran across what is now France from Brittany to the Mediterranean. The Spanish peninsula stood as a detached island. The future Alps rose as a long, low ridge, to the north of the eastern edge of which lay another insular space, where now we find the high grounds of Bavaria and Bohemia. The shallow waters that wound among these scattered patches of land were gradually silted up. Many of them became marshes, crowded with a most luxuriant cryptogamic vegetation, specially of lycopods and ferns, while the dry grounds waved green with coniferous trees. By a slow intermittent subsidence, islet after islet sank beneath the verdant swamps. Each fresh depression submerged the rank jungles and buried them under sand and mud, where they were eventually compressed into coal. To this united co-operation of dense vegetable growth, accumulation of sediment, and slow subterranean movement, Europe owes her coal-fields.

All this time the chief area of high ground in Europe appears still to have lain to the north and northwest. The old gnarled gneiss of that region, though constantly worn down and furnishing materials towards each new formation, yet rose up as land. It no doubt received successive elevations during the periods of disturbance, which more or less compensated for the constant loss from its surface.

The next scene we may contemplate brings before us a series of salt lakes, covering the centre of the continent from the north of Ireland to the heart of Poland. These basins were formed by the gradual cutting off of portions of the sea which had spread over the region. Their waters were red and bitter, and singularly unfavourable to life. On the low intervening ridges a coniferous and cycadaceous vegetation grew, sometimes in quantity sufficient to supply materials for the formation of coal seams. The largest of these salt lakes stretched from the edge of the old plateau of Central France

along the base of the Alpine ridge to the high grounds of Bohemia, and included the basin of the Rhine from Bâle down to the ridge beyond Mayence, which has been subsequently cut through by the river into the picturesque gorge between Bingen and the Siebenge-birge. This lake was filled up with red sand and mud, limestone, and beds of rock salt. Where the eastern Alps now rise the opener waters were the scene of a long-continued growth of dolomite, out of which in later ages the famous dolomite mountains of the Tyrol were carved.

These salt lakes of the Triassic period seem to have been every-where quietly effaced by a widespread depression, which allowed the water of the main ocean once more to overspread the greater part of Europe. This slow subsidence went on so long as to admit of the accumulation of masses of limestone, shale, and sandstone, several thousand feet in thickness, and probably to bring most of the insular tracts of Central Europe under water. To this period, termed by geologists the Jurassic, we can trace back the origin of a large part of the rock now forming the surface of the continent, from the low plains of Central England up to the crests of the northern Alps, while in the Mediterranean basin, rocks of the same age cover a large area of the plateau of Spain, and form the central mass of the chain of the Apennines. It is interesting to know that the northwest of Britain continued still to rise as land in spite of all the geographical changes which had taken place to the south and east. We can trace even yet the shores of the Jurassic sea along the skirts of the mountains of Skye and Ross-shire.

The next long era, termed the Cretaceous, was likewise more remarkable for slow accumulation of rock under the sea than for the formation of new land. During that time the Atlantic sent its waters across the whole of Europe and into Asia. But they were probably nowhere more than a few hundred feet deep over the site of our continent, even at their deepest part. Upon their bottom there gathered a vast mass of calcareous mud, composed in great part of foraminifera, corals, echinoderms, and molluscs. Our English chalk which ranges across the north of France, Belgium, Denmark, and the North of Germany, represents a portion of the deposits of that sea floor, probably accumulated in a northern, somewhat isolated

basin, while the massive hippurite limestone of Southern Europe represents the deposits of the opener ocean. Some of the island spaces which had remained for a vast period above water, and had by their degradation supplied materials for the sediment of successive geological formations, now went down beneath the Cretaceous sea. The ancient high-grounds of Bohemia, the Alps, the Pyrenees, and the Spanish tableland were either entirely submerged, or at least had their area very considerably reduced. The submergence likewise affected the northwest of Britain; the western highlands of Scotland lay more than 1,000 feet below their present level.

When we turn to the succeeding geological period, that of the Eocene, the proofs of widespread submergence are still more striking. A large part of the Old World seems to have sunk down; for we find that one wide sea extended across the whole of Central Europe and Asia. It was at the close of this period of extreme depression that those subterranean movements began to which the present configuration of Europe is mainly due. The Pyrenees, Alps, Apennines, Carpathians, the Caucasus, and the heights of Asia Minor mark, as it were, the crests of the vast earth-waves into which the solid framework of Europe was then thrown. So enormous was the contortion that, as may be seen along the northern Alps, the rocks for thousands of feet were completely inverted, this inversion being accompanied by the most colossal folding and twisting. The massive sedimentary formations were crumpled up, and doubled over each other, as we might fold a pile of cloth. In the midst of these commotions the west of Europe remained undisturbed. It is strange to reflect that the soft clays and sands under London are as old as some of the hardened rocks which have been upheaved into such picturesque peaks along the northern flanks of the Alps.

After the completion of these vast terrestrial disturbances, the outlines of Europe began distinctly to shape themselves into their present form. The Alps rose as a great mountain range, flanked on the north by a vast lake which covered all the present lowlands of Switzerland, and stretched northward across a part of the Jura Mountains, and eastward into Germany. The size of this fresh-water basin may be inferred from the fact that one portion only of the sand and gravel that accumulated in it even now measures 6,000 feet

in thickness. The surrounding land was densely clothed with a vegetation indicative of a much warmer climate than Europe now can boast. Palms of American types, as well as date palms, huge Californian pines (Sequoia), laurels, cypresses, and evergreen oaks, with many other evergreen trees, gave a distinctive character to the vegetation. Among the trees too were planes, poplars, maples, willows, oaks, and other ancestors of our living woods and forests; numerous ferns grew in the underwood, while clematis and vine wound themselves among the branches. The waters were haunted by huge pachyderms, such as the dinotherium and hippopotamus; while the rhinoceros and mastodon roamed through the woodlands.

A marked feature of this period in Europe was the abundance and activity of its volcanoes. In Hungary, Rhineland, and Central France, numerous vents opened and poured out their streams of lava and showers of ashes. From the south of Antrim, also, through the west coast of Scotland, the Faröe Islands, and Iceland, even far into arctic Greenland, a vast series of fissure-eruptions poured forth successive floods of basalt, fragments of which now form the extensive volcanic plateaux of these regions.

The mild climate indicated by the vegetation in the deposits of the Swiss lake prevailed even into Polar latitudes, for the remains of numerous evergreen shrubs, oaks, maples, walnuts, hazels, and many other trees have been found in the far north of Greenland, and even within 8° 15′ of the pole. The sea still occupied much of the lowlands of Europe. Thus it ran as a strait between the Bay of Biscay and the Mediterranean, cutting off the Pyrenees and Spain from the rest of the continent. It swept round the north of France, covering the rich fields of Touraine and the wide flats of the Netherlands. It rolled far up the plains of the Danube, and stretched thence eastward across the south of Russia into Asia.

By this time some of the species of shells which still people the European seas had appeared. So long have they been natives of our area that they have witnessed the rise of a great part of the continent. Some of the most stupendous changes which they have seen have taken place in the basin of the Mediterranean, where, at a comparatively recent geological period, parts of the sea floor were upheaved to a height of 3,000 feet. It was then that the breadth of the

Italian peninsula was increased by the belt of lower hills that flanks the range of the Apennines. Then, too, Vesuvius and Etna began their eruptions. Among these later geographical events also we must place the gradual isolation of the Sea of Aral, the Caspian, and the Black Sea from the rest of the ocean, which is believed to have once spread from the arctic regions down the west of Asia, along the base of the Ural Mountains into the southeast of Europe.

The last scene in this long history is one of the most unexpected of all. Europe, having nearly its present height and outlines, is found swathed deep in snow and ice. Scandinavia and Finland are one vast sheet of ice, that creeps down from the watershed into the Atlantic on the one side, and into the basin of the Baltic on the other. All the high grounds of Britain are similarly buried. The bed of the North Sea as well as of the Baltic is in great measure choked with ice. The Alps, the Pyrenees, the Carpathians, and the Caucasus send down vast glaciers into the plains at their base. Northern plants find their way south even to the Pyrenees, while the reindeer, musk-ox, lemming, and their arctic companions, roam far and wide over France.

As a result of the prolonged passage of solid masses of ice over them, the rocks on the surface of the continent, when once more laid bare to the sun, present a worn, flowing outline. They have been hollowed into basins, ground smooth, and polished. Long mounds and wide sheets of clay, gravel, and sand have been left over the low grounds, and the hollows between them are filled with innumerable tarns and lakes. Crowds of boulders have been perched on the sides of the hills and dropped over the plains. With the advent of a milder temperature the arctic vegetation gradually disappeared from the plains. Driven up step by step before the advancing flora from more genial climates, it retired into the mountains, and there to this day continues to maintain itself. The present Alpine flora of the Pyrenees, the Alps, Britain, and Scandinavia, is thus a living record of the ice age. The reindeer and his friends have long since been forced to return to their northern homes.

After this long succession of physical revolutions, man appears as a denizen of the Europe thus prepared for him. The earliest records of his presence reveal him as a fisher and hunter, with rude flint-

pointed spear and harpoon. And doubtless for many a dim century such was his condition. He made no more impress on external nature than one of the beasts which he chased. But in course of time, as civilisation grew, he asserted his claim to be one of the geographical forces of the globe. Not content with gathering the fruits and capturing the animals which he found needful for his wants, he gradually entered into a contest with nature to subdue the earth and to possess it. Nowhere has this warfare been fought out so vigorously as on the surface of Europe. On the one hand, wide dark regions of ancient forest have given place to smiling cornfields. Peat and moor have made way for pasture and tillage. On the other hand, by the clearance of woodlands the rainfall has been so diminished that drought and barrenness have spread where verdure and luxuriance once prevailed. Rivers have been straitened and made to keep their channels, the sea has been barred back from its former shores. For many generations the surface of the continent has been covered with roads, villages and towns, bridges, aqueducts and canals, to which this century has added a multitudinous network of railways, with their embankments and tunnels. In short, wherever man has lived, the ground beneath him bears witness to his presence. It is slowly covered with a stratum either wholly formed by him or due in great measure to his operations. The soil under old cities has been increased to a depth of many feet by the rubbish of his buildings; the level of the streets of modern Rome stands high above that of the pavements of the Cæsars, and that again above the roadways of the early Republic. Over cultivated fields his potsherds are turned up in abundance by the plough. The loam has risen within the walls of his graveyards as generation after generation has mouldered into dust.

It must be owned that man, in much of his struggle with the world around him, has fought blindly for his own ultimate interests. His contest, successful for the moment, has too often led to sure and sad disaster. Stripping forests from hill and mountain, he has gained his immediate object in the possession of their abundant stores of timber; but he has laid open the slopes to be parched by drought, or swept bare by rain. Countries once rich in beauty, and plenteous in all what was needful for his support, are now burnt and barren,

or almost denuded of their soil. Gradually he has been taught, by his own bitter experience, that while his aim still is to subdue the earth, he can attain it, not by setting nature and her laws at defiance, but by enlisting them in his service. He has learnt at last to be the minister and interpreter of nature, and he finds in her a ready and unrepining slave.

In fine, looking back across the long cycles of change through which the land has been shaped into its present form, let us realise that these geographical revolutions are not events wholly of the dim past, but that they are still in progress. So slow and measured has been their march, that even from the earliest times of human history they seem hardly to have advanced at all. But none the less are they surely and steadily transpiring around us. In the fall of rain and the flow of rivers, in the bubble of springs and the silence of frost, in the quiet creep of glaciers and the tumultuous rush of ocean waves, in the tremor of the earthquake and the outburst of the volcano, we may recognise the same play of terrestrial forces by which the framework of the continents has been step by step evolved. In this light the familiar phenomena of our daily experience acquire an historical interest and dignity. Through them we are enabled to bring the remote past vividly before us, and to look forward hopefully to that great future in which, in the physical not less than in the moral world, man is to be a fellow-worker with God.